The
Wordsearch
Collection

p

This is a Parragon Publishing Book

This edition is published in 2007

Parragon Publishing
Queen Street House
4 Queen Street
Bath BA1 1HE, UK

Cover design by: Talking Design

ISBN 978-1-4054-7509-9
A copy of the British Library Cataloguing-in-Publication Data is
available from the British Library.

Printed and bound in China

ONE WORD "S" CINEMA

In the 2001 animated film SHREK, an ogre, a donkey, and a princess become fast friends. Search for Shrek and 26 other one-word "S" films.

SABRINA

SCANDAL

SCARFACE

SCREAM

SCROOGED

SERPICO

SHADOWS

SHAFT

SHAMPOO

SHINE

SHREK

SIGNS

SINGLES

SNEAKERS

SPAWN

SPECIES

SPHERE

SPLASH

STAGECOACH

STARMAN

STEEL

SUDDENLY

SUPERMAN

SUSPIRIA

SWIMFAN

SWINGERS

SWITCHBACK

```
N H U R A I R I P S U S Y N
Y D K S T E E L F U I L S U
E E I N R N P O D P N A W S
N C C E W M A E M E B A I I
I S H A F T G A D R S H M Y
H P P K F O E D I M C G F K
S S E E O R U N B A S Y A F
N O U R C S A S O N C G N O
K H C S W I T C H B A C K O
D S W I N G E R S A N P W P
O A G I P G H S K U D I A M
P L S T A R M A N Y A O B A
S P D T U K E R H S L G W H
Y S S N G I S S E L G N I S
```

DOGGIE DAY CARE

If you worry about Fido being left alone while you're at work, you can always send him to a day-care center that caters to CANINES. The CARE-TAKERS at these facilities will PAMPER your pooch with plenty of ATTENTION and playful ACTIVITY to keep him busy throughout the day.

ACTIVITY

ATTENTION

BATH

BRUSH

CAMP

CANINES

CARETAKERS

COMFORT

CONTACT

COST

EXERCISE

FACILITY

FREEDOM

GROOM

GROUP

GUESTS

MEALS

NAP TIME

OUTDOORS

PAMPER

PLAYTIME

POOL

ROAM

ROUTINE

SERVICE

SNACKS

SOCIALIZE

SWIM

TRAINING

TREATS

WALKS

```
H W G R O U P A M P E R T F
A T T E N T I O N V G R I H
M K L C O S D C A N I N E S
S O S I S E E N I T U O R R
M T O V E W V N T C S E Y O
E C A R P S I R A A K L B O
A M F E G A O M C A L N R D
L X I S R F P C T R A N U T
S O I T M T O E I O W A S U
T K O O Y N R F V A T P H O
S L C P T A E T I M L T C S
E F F A C I L I T Y A I G S
U L C X N A N P Y B G M Z M
G T S O C S E S I C R E X E
```

There are nearly a hundred bays in the islands of Great Britain and Ireland. In Scotland they are called firths or lochs, and in Ireland many are known as loughs.

BALLIN-SKELLIGS

BLACKSOD

BROAD

BROOM (Loch)

CLYDE (Firth of)

DROGHEDA

DULAS

EDDRACHILLIS

FALMOUTH

FISHGUARD

FORTH (Firth of)

FYNE (Loch)

HERNE

LAXFORD (Loch)

LONG (Loch)

LORN (Firth of)

LUCE

NEWPORT

PADSTOW

PEGWELL

PORT ISAAC

RED WHARF

SAND

SHEEP

SLIGO

START

ST. AUSTELL

ST. IVES

TARBERT (Lough)

TRALEE

```
G C B B S T F A S V W Y D E
F C A A R G N O L W W Y E N
H A L A T O A N R N I B H Y
L U L Y S T A U S T E L L F
D E I M D I P D N Y H A H H
E I N Y O E T F E R H C H H
F I S H G U A R D H N K M W
L X K W D N T A O E G S O O
T R E B R A T H I P T O O T
I L L O O H R W E I W D R S
L F L G F E A D V R N E B D
B I I U X C T E G A N Y N A
W L G F A U S R S S H E E P
S L S I L L I H C A R D D E
```

WHERE DOES IT ALL GO?

If you're like most people, there are likely times when you ask yourself, "Where did all my money go?" Below are some things that may figure into your household budget.

AUTOMOBILE

BOOKS

CLOTHES

COLLEGE

DINING OUT

ELECTRIC (bill)

FOOD

FUEL

GIFTS

HAIRCUTS

HEALTH CLUB

HEATING (bill)

INSURANCE

MAGAZINE (subscriptions)

MORTGAGE

NEWSPAPERS

PHONE (bill)

PLUMBING

RENT

SHOES

STAMPS

TAXES

TOLLS

TOOLS

TRAVEL

TUITION

WATER (bill)

```
M H A I R C U T S M T N L S
D V D E N E W S P A P E R S
O I M U T S P A N G V T U Z
O G N I B M U L P A O K G P
F N K I A T M R R Z L C H B
W I C T N U B T A I V O U A
A T S N S G T M N N N L V C
T A X E S K O O B E C L L I
E E O R H R I U M H T E G R
R H B V T T X S T O U G I T
S L R G I D O L O F B E E C
K S A U I A A L S T F I G E
B G T L Z E S O C W T H L L
E X W W H V E T W N S I I E
```

STREETS OF ISTANBUL

Istanbul is Turkey's largest city. Called Constantinople until 1930, it's the country's chief seaport and producer of cement and tobacco products. If you visit this city, you may one day walk along the 35 streets listed in our puzzle.

AKSEKI

ALTAY

AMELE

ANKARA

ARMA

ATATURK

AYKAPI

BARBAROS

CIBALI

CUMHURIYET

DRAMAN

FAITH

HASEKI

HAYDAR

HORHOR

KIREMIT

KOSKA

MARMARA

MERCAN

METE

MILLET

MUSALLA

ODALAR

ORDU

PALANGA

RUMELI

SPOR

TAKSIM

TERSANE

TIYATRO

TOPKAPI

TURAN

VATAN

VEZIR

VODINA

```
B F O T R A D Y A H K V Y I
T A K S I M K V O D I N A L
E I G D R Y R S A V R R D E
L T M N B B A O E A E T E M
L H E L A N L T P K M Z V U
I T R Y A L L B R S I O I R
M L C M I P A K P O T P K R
O D A L A R S P E K A R E F
P R N B B R U V A K T N S G
D Y D A I I M H Y N A T A V
N A R U T C D A M S K L H M
H O R H O R T K R U T A T A
S V K M Z E L E M A C C R I
R G C Y A T T M Y N Y B R A
```

HORSING AROUND

At a horse SHOW, a JUDGE looks at ability, appearance, and ring manners. If you have the SKILL to HARNESS all 32 terms related to showing horses, it's TROPHY TIME for you.

ARENA
BUILD
CANTER
CLASS
CONTROL

DIVISION
DRESSAGE
ENTRY
EVENT
HALTER

HARNESS
HUNTER
JUDGE
JUMP
MANEUVERS
OLYMPIA
PACER
PERFORM
PIVOT
POLO
RACE
RODEO
SHOW
SKILL
SLIDE
SPEED
SPIN
TASK
TEMPERAMENT
TIME
TROPHY
TROT

```
R O D E O E E K U S D P R G
N H C V N P S T E J M V M H
T A N E R A U N R U I N A A
R P M N T I M E J D E L P C
C R E T N U H M R G T I O I
K E D R E S S A G E V I S M
N C I Y F W R R R O L S A S
O A V Y O O R E T N A C L Y
A P I H S H R P V L E I V H
T M S P D O S M C U D S W R
V R I O M L K E D E E P S T
A N O R T Y I T V C T N K C
C O N T R O L U Y P W P A Y
G H C C P O L O B R J L U M
```

THE VALKYRIES

7

In Germanic mythology, Valkyries are maidens dressed in mail who serve Odin, the ruler of the gods. Their job is to preside over battles, choose those who were to die, and bring the souls of the slain heroes back to Valhalla. BRYNHILD is their chief, and they are depicted as riding through the air on horseback, wearing helmets and carrying spears.

BRYNHILD	ROTA	SKEGGJOLD
GEIRAHOD	SANGRIDR	SKULD
GEIROLUL	SIGRDRIFA	SVAFA
GOLI	SIGRLINN	SVIPUL
GONDUL	SIGRUN	THRUD
GUNDR		
GUNNR		
GUTH		
HERFJOTUR		
HERVOR		
HILDR		
HLATHGUTH		
HLOKK		
HRIST		
JUDUR		
KARA		
MIST		
OLRUN		
RANDGNOR		
RATHGRITH		
REGINLEIF		

```
M V N P E T M D E R K M M J
D L U K S I U G U N D R P K
O J E V S R H D O J N A P A
H L A T H G U T H N A D F R
A U A T D J H E U F D B I A
R P U T L J R G I G H U E N
I I S D O F B R Y N H I L D
E V L I J R D S I G R U N G
G S D O G R T H R T L P I N
R A T H G R I T H O S I G O
M U P I E R L I R L V I E R
R M S K K V L I P R O R R L
A F A V S D E A N U I K E H
U R D I R G N A S N V K K H
```

9

SWITZERLAND CITIES & TOWNS

Most of the population of Switzerland lives on a plateau that extends
between the Alps and the Jura Mountains. This is where the capital city
of BERN, as well as Switzerland's largest city, ZURICH, are found.

AARAU

ALTDORF

ARTH

BAAR

BADEN

BASEL

BELP

BERN

BIEL

BRUGG

BUCHS

BULLE

CAROUGE

CHUR

DAVOS

FLAWIL

FRIBOURG

GENEVA

KRIENS

MEILEN

MONTHEY

NYON

OLTEN

PAYERNE

PULLY

SAANEN

SARNEN

SIERRE

SION

SPIEZ

SURSEE

THUN

USTER

UZWIL

VEVEY

WALD

ZURICH

```
Y C K T N W R A P T Y B T E
U U S O H D I C W L N O Y N
G Z I R N P A Y E R N E C R
G S W E S R Y G H T H S C P
U A D I O L A R H T H O T E
R A B U L L E U N C R V B M
B N G U T F N O U A R A A B
S E P D E S M B Y F W D S G
H N O S N M U I U E N A E P
O R E P H C I R U Z V R L R
F A L I W A L F S E R E E D
U S T E R C K E N E B U V B
P Z A Z L K M E I L E N H C
V K V T E G G S T B P H O C
```

EAT YOUR WORDS

A **MANGO** is a tropical fruit that's eaten fresh or used in making desserts and preserves. It can be kidney-shaped, oval, or round with a leathery skin and juicy pulp. The list below contains mango, along with 39 other names of foods containing two vowels. In this puzzle, "Y" is considered a consonant.

BACON
BAGEL
BEAN
BREAD
BURGER
CARROT
CELERY
CHEDDAR
CHICKEN
CHICORY
CHILI
GRAPE
GUMBO
LEMON
LIME
LOBSTER
MANGO
MELON
OYSTER
PASTA
PEACH
PEAR
PECAN
PEPPER
PICKLE
PITA
PIZZA
POPCORN

PRETZEL
PRUNE
PUMPKIN
RASPBERRY
RICE
SALAD

SOLE
SPINACH
STEAK
SUSHI
TROUT
TUNA

```
K C I C P M U T O G N A M Z
P E H H R E P T U O R T Y T
E I L I H C N M O N G I L H
C K C C C O B U Y B A P P A
A E A K L O S R R N O C A B
N E C E L E R Y E P A R G M
P I M N T E E Y C A E M I L
R O K A B S G O L L D H L P
N P E P P E R A O Y S T E R
M K S I M N U S B U A O Z P
H A Z D A U B D S C L R T B
R Z A T S A P S T S A R E B
A S P I N A C H E D D A R A
Z E C L G P E A R Z N C P B
```

The term "plant" includes everything from the simplest, smallest algae to the most complex, largest tree. Many plant species are composed of different parts, and 30 of them can be found in the diagram.

AXIL	BRANCH	GLUME
BARK	BURR	HULL
BEARD	CATKIN	LIGULE
BINE	CONE	PERICARP
BOLL	DRUPE	PLUMULE
		RACEME
		RHIZOME
		RUNNER
		SAMARA
		SCALE
		SCAPE
		SPADIX
		SPATHE
		STIPULE
		STROBILE
		TENDRIL
		THORN
		TRUNK
		TUBER
		UMBEL

```
C G E L I G U L E N D N X D
S A L B I L P M L E G O E H
N O T S T R O B I L E B M U
B I L K Z Z D K U U P O X L
K D T Z I R G N X P U T D L
C B G H A N K U E I R S B D
T P R E O M B R B T D R I X
B L B L C R I T A S E A U S
B U M E H C N A R B N R P B
E M E C A R E R U E P A C S
N U O R X N H T N H T M C M
T L P Z I L T O N H G A K R
S E M U L G C T E A L S N H
K U E X N O D T R E O A S H
```

It's early to bed and early to rise for the rancher. His days are long and the work is hard. His faithful companion, the horse, gets him around quickly to check the stock and fences. Listed below are some terms associated with the life of a rancher.

AUGER
BALER
BILLET
BINS
BLANKET
BOOTS
BRIDLE
CHAPS
CINCH
CURB BIT
FESCUE (grass)
GLOVES
HALTER
HAMMER
LARIAT
LATIGO
MOWER
NAILS
NIPPERS (tools for grasping or severing wire)
PARKA
PITCHFORK
PLIERS

POST
RAKE
RASP
REINS
SADDLE
SHOVEL

TARP
TRACTOR
TWINE
WAGON
WIRE

```
O R M T D E K A R A S P B O
A S E V O L G F D P L O G N
T M A S E E W I R E I D W O
R S B V E U P A R K A M G G
K R O F H C T I P E N I R A
E H O P R S N I E R T F E W
S M T L I E T T P A B L L F
O T S E M F M W L L D S A C
B R I D L E H M I D I R B H
N A E B R L B L A N K E T A
R C C E B I I S C H E P R P
E T W I N R V B O L N P R S
M O H S G G U C L A R I A T
M R E G U A H C N I C N N O
```

CANADIAN OAKS AND PINES

In this puzzle you'll be searching for nine different types of oak trees and 21 pine trees native to Canada. "Oak" and "Pine" do not appear in the grid.

BLACK

CHESTNUT

DURMAST

ENGLISH

GARRY

POISON

SCARLET

SWAMP (White)

WHITE

AUSTRIAN

BANKSIAN

BULL

HARD

JACK

LIMBER

LODGEPOLE

MUGHO

NORWAY

OREGON

PITCH

PONDEROSA

SCOTCH

SCOTS

SCRUB

SHORE

SILVER

SOFT

STONE

WEYMOUTH

YELLOW

```
Y A W R O N A I S K N A B B
P P N P R C P O C H S F J L
H O S V K H L A H O C D N E
L S I C M E J F R G R T A L
L I A S O S L E I A U Y I E
U L S W O T D O H R B M R P
B V I A P N C K P O B E T T
W E Y M O U T H R E N D S H
O R N P R T H E R G G A U N
L G M O F F B O L A M D A I
L T J L T O H I O R E G O N
E P C C S S S O U R A S L L
Y O E T I H W D K Y L C I C
E J W M Y J A K S C O T S A
```

CASTLES OF WALES

Some of the finest examples of medieval castle construction can be found in Wales, which is often called the "Land of Castles." You can visit these fabulous reminders of a distant age by searching the diagram below.

BUILTH

CAERPHILLY

CALDICOT

CARDIFF

CARDIGAN

CAREW

CHEPSTOW

CHIRK

COITY

CONWAY

DINBAUD

DIXTON

FLINT

FONMON

HARLECH

HOLT

KENFIG

MOLD

NEATH

NEWPORT

OGMORE

PENARD

PENHOW

PENRICE

PICTON

POWIS

RADNOR

RAGLAN

TENBY

UPTON

WHITE

```
R O M M F H A R B K U K N T
I R F O O Y Y Y F D G H D A
U H A L E T A F I S C H E D
L P T D I W O X F I A C S Y
H K T O N N T H C I R E L N
U E C O M O T O C I D L A C
O N C O N L R G H I I R C P
C F N I I D O M E H G A A I
O I O U R I P O P P A H R C
S G B H Y N W R S P N W E T
S E K H T B E E T I H W W O
Y R A G L A N P O W I S F N
K R I H C U E E W O H N E P
P E N A R D R N T K F H Y K
```

In the Middle Ages, the highest aspiration for a young man was to become a knight in shining armor. This was no easy task, though, for the candidate needed the character of a saint plus the athletic ability of an all-star! Get in the SPIRIT and PLUCK these knightly traits from the diagram.

BRAVERY

COURAGE

DARING

DASH

EFFORT

ÉLAN

ENDURANCE

ENERGY

FIRMNESS

FORTITUDE

GRIT

HEART

HONESTY

HONOR

INTEGRITY

NERVE

PATIENCE

PLUCK

SPIRIT

SPUNK

STAMINA

STRENGTH

TENACITY

VALOR

VERVE

VIGOR

VITALITY

WILL

```
M V I T A L I T Y A W D U I
B L E E F F O R T V D B K I
R O L A V M R B I I H T C E
A E A O G R E O R T R G U L
V N N R L G E H G T R I L C
E G K D A E C N E I T A P T
R D N R U A E N T A V A N S
Y H U A H R A E N E R G Y I
G O P T T C A N I M A T S C
C N S S I E R N V D S D T D
U O I T W T W E C E T A N F
T R Y R F I R M N E S S M S
T W S C A V L O K V Y H N Y
M C E O E D H L F A B T T B
```

ARABIC ORIGINS

Many important words that we use today can be traced back to the Arabic language. This Arab influence began in the early Middle Ages and has continued for centuries. Below are 28 English words that were originally derived from Arabic.

ADMIRAL

ALCHEMY

ALCOVE

ALFALFA

ALKALI

ARTICHOKE

AZURE

CALIBER

CARAFE

CARAT

CARAWAY

COFFEE

COTTON

ELIXIR

HENNA

LUTE

MACRAMÉ

MAGAZINE

MOHAIR

MUSLIN

NADIR

SAFFRON

SHERBET

SIROCCO

SOFA

TARIFF

ZENITH

ZERO

```
N  E  N  L  S  E  Z  E  L  I  X  I  R  C
O  B  F  M  K  U  S  U  E  E  N  I  R  B
T  N  S  N  M  F  X  A  K  F  R  V  M  E
T  C  S  O  F  A  F  H  O  N  F  U  V  Y
O  A  O  I  R  L  E  C  H  F  S  O  Z  G
C  R  R  M  A  C  C  N  C  L  R  Z  C  A
S  A  F  F  R  O  N  T  I  L  A  K  L  A
T  W  L  I  R  V  T  N  T  Z  L  R  D  L
N  A  D  I  R  E  M  A  R  C  A  M  D  C
Y  Y  S  W  B  B  C  O  A  A  I  G  Y  H
B  T  R  R  B  E  A  T  H  R  N  A  A  E
O  R  E  Z  T  F  R  E  A  A  S  N  Z  M
E  H  D  U  Y  O  A  L  M  F  I  Y  E  Y
S  W  L  D  X  H  T  I  N  E  Z  R  O  H
```

You can take a BRIEF solving break, if you wish, before tackling this puzzle. As you can see, all of the words below are adjectives related to time.

ANCIENT

ANTIQUE

APERIODIC

ARCHAIC

BRIEF

CHRONIC

COEVAL

CONSTANT

CONTINUAL

DATED

EARLY

EPHEMERAL

ERSTWHILE

FORE

FORMER

FREQUENT

IMPROMPTU

INTERIM

LAST

LATE

OFF-PEAK

PREVIOUS

PRIOR

RECENT

TARDY

TEMPORAL

TIMELY

VINTAGE

```
L O G L A T E M P O R A L A
Y A F O R M E R R F L A G A
C K U B R I E F O L L R F N
I H A N E V B C H F A Q A C
A E R E I U T P M O R P M I
H S E O P T N E U Q E R F E
C E U N N F N S P R M O L N
R S Q E Q I F O I M E I T T
A N I T F Y C O C G H R I Q
N D T A L L D U A W P P M A
C A N R E I A T T N E C E R
N T A D C O N S T A N T L M
I E O Y M I R E T N I Q Y F
A D L A V E O C K S T D D F
```

MANY NUMBERED THINGS

If you're a number cruncher, you may want to break out the ol' CAL-CULATOR to determine just how much puzzle fun is contained in this puzzle! All of the entries hidden in the diagram are things that have numbers, so sharpen your pencil and start solving!

APARTMENT

CALCULATOR

CALENDAR

CHECK

CLOCK

DARTBOARD

ELEVATOR

HIGHWAY

HOUSE

INVOICE

KEYBOARD

LOCKER

MAILBOX

MONEY

RACE CAR

RADIO

RULER

SCALE

SCORECARD

STAMP

SUNDIAL

TAPE MEASURE

TELEPHONE

THERMOMETER

TIMER

WATCH

YARDSTICK

```
Y L E R U S A E M E P A T N
R C Y A W H G I H R P K K S
R M A I L B O X G A X C C T
O A R L O C K E R M O O E W
K T D E C N S T I R R L H X
I S S I T U M D E E C C K
N U T T O E L R C P S L E E
V N I H N H M A H H M Y U V
O D C T C K R O T H B A V R
I I K P W D N B M O C N T H
C A M O N E Y T A R R T M S
E L E V A T O R A C E C A R
S C A L E N D A R D Y H T W
H W L B G V T D R E M I T X
```

The subject of this puzzle is words containing the letters "BY."

BABY	BYPLAY	BYWORD
BOBBY	BYRE	CABBY
BUSBY	BYROAD	CUBBY
BYGONE	BYSTANDER	GABBY
BYLAW	BYSTREET	GOODBYE
BYLINE	BYTE	GRUBBY
BYNAME	BYWAY	HOBBY
		HUBBY
		LABYRINTH
		LOBBY
		LULLABY
		NEARBY
		NOBBY
		NUBBY
		RUBY
		RUGBY
		SCRUBBY
		STUBBY
		TRILBY
		WALLABY

```
R L Y G L W Y P Y I T W H D
G U B O C A B B Y W O R D I
Y O B N W L A Y U R E I R W
G B O Y B L I R T D A M A N
Y N B D L A D O N I P L W O
S C R U B B Y A L P Y B A B
L C L H T Y T D T B Y D T B
Y E E B B S E T B G C O R Y
A I M R Y T G E O E A H B E
U L A B Y R I N T H O B E Y
A E N B U E E I B B U S B Y
N S Y B T E C L B C Y G D Y
I I B P W T S Y B B U H G N
H Y C D N U B B Y R R C E T
```

DOUBLE-CHECK

Hopefully this puzzle won't BAFFLE you as the word list is comprised of 32 words that are spelled with double letters.

ADDITION

ALLEY

APPLE

BAFFLE

BANNER

BEECH

BOOTH

BREED

BRILLIANT

BROOD

BUTTER

BUZZARD

CARELESS

CHEESE

CHESS

DRESS

EFFECT

FEELING

FILLER

FLATTEN

FLEECE

FOOLISH

FUNNY

GOOEY

GOOSE

HALLWAY

HAPPY

INNING

LATTER

LESSON

LETTER

LITTLE

```
F B C F L Y A L L E Y A T P
S B U A W G P T L H I S Z C
F O U Z R G R P D E E R B O
I L I T Z E P Y A W L L A H
L N E T T A L F E H E D N T
L L E T T E R E A S D P N O
E F A N B G R D S I O A E O
R L T I B H N O T S I O R B
R E T E O Y N I E L E H G G
B E E T N F O O L I S H O B
O C G N I N N I F E E O C A
H E U Y P L R E F F E C T Y
I F H G N B I A A Y H F L Y
S S E R D O O R B D C B E W
```

CONCERT PAVILIONS

Here at the outdoor concert pavilion, the STAGE is set, so prepare yourself for the PLEASURE of solving this puzzle by putting down your conductor's baton and picking up your pencil. Ready? Begin!

ACOUSTICS

AUDIBLE

AUDIENCE

BAND

BLEACHERS

CITY

CONCERTS

HARMONICS

HEAR

JAZZ

MELODY

MUSIC

OPEN AIR

ORCHESTRA

PARK

PERFORMERS

PLATFORM

PLEASURE

RECITAL

ROWS

SEATS

SECTION

SINGER

SNACKS

SOLO

SONGS

SOUND

SOUVENIR

SPEAKERS

STAGE

TICKET

VOCALIST

```
E I W L S O U V E N I R R S
L G S D A Z R T G G J W T Y
B K C N Y T I C K E T A D S
I O I M U S I C H G G O Z T
D P T S R E H C A E L B S Z
U L S E R O B Z E E S R W V
A E U C I E F I M R E T O S
U A O T A S M T O K A C R N
D S C I N O M R A H A E G A
I U A O E N S E O L O S H C
E R B N P G P O I F P T J K
N E A E O S G S U G R A L S
C O N C E R T S I N G E R Z
E J D G Y T R Z Y D D S P K
```

"S" WORDPLAY

21

Situated in the sWELL sPACE are 44 terms that form new words when preceded by the letter "S." If you sTART now, you'll sPRINT past those solving at a sNAIL's pace!

CANT	TART	TUMBLE
CARE	TEAL	WARM
COLD	TEAM	WELL
COWL	TONE	WINE
CREAM	TORE	WING
CREW	TRAIN	WIPED
EATING	TRAP	WITCH
EVEN		
EVER		
HARES		
HOVEL		
KETCH		
LACK		
LATE		
LEDGE		
LEEK		
LENDER		
NAIL		
PACE		
PARE		
PARK		
PEAR		
PLATTER		
PRAY		
PRIG		
PRINT		
TABLE		
TAKES		
TALE		
TALK		

```
V R P L T H L D E H S V L K
M T H H C G L T T V Y V H L
T N M O E G N N E V E A E G
G A S V K C R I M N R R R D
S C B E N I A R T E O U A P
O W E L L E A P S A T T P T
O L E B E W L E D G E P C C
C H R M I A K A H E A T O B
L G C U T A C R T R M L W K
P A R T T A R T K E D C L R
P I E G I L E N D E R A C M
I R W T N W A D P N T S V Y
R N I I B I M I R I K C A L
K G B G L B W C Y W S H H A
```

23

Seashell collecting is very popular with beachcombing tourists. Not only do they make attractive mementos and gifts, but the sorting and researching extends the holiday after returning home. Scour the diagram to find 37 "buried" seashells.

ABRA	BUBBLE	COWRIE
ACAR	CALICO	DOVE
ARCA	CARRIER	FROG
ARK CLAM	CONCH	HELMET
AUGER	CONE	HORN
BONNET	CORAL	JEWEL BOX
		LIMPET
		LION'S PAW
		MOON
		NUT CLAM
		OLIVE
		PERIWINKLE
		PHOS
		RAZOR
		ROCK
		SCALLOP
		SLIPPER
		SLIT
		STAR
		TULIP
		TURRET
		TUSK
		VASE
		VENUS
		WORM

```
D D M G E W T B E U P H O S
G X O B L E W E J I O U L N
D E E F N R A Z O R R I O N
H C V N A C P G N Z P W B U
I C O I O I S T T P K O O T
J B D N L V N R E I R R A C
O E E U C O O R P R H M H L
M A T H F H I O M E R B W A
C O R R E W L Z I G S U V M
O L O C I L A C L U V B T L
R G C N A R M K N A R B A X
A R K C L A M E S A J L X J
L L S L D C V E T U X E M Z
E K S E K A J S L I T X S T
```

SILENCE IS GOLDEN

23

SILENCE is golden for those who take a BREAK from their hectic lives and the pressures of work by indulging in QUIET contemplation. Many religious centers offer RETREAT packages. For more information, check out your local Yellow Pages to locate a center near you.

ABBEY

ALONE

BALANCE

BREAK

CALM

CHAPEL

COMFORT

CONTEM-
PLATE

CONVENT

INDULGE

LISTEN

MEDITATE

MONASTERY

PONDER

PRAYER

PRIVATE

QUIET

REFLECT

RELAX

RETREAT

SECLUDED

SERENITY

SILENCE

SOLITUDE

STRENGTH

THINK

TIME

TRANQUIL

WONDER

```
P W T H Y L T D S F C X T A
R F I C Q U I E T K F M K A
A L O N E K C S O O H H N B
Y E C N A L A B T S T R I B
E G F O U Q F E O E G X H E
R L Q D N S S E R E N I T Y
E U E T F T P L R B E M R T
D D P O N D E R E T R E A T
N N U A Y P C M F Q T D N R
O I E T A V I R P S S I Q O
W C R H I T E I A L M T U F
I I C S I L E N C E A A I M
S H M L A C O N V E N T L O
L N T X N M D S L Y R E E C
```

Ladies' fans were introduced into 16th-century Europe by Portuguese sailors who brought them back from Japan. Their popularity spread and intricately DECORATED HANDHELD fans would become an indispensable fashion ACCESSORY for women during the 17th and 18th centuries. The word list below offers terms related to making an ordinary fan go from "fan to FANCY."

ACCESSORY

BAMBOO

BREEZE

CIRCULAR

COLORFUL

DECORATED

DELICATE

DESIGN

ELEGANT

EMBROIDERED

FANCY

FEATHERS

FOLD

FRAME

HANDHELD

HANDLE

LACE

MATERIAL

PAINTED

PAPER

PIVOT

PLEATS

RIBBON

SHAPES

SILK

STICKS

STRAW

TASSELS

WOOD

```
N G I S E D T T W U K L I S
F O L B A M B O O E I N K L
O A B U N T O G Z V C C A S
L N N B F D A E L I I I T V
D V S C I R E S B T R P N S
E Z E M Y R O S S E C C A N
C M P T B F P L T E U N G A
O I A E A A E A O R L L E B
R R H R I C M A M C A S L N
A E S N F V I P T C R W E P
T D T H A N D L E H D N A H
E E M B R O I D E R E D S H
D C V L F T N A K D B R O G
R Z O R E P A P L E A T S F
```

DINING GUIDE

When it comes to picking a place to eat, the choices are practically endless. Here's a list of dining spots ranging from the simple to the elaborate, so bring your pencil as well as your appetite.

AUTOMAT

BEANERY

BISTRO

CABARET

CAFETERIA

CANTEEN

CANTINA

CLUB

COFFEE SHOP

DELI

DINER

EATERY

GARDEN

GRILL

HASH HOUSE

LODGE

LUNCHEON-
ETTE

MESS HALL

PIZZERIA

RESORT

RESTAURANT

ROADHOUSE

SALOON

SNACK BAR

TAVERN

TEAROOM

TRATTORIA

```
L K M S O P I Z Z E R I A L
L F C A B A R E T S C I U I
A A U T O M A T L U R N L B
H K R Z Y D B P L O C E P N
S V C M T Y K C T H D O H R
S A L O O N C T E H H G A E
E S U O H D A O R S I E E V
M Y B R M R N R E A C T C A
E D R A T E S E U H A A O T
A I R E T E F A C A N R L R
T N Z T N F M F D T T L O O
E E E D O A F V E S I S U S
R R K C L U E E I R N A E E
Y G A R D E N B G N A Y M R
```

For more than 30 years, Samuel Goldwyn (1882-1974) was one of Hollywood's most prominent producers, but he was also known for his misuse of the English language. His many malapropisms became known as "Goldwynisms" and included such gems as "A verbal contract isn't worth the paper it's written on" and "In two words: im-possible."

BLOOPER

BLUNDER

BOBBLE

BONER

BOO-BOO

BOTCH

DEFECT

ERROR

FALLACY

FAULT

FAUX PAS

FLAW

FLUFF

FUMBLE

GAFFE

GLITCH

GOOF

LAPSE

MALAPROP

MISDEAL

MISHAP

MISPLAY

MISPRINT

MISTAKE

OMISSION

OVERSIGHT

SLIP

TYPO

WRONG

```
V S O V R E F H W O U S B F
P V D O H C T I L G S H G P
A V R E N O B N O M W N O O
F R E L B B O B I U O F V R
E F F A G I R S W R F X E P
S L I P S C H T W U P D R A
H M I S T A K E L Y N S S L
U M I E P G R F C U A D I A
O M I S D E A L L P A E G M
O Y G T P L U B X Y T F H M
B I Y O L L F U M B L E T E
O P O A O K A L B O T C H B
O L C T S F K Y A A M T H T
B Y T K U A W L H W R B F G
```

WORDS STARTING WITH "F"

Nothing FANCY here . . . just 30 unrelated words that FEATURE "F" as their first letter.

FACADE

FACIAL

FACTORY

FACTS

FACULTY

FADED

FAINT

FAIRY

FAITH

FAMILIAR

FAMOUS

FANCY

FARCE

FARMER

FATHER

FAUCET

FAVORITE

FEATHER

FEATURE

FEDORA

FICTION

FIFTY

FIXED

FLAME

FLOWER

FORMAL

FORTH

FRAIL

FRAMED

FRONT

```
X S Y T F I F L F F W E R X
S D E M A R F A C A D E C C
H W X W R E R I V M W L F V
M H X T M C F C T O V F V S
I R T A E A I A L U R A Y L
M E L I R F C F T S V I S A
A F C F A C T O R Y S R T X
R C E I I F I F A N C Y F E
S E N M L A O R E H T A F O
I T H V I R N R U L U R T D
C U C T M O U V U C I N C E
V F A A A D L C E F O A V D
F N L E F E A T U R E A R A
A H T R O F F T F D E X I F
```

The canna is a broad-leafed, ornamental tropical plant. Its numerous varieties range in size from 1 1/2 to 7 feet, with foliage streaked with yellow, silver-blue, or maroon. During late summer, a combination of some of the varieties below can produce flowers that will blanket your garden with a brilliant mixture of color.

AIDA

BROCADE

COLE (Rosamund)

CREMORA

CROZY (Madame)

CUPID

DUPONT (Mrs. Pierre S.)

FIESTA

FLAME (Pygmy)

FLAMINGO

FRECKLES

GAIETY

GARBO

GOLD MINE

GRANDE

INTRIGUE

MOHAWK

NEW DAY

NIRVANA

OMEGA

PANACHE

PRETORIA

RED STRIPE

ROSALINDA

ROSEVER

TAJ MAHAL

TOPAZ

TRAVIATA (La)

WYOMING

```
L Z S O P A N A C H E Y U H
A A B L K F D I P U C A U W
H P S R I W O R R I L D N Y
A O C E O M A E E V P W U O
M T S U E S D H T V A E G M
J T A G T S A C O L E N Y I
A Z A I T S T L R M I S A N
T D D R V G E N I M D L O G
Y U I T J A E L A N N Y N R
T P A N Y M R L K P D I C A
E O P I A Z F T G C S A Y N
I N Z L B R O C A D E A Z D
A T F V J T A R O M E R C E
G A R B O Z P M C L D W F M
```

WOODS OF OLD

Many secrets about the past are revealed thanks to PETRIFIED (fossilized) WOOD. Formed in prehistoric times, these remnants of the Earth's life from millions of years ago help UNCOVER clues to the past, such as what plants grew where, and that, in turn, gives clues to climates and climatic changes throughout the ages.

BRANCH
BURIED
CAVITY
CHIP
COLOR
CRACKS
DARK (colors)
DATA
DISCOVER
EARTH
FOREST
FOSSIL
FRAGMENT
IDENTIFY
KNOT
LIGHT (colors)
MINERALS
PATTERNS
PETRIFIED
PRESERVED
PRESSURE
RINGS
ROOT

SEDIMENTS
SLAB
SPECIMEN
STEM
STRUCTURE

STUDY
STUMP
TRUNK
UNCOVER
WOOD

```
Y T S T E M M P I H C C V I
K D F G N S M A R L R V D V
Y B U W N U K T H I E N E F
A U M T T I R T U S V R V O
P R E S S U R E T S O D R M
D I T N N A T R T O C A E I
I E U K E R N N T F N R S N
S D H F O R E S T H U K E E
C V E L H M M K K T G M R R
O A O N I B G N C C I I P A
V C V D T F A U O C A I L L
E D E I F I R T E P T R G S
R S V M T T F P B R A N C H
U B A L S Y S Y E N D O O W
```

UNISEX BABY NAMES

Unisex names can be used for boys or girls. For instance, there is actress and producer DREW Barrymore, and NFL quarterback Drew Bledsoe. You can pick the names by gender as some meanings differ for both sexes. The following is our list of 33 common as well as unusual unisex baby names.

ALEX

AVERY

BEVERLY

BRYN

CAMERON

DALE

DREW

EMERY

FLYNN

GALE

GENE

HOLLIS

INNIS

JORDAN

KELSEY

LINDSAY

MERLE

NOWELL

OAKLEY

PRICE

QUINN

RANDY

ROBIN

SANDY

SHELLEY

TERRY

TYLER

URIAH

VAIL

WHITNEY

XERES

YANCY

ZANE

```
Y M J O S A N D Y V O V H Q
D Y A D W V Y R P E D D H J
X C R Z V Q C E Y E L A D C
M I G A R H C W L R I K C B
Q U I N N I K Y Y R E V A O
T L H E R D Y L U L E M M O
R I G P D Z Y R S O G M E Y
H G G Y F E X E R E S A R R
O B X E L A Y V N A D R O J
L H R L Y C S E O T E B N M
L E E Y N Z I B W T I U A F
I H L A N X N P E N O H I K
S R Y A S D N I L P X C W T
V M T B G P I J L O D F J C
```

STREETS OF SEATTLE

Settled in 1851 by New Yorker David DENNY, Seattle was named after Sealth, the chief of the local Duwamish tribe. Known today as the "Emerald City," Seattle is admired for its lush greenery produced by its misty climate. Gain your footing in the Pacific Northwest by finding 38 Seattle streets in the diagram below.

ALASKAN
ALDER
ALOHA
BELL
BOREN
BROAD
CEDAR
CHERRY
DENNY
DEXTER
EAGLE
EAST ROY
ELLIOTT
FAIRVIEW
JACKSON
JAMES
JOHN
KING
LENORA
MADISON
MAIN
MARION
MELROSE
MERCER
MINOR
OLIVE

PIKE
PONTIUS
REPUBLICAN
SENECA
STEWART
TERRY

THOMAS
VINE
WALL
WESTERN
YALE
YESLER

```
W  P  S  E  Y  R  Y  D  H  H  X  L  R  R
R  A  A  J  R  E  K  I  N  G  K  E  O  I
I  L  L  T  S  U  I  T  N  O  P  N  B  N
P  S  D  L  T  E  R  R  Y  U  I  O  R  N
I  V  E  T  S  E  P  D  B  M  L  R  O  S
K  R  R  N  T  W  W  L  W  I  R  A  A  A
E  R  L  X  E  O  I  E  V  I  N  E  D  M
S  A  E  N  W  C  I  E  S  E  M  A  J  O
O  D  E  C  A  V  A  L  N  T  X  S  U  H
R  E  L  N  R  K  D  Y  L  E  E  T  D  T
L  C  G  I  T  E  S  C  H  E  R  R  Y  M
E  L  A  Y  N  S  M  A  D  I  S  O  N  A
M  F  E  N  V  A  H  O  L  A  B  Y  B  I
J  V  Y  B  N  O  S  K  C  A  J  O  H  N
```

32 — STREETS OF ST. AUGUSTINE

A busy seaport in Florida, St. Augustine is known as the oldest city in the United States. In 1513, Juan Ponce de León took possession of the region for Spain after he landed there in search of the legendary Fountain of Youth. This puzzle features 28 streets of St. Augustine.

ARTILLERY

AVILES

BRIDGE

CADIZ

CARRERA

CASTILLO

CATHEDRAL

CHARLOTTE

CORDOVA

CUNA

DE HAVEN

GRANADA

GROVE

HYPOLITA

KING

MARINE

MAY

MYRTLE

OCEAN

ORANGE

RIBERIA

SARAGOSSA

SOUTH

SPANISH

ST. GEORGE

TREASURY

VALENCIA

WASHING-
TON

```
M A O I A G G Y A E W B D C
E I I C S A R A G O S S A A
G R O V E U C R K Z S T E D
N E R Y S A O I C S H V W I
A B A A R E N A O E O A T Z
R I E R G G V L D G S U Z D
O R E T T O L R A H C S T E
T R S L D I A T I L O P Y H
A U U R T L L N C R S A E A
W S O S Z R G L N K V N G V
E C A I A T Y T E I I I D E
O C U Z O S E M L R U S I N
G R A N A D A E A I Y H R C
T U C H A C S M V Y V C B K
```

Many CARACAS streets, schools, statues, parks, and plazas honor the South American liberator Simón BOLÍVAR, born in this Venezuelan capital in 1783. Today, this prosperous, sophisticated city offers many cultural activities, including theater, concerts, dance, film, and museums. Take a stroll for a glimpse of Caracas high life.

ACACIAS
ALAMEDA
APAMATE
ÁVILA
BALDO
BARALT
BLANDÍN
BOGOTÁ
BOLÍVAR
BOYACA
CARACAS
CARONI
CERRITOS
CHACAITO
COLEGIO
COROMOTO
GAMBOA
LIBERTAD
LIMA
LINCOLN
MADRID
MIRANDA
OLIMPIO

PANTEÓN
PELOTA
PLAYA
REAL
SOLANO

SUCRE
TAMANACO
URDANETA
VEROES
VOLLMER

```
P C P E L O T A V S U C R E
B A L D O L A O D U R O Y V
V G N L A V I L A N D M O G
M V A T O G O B A R A L T I
S E O R E V M T E M N R R L
R A O L S O T I R R E C I C
O S O I A L N L D N T D H M
R C A N P L A Y A S A A A A
A S A C G M N U O C C M D P
V U C O A E I L U A A I I A
I T A L M R A L I R C L R M
L A Y N B N A T O O I S D A
O T O M O R O C A N A M A T
B V B L A N D I N I S B M E
```

THE ALEUTIAN ISLANDS

A chain of more than 150 islands in southwestern Alaska, the Aleutians extend westward in an arc of 1,100 miles. The names of 35 of these treeless, rugged, foggy islands are hidden in this puzzle.

ADAK

AGATTU

AKUN

AKUTAN

ALAID

AMCHITKA

AMLIA

ATKA

ATTU

BOBROF

BOGOSLOF

BULDIR

CHUGUL

DAVIDOF

DELAROF

GARELOI

HERBERT

KAGAMIL

KANAGA

KAVALGA

KISKA

SAMALGA

SEDANKA

SEGUAM

SHEMYA

TAGALAK

TANADAK

TANAGA

TIGALDA

ULAK

UMAK

UMNAK

UNALASKA

UNIMAK

YUNASKA

```
A D K S E G U A M L I A D F
L G C A R K G T V I A E A V
A D A K A A M M T S L K K U
I F T N N L A D L A G I T V
D L M A A U T I R M G T I A
H U T D N K M O C A A A H S
E G V E T A F K H L A U C H
R U D S G O D O G G M H M E
B H N A D U N A L A S K A M
E C K I K N R A K S A N U Y
R V V N M E V Y N U O R U A
T A G A L A K U T A N G T I
D S A O K A K S I K E K O R
B R I D L U B G F O R B O B
```

SAY CHEESE!

Although the U.S. produces more cheese than any other country, France consumes the most. You'll find lots of your favorite cheeses in the list below.

ASIAGO

BEL PAESE

CAMEMBERT

CHEDDAR

CHESHIRE

COLBY

DANBO

DERBY

DUNLOP

EDAM

ESROM

FONTINA

GOUDA

GRUYÈRE

HAVARTI

JARLSBERG

LEYDEN

LIMBURGER

MYSOST

PROVOLONE

RICOTTA

ROMANO

ROQUEFORT

SAGA

SAPSAGO

SBRINZ

STILTON

ST. OTHO

SWISS

TILSIT

```
A C C Y D U N L O P R B W M
B P E O N A M O R G O U D A
R Y S T I L T O N T A L B D
A S R M R F V T I L S I T E
D R O H T O T S O S Y M S U
D E M Z L N Q G G C T B H A
E Y Z O S T E U R R I U H V
H R N S Y I A O E U S R A L
C E I B J N G B B F Y G V E
S W R H H A M J S Q O E A Y
S E B E S E A P L E B R R D
D A S P M E C G R S N Y T E
Y I A A Y T H Y A O A F I N
T S C O L B Y C J S D R E H
```

What's your IMPRESSION of a puzzle in which the CONCEPT is to uncover 28 THOUGHT processes? We hope you think it's a great IDEA!

BELIEF

CONCEPT

DAYDREAM

DOUBT

FANCY

FANTASY

HYPOTHESIS

IDEA

IMAGE

IMPRESSION

INKLING

INSPIRATION

MEDITATION

MEMORY

MUSING

NOTION

QUESTION

REFLECTION

REVERIE

SENTIMENT

SPECULATION

SUPPOSITION

SURMISE

THEORY

THESIS

THOUGHT

VIEW

WHIM

```
S P E C U L A T I O N N Y G
I I R L P E N P B C F D R N
S N M I H W W O O U A I O O
E K S A G L B N I Y O I E I
H L N P G N C E D T T D H T
T I O K I E I R L I O H T C
O N I M P R E S S I O N H E
P G T T Y A A O U I E U O L
Y M A G M S P T F M S F U F
H E T I N P A V I A W E G E
C M I Q U E S T I O N Q H R
H O D S D S N B N E N C T T
M R E I R E V E R A W M Y F
I Y M E S I M R U S F V E N
```

TREE-FOR-ALL

Become one with nature as you search through the UNDERBRUSH of this puzzle for the following terms related to trees. You'll find everything from a SAPLING to a FOREST full of FOLIAGE in the grid below.

BARK

BOUGH

BRANCH

BRUSH

CHAPARRAL
(thicket of shrubs)

FOLIAGE

FOREST

FROND (leaf)

GROVE

HEATH

HEDGE

JUNGLE

KNOT

LEAF

LIMB

LUMBER

ORCHARD

PULP

RAVINE

ROOTS

SAPLING

SHRUB

SPRIG

STUMP

THICKET

TIMBER

TRUNK

TWIG

UNDERBRUSH

VEGETATION

VINE

WOODLAND

```
P M U T S T S E R O F U F P
R I G S H C N A R B H A S W
J E V E T I C M P J E U T K
U L D O V O C H H L N W N R
H G A A L R O K B D I U V P
E N R R P C T R E G R N E T
A U B U R H S R L T B R G R
T J L K R A B E V I N E E A
H P A G I R P S G G B B T G
J O H M U D C A E A M M A W
D O K S B N T V H I I U T J
R H H G U O O W T C L L I V
A L D D N R D N A L D O O W
H F C K G F B O U G H T N F
```

Undoubtedly, Mark Twain was a man of many words. Now let's see if you can find the following words that have been created by using the letters in his real name — Samuel Langhorne Clemens.

ALLEGE

AMONG

ANGEL

CAMEL

CAUSE

CHALLENGE

CLEANER

COLLEGE

COMMA

EAGER

ERASE

GENERAL

GLEAN

GROUSE

HAMMER

HUMAN

LANGUOR

LASER

LEASE

LEMON

LESSON

MANAGER

MANNER

NAMER

NUMERAL

ORANGE

REACH

SALON

SCALE

SCANNER

SEASHELL

SHALL

SHORE

SMALLER

SUMMER

SUMMON

```
G N O S S E L C H L O L M M
H N S R S A H E L A C S N S
M U H U E N N E S N M A U U
S A O C L M U E S G O M A U
H R R E L L A M S U M M E R
G C E L H S M N E O A O E R
N N A N H M S G N R L C S L
E H N E A R N O G E A O A E
S A L O R E O L L C R L E M
A L S R L G L R E G E L L A
R S R L N A S C A N N E R C
E L A O S E S O N N E G U E
M H M E H U M A N A G E R A
C A R S N M E S A N G E L G
```

CEREALS & THEIR PRODUCTS

Whole or ground, the edible seed-like fruits of CEREAL grasses have supplied the principal food of man and domestic animals for thousands of years. You'll find some grains and a few of the foods we make from them today camouflaged below.

BAGELS

BISCUITS

BRAN

BREAD

BUNS

CAKE

CEREAL

COOKIES

CORN

CRACKERS

DUMPLINGS

FARINA

FLOUR

GRITS

HOMINY

MACARONI

MEAL

MILLET

NOODLES

OATS

PANCAKES

PASTRY

PRETZELS

RAVIOLI

RICE

ROLLS

SCONES

SESAME

SPAGHETTI

WAFFLES

WHEAT

```
I  T  T  E  H  G  A  P  S  M  V  E  E  A
N  R  E  M  O  O  R  C  E  C  I  R  B  F
O  W  S  K  M  S  T  A  O  M  O  E  B  W
R  O  W  G  I  F  L  O  U  R  S  N  R  T
A  R  A  R  N  A  K  E  S  F  N  Z  E  H
C  M  F  I  Y  I  M  E  G  L  T  L  A  S
A  S  F  T  E  A  L  T  A  A  L  G  D  S
M  S  L  S  S  D  F  P  E  I  B  O  R  T
B  Z  E  E  O  Y  K  H  M  C  W  E  R  I
I  U  S  O  Z  R  W  V  E  U  K  V  S  U
T  S  N  K  K  T  E  R  A  C  D  K  I  C
O  Z  A  S  U  S  E  K  A  C  N  A  P  S
F  A  R  I  N  A  S  R  A  V  I  O  L  I
S  M  B  E  L  P  C  Y  P  C  E  T  M  B
```

40

ON THE CARPET

Hopefully you won't be fooled by this puzzle. Just "loop" BROAD-LOOM, SHAG, and 31 other terms associated with carpeting.

ACTION BAC

ANTIMICROBIAL

AXMINSTER

BECK

BERBER

BROADLOOM

CONTRACT

CUT PILE

DENIER

DENSITY

FIBER

FILAMENT

GAUGE

GRAPHIC

JUTE

KUSTER

LATEX

LEVEL (loop)

OLEFIN

PILE (height)

PIN DOT

PLUSH

POLYESTER

SHAG

SKEIN

SOLUTION

SPACE

STATIC (control)

TEXTURED

TUFT

URETHANE

VELVA (loop)

WOOL

```
C F S I T D I D X E T A L P
F R K A E N E S C Y X J L D
I K E N V N E A T M D U Y E
B J I T S L B M I A S T R R
E E N I S N E N A H T E R U
R X T M O E S V I L C I K T
B Y F I A T Y G E F I X C X
E E T C E C E L W L E F E E
R C B R O A D L O O M L B T
A A X O S R V O I P I G O O
J P T B H T W P F P V A X D
I S F I A N O I T U L O S N
E G U A G O K U S T E R S I
R B T L K C C I H P A R G P
```

42

CASTLES OF SCOTLAND

Scotland is famous for its lochs, or lakes (and a monster that may reside in one!), but it's also known for its castles. Here are just some of the hundreds that are found throughout the land.

ANNAN
BEAULY
BOTHWELL
CAWDOR
CRAIL
CRATHES
CULLEN
DOON LOCH
DRUM
DUFFUS
DUMFRIES
DUNS
EDZELL
ELCHO
ELGIN
FINTRY
FYVIE
GLAMIS
GLEN COVA
GUTHRIE
HAILES
INSCH
KEITH

KELLIE
KILLIN
NEWARK
OYNE
ROSYTH
TOWARD

TURRIFF
UDNY
WICK
WYRE
YARROW
YESTER

```
E S U F F U D L G K C I W D
R K N Y S R L L E W H T O B
Y E V E U I E I V K A O R O
W I T M L N L H F I N T R Y
E T C S C L T F L L N N A N
K H I O E Y U D O L S S Y E
T L V K S Y D C M I E N C O
K A Y O Z A H U M N F Z U H
Y R R T K I Y A M W F S D D
M E A O H C L E S F I E N E
M L N W D G W I B D R L Y B
B G N A E W G U T H R I E Z
L I A R C N A Y Y L U A E B
M N N D B V U C R A T H E S
```

43

Hidden in the diagram below are 37 items commonly found at a flea market, from BOOKS to YARN. So put on your hunting caps, solvers, and see how quickly you can bag these bountiful bargains.

BOOKS
BUTTONS
CAMERAS
CARDS (baseball)
CERAMICS
CHINA
CLOTHES

COINS
COLOGNE
CUPS
CUTLERY
DISHES
DVDS
FANS

GAMES
GEMS
GLASSWARE
LAMPS
LINENS
MACRAMÉ (items)
MAPS
MEDALS
MODELS
MONEY (foreign)
MUSIC (sheet)
PANS
PERFUME
PEWTER
POTS
RECORDS
RUGS
SHELLS
STAMPS
STATUES
TOOLS
VIDEOS
YARN

```
V S L L E H S L A D E M S C
P T C U C O R T V I D E O S
U T C I W G L C A I H L B T
O N O U M L B U T T O N S O
Y C R O P A A T O G U D E P
E N H E L S R L N A R E H D
B M B I T S C E L A M P S Y
C O U T N W M R C E S P I S
D N O F L A E Y S O A U D M
V E N K R R S P Y N R G L N
D Y R C S E M N S L E D O M
S N A F M A P S I M M N S V
I M Y A T S K T S O A L I G
R U G S T I M U S I C I R L
```

With a population of 3.2 million, Melbourne is Australia's second largest CITY after Sydney. Internationally known for its excellent food, beer, wines, and festivals, Melburnians love any excuse to hold a party. Sports-minded Melbourne is also Australia's financial hub and fashion center, and its broad, tree-lined boulevards make the city perfect for strolling.

A'BECKET
ALBERT
BATMAN
BOURKE
CECIL
CITY
CLOWES
COLLINS
COVENTRY
DORCAS
DUDLEY
ELIZABETH
FLINDERS
GEORGE
GRANT
GREY
HODDLE
HOTHAM
KING
LATROBE
LORIMER
LYGON
MARKET
MORAY

POWLETT
QUEEN
SIMPSON
SPRING
ST. KILDA

STUART
SWAN
THERRY
VICTORIA
WALSH

```
C  S  C  K  E  K  R  U  O  B  K  L  N  H
H  E  G  R  O  E  G  H  M  I  V  A  O  C
G  U  C  D  M  D  A  D  L  I  K  T  S  F
C  O  A  I  U  M  B  I  C  Y  H  R  P  P
P  O  R  D  L  C  I  T  Y  A  R  O  M  A
U  O  L  M  Z  H  O  R  M  R  M  B  I  L
L  E  W  L  S  R  T  T  Q  R  E  S  B
Y  K  F  L  I  N  D  E  R  S  U  E  G  E
G  E  A  A  E  N  S  K  B  W  C  E  H  R
O  W  R  V  O  T  S  C  M  A  R  K  E  T
N  M  O  G  U  C  T  E  G  N  Z  G  H  N
C  C  N  A  M  T  A  B  S  P  R  I  N  G
K  I  R  D  O  R  C  A  S  E  W  O  L  C
K  T  N  A  R  G  V  G  H  O  D  D  L  E
```

In 1874, Mennonite immigrants from Russia brought the Turkey Red variety of winter wheat with them to Kansas. The successful agricultural production of this crop has earned Kansas the nickname "Breadbasket of America." Join the search to find 45 towns dotting the plains of the 34th state of the Union.

AETNA
AGRA
ALAMOTA
ARMA
BALA
BERN
BUXTON

CAIRO
CHETOPA
CORA
ERIE
FORMOSO
GAS CITY
GRETNA

HARRIS
HAYS
HEALY
HIAWATHA
HOXIE
HOYT
HYMER
IONIA
JUNIATA
KEATS
LYLE
MILO
MODOC
NEOLA
NILES
ORION
OTIS
RENO
ROLLA
SAXMAN
SHAW
STULL
TASCO
TICE
TOULON
TREGO
TROY
TYRO
XENIA
YODER
ZOOK

```
J H X S Z O O K O T H H E N
N I Y O S H C R K I S R J A
D A O R E Y Y S X C I H L B
H W R I L T W M A E H Z A O
Z A T A I N U J E T N C R W
N T E C N S E D T R E I G I
J H S L R K I O N A O O A O
R A A E Y N U T A N L L S N
G C D P A L A M O T A I L I
F O R M O S O O N E R M R A
Y R X N O T X U B R I E R X
B A L A R A E W A G C X G A
S T U L L E A H O Y T F O O
S M M X O K B O C O D O M H
```

STREETS OF BUENOS AIRES

Buenos Aires, Argentina, is a walking city, full of parks, wide boulevards, and narrow lanes lined with turn-of-the-century architecture. After relaxing in one of its many plazas, take a walk to the magnificently gilded COLÓN Theater where musicians say the acoustics make it one of the finest concert halls in the world.

ALCORTA

ALVEAR

ARENALES

ARROYO

AYACUCHO

BALCARCE

BOLIVAR

BOLLINI

CALLAO

CERRITO

CHILE

COLOMBIA

COLÓN
  (Plaza)

CÓRDOBA

DEFENSA

FLORIDA

ITALIA (Plaza)

JUNCAL

JUNIN

LAS HERAS

LAVALLE

MAIPÚ

MAYO (Plaza)

ORO

PAMPA

PENA

PERÚ

POSADAS

SAN MARTIN (Plaza)

SANTA FE

SUIPACHA

VIAMONTE

```
T F C T U T U M A N H U Q S
A L C O R T A P A I O P U A
C O O C L K B Y E T G I B R
O R R A B O A R I R P A O E
L I E O L C M R W A U M L H
O D L L U L R B C M N A I S
N A I C F E A H I N V A V A
A N H E C R A C L A B R A L
I O C O J O X P L S A E R A
V J Y U M P R L M E N N R C
S A N T A F E D V A E A O N
M I T A L I A L O D P L Y U
N E T N O M A I V B Z E O J
Y D D E F E N S A D A S O P
```

COMMUNITY centers are where the people of a NEIGHBORHOOD can get together for cultural, recreational, or SOCIAL ACTIVITIES. It's at these meeting places that friendships are formed with other MEMBERS of the community.

ACTIVITIES

ADULTS

BINGO

CHILDREN

CITY

COMMUNITY

CONCERTS

CRAFTS

CULTURE

DANCES

EDUCATION

EVENTS

GAMES

GATHER

LEARN

LECTURES

MEETINGS

MEMBERS

MUSIC

NEIGHBOR-HOOD

PLAYS

READ

RECREATION

SHARE

SOCIAL

SPORTS

TEENS

THEATER

TOWN

VOLUNTEERS

WORKSHOPS

```
T C D P L A Y S O C I A L G
H S P O H S K R O W C E B A
E T E C O N C E R T S V K M
A L M R F H C P I S T E I E
T U Y Y U R R V K D R N C S
E D U C A T I O N W O T H R
R A A F O T C I B I P S I E
U E T N I M O E T H S W L B
T S H E C G M A L O G Y D M
L H S T N E E U C S T I R E
U A P I A R S G N I T E E M
C R B O C G A E C I S K N N
O E R E A D E E B S T U T D
B S R E E T N U L O V Y M I
```

ALL ABOARD

Amtrak Railroad's official name is the National Railroad PASSENGER Corporation. Only 25 employees worked for Amtrak when its service started on May 1, 1971, compared to the 22,000 working for the company today. Of its 2,141 railroad cars, Amtrak operates 760 COACH cars while BAGGAGE cars make up the rest of the fleet. Enjoy your trip as you search for these railroad terms.

BAGGAGE

BERTH

BRAKES

COACH

COMMUTER

CONDUCTOR

CROSSTIE

DEPOT

DINER

ENGINEER

FREIGHT

LOCOMOTIVE

MAIL

MONORAIL

PASSENGER

PORTER

REFRIGERATOR

SEATS

SIGNALS

STATION

TERMINAL

TOURISTS

TRANSPORT

TRESTLE

VEHICLE

VIADUCT

```
S S B G S L A N G I S A G M
P T S E T L L O S E K A R B
K A A G H I B A G G A G E C
O E S T G A A O N E E V F T
V S T S I R U O T I I F R T
I P T F E O E A F T M A I L
A R R A R N N T O S N R G D
D K E T F O G M R S G H E T
U I E T I M O E P O T D R T
C O N D U C T O R R P E A P
T A I E O M R T E C S P T A
R F G L R T M B D T N O O R
K G N P G H K O L C P T R A
B V E H I C L E C O A C H I
```

"Y," IT'S A GIRL!

Although she may not be as famous as MARILYN Monroe, JAYNE Mansfield was one of Hollywood's most colorful personalities. Bigger than life, she was the epitome of the blonde bombshell of the 1950s. Throughout her career she would portray cartoonish, dizzy blondes even though it's been reported that she possessed a genius IQ! Sadly, like Marilyn before her, she also died tragically young. We've hidden 35 female names containing the letter "Y" in the grid below.

ABBY   CATHY   EMILY

BETTY   CHERYL   EVELYN

CAROLYN   CINDY   FAYE

CARYN   ELYSE   GAYLE

HOLLY JAYNE JOYCE JUDY KELLY LUCY LYDIA LYNN MARILYN MARY MERYL MOLLY NANCY PENNY PHYLLIS RUBY SALLY SHERRY SHIRLEY TAMMY TIFFANY YOLANDA YVONNE

```
O Y G E Y L A U V M L A J P
I L J E A C D M Y S H I A Y
S L D A V H U O A J U D Y B
D E S Y L E J L M R N Y N A
F K T I K R L L G A Y L E R
C A R O L Y N Y L I R A M J
B N Y B E L H O N E A B J J
S E P E N N Y A A N C B P I
Y H T A C E N H O L L Y R N
E L E T L C A O P D Y U O F
J F I R Y I F V V M B L H J
J F I M R G F V M Y D N I C
C H R G E Y I A Y S E P M T
S E P A M I T V I L G G J F
```

SHARK SPECIES

It's been almost 30 years since Steven Spielberg released *Jaws*, a film that kept people in theaters — and out of the ocean! Swimming around in the dark depths of the diagram below are 30 species of shark, including the "star" of that summer blockbuster, the GREAT WHITE. See how long it takes you to net these evasive underwater animals.

ANGEL

BASKING

BIGNOSE

BLACKTIP

BLUE

BRAMBLE

DOGFISH

DUSKY

FINETOOTH

GREAT WHITE

GREENLAND

HAMMER-
HEAD

INSULAR

KITEFIN

LEMON

MAKO

NIGHT

NURSE

PORBEAGLE

PORTUGUESE

REEF

SAND

SILKY

SIXGILL

SMALLTAIL

SMOOTHHOUND

SPINNER

THRESHER

TIGER

WHALE

```
T N H P E A B S F H X U W S
H E U O B L A C K T I P M I
B L R R B H L E M O N O N X
D B R B S A N D L O O G E G
O M E E S E U G U T R O P I
G A H A M M E R H E A D H L
F R S G C R N H A N N W F L
I B E L E I O T T I G E R E
S A R E F U W I G F E A S L
H S H E N H L H O R L O I A
M K T D I L T B G U N K L H
L I A T L L A M S G W A K W
K N E S R E N N I P S M Y F
D G Y C T X I B D U S K Y U
```

50 LOST & FOUND

It's important to WATCH your personal belongings whenever you're out-and-about, otherwise they'll end up in a lost-and-found bin or, if you're lucky, in the hands of a good Samaritan. This list is comprised of items that have appeared in lost-and-found listings.

ARTWORK

BACKPACK

BOOKS

BRACELET

BROOCH

CALCULATOR

CELL PHONE

COAT

EARRINGS

GLASSES

GLOVES

HANDBAG

HATS

INSTRUMENT
(musical)

JACKET

KEYS

MAKEUP
CASE

MONEY

NECKLACE

PETS

PURSE

RING

SCARF

SHOES

SWEATER

UMBRELLA

WALLET

WATCH

ZIP DISK

```
V U E S R U P I D A H H H I
L D S A G W I U T E L L A W
B I B E T N E M U R T S N I
F O R N S T I B B R C M D J
G L O V E S M R D O I O B C
V K O K E C A E R T K N A S
V P C O S C K L E A R E G T
R A H A E P E L G L E Y F E
J S R L P V U A A U T L E P
K V E Y S K P H S C A R F K
R T D W A T C H Z L E C E S
K R O W T R A A E A W Y T C
D Z I P D I S K B C S A K O
U H T P P C E L L P H O N E
```

STREETS OF PITTSBURGH

Pittsburgh, Pennsylvania, one of the world's largest inland ports, is a center for research, commerce, and the steel industry. It is also the home of three professional sports teams: the Penguins, the Pirates, and the Steelers.

ALCOR

ARCH

ATWOOD

AVERY

BATES

BEELEN

CATO

CEDAR

CENTRE

COLWELL

CRAFT

DAKOTA

DESOTO

ETNA

FORBES

FORT PITT

FRANCIS

FRENCH

GRANT

HODGE

ISABELLA

LIBERTY

LOCUST

LYTTON

MAGEE

OHARA

OLIVER

PENN

REED

RIDGE

RIVER

ROBERTS

WARD

WEBSTER

WOOD

WYLIE

```
K H C Q T S U C O L W E L L
N Y T R E B I L T F K N Z D
N W N G A Q Y X O J E H M A
E R D P E F N R S L P C D K
P I J O V S T R E B O R E O
R V L R O P J E D V H A E T
E E B Y I W B H Q R A Z G A
T R A T W O O D F L E L A L
S E T Z Y D F N C O G E M L
B V E N G R O O D C R W D E
E I S E E T R H Z S A B Q B
W L C N T C E D A R N T E A
K O C Y N F X R D R T Z O S
N H L J A M S I C N A R F I
```

Mountain biking combines the ADVENTURE of OFF-ROAD excitement with the speed of cycling. Bikers wear a HELMET and GLOVES to protect themselves from a rough ride in the WOODS, and the bikes are made with lightweight frames, absorbent SHOCKS, durable GRIPS, and TOE CLIPS.

ADVENTURE

BIKE

BRAKES

CLIMB

COURSE

CRANK

CRUISE

EXERCISE

FRAME

GEARS

GLOVES

GRIPS

HELMET

HILLS

JUMP

MILES

OFF-ROAD

PEDAL

PUDDLES

RACE

ROCKS

SHIFT

SHOCKS

SPORT

TERRAIN

TIRES

TOE CLIPS
(connect a rider's feet and toes to the pedals)

TRACTION

TRAIL

TRAIN

WATER BOTTLE

WOODS

```
V M H R T R F E T C J I D I
K P H I L L S S O T K B C T
M S R B I S N K E B R W W C
H E R A I P C X C L N O W H
S J R A W I E L L O D O P P
J T O T E R R A I N H D I S
D B C F C G D T P M V S U B
U I K I D E C S S K B S C P
H K S H P A D V E N T U R E
O E E S R U O C F K R T A S
B E L T T O B R E T A W N I
E R I M U R A V F N I R K U
J U M P E M A F R F N R B R
B R A C E T J S E V O L G C
```

BROWSING FOR BARGAINS

Have you ever visited a consignment shop? It's a great place to find inexpensive CLOTHING, FURNITURE, or JEWELRY if you're on a tight budget. Browse through the list of 28 words associated with this type of shop, and then try to find them in the grid below.

ACCEPTANCE

ACCESSORY

ANTIQUE

BUSINESS

CLOTHING

CONDITION

CONTRACT

COUNTER

CRAFT

DEAL

DISPLAY

EXCHANGE

FURNITURE

HARDWARE

INVENTORY

JEWELRY

MERCHAN-
DISE

OWNER

POLICY

PRICE

PURCHASE

RACK

REDUCTION

RETURN

SHELF

SIZE

VALUE

VARIETY

```
P A M Y T E I R A V L U P N
O W N E R C O N D I T I O N
B D L Y R O S S E C C A L R
E U L A V C T K O D C V I U
R M S E E F H N C C F Z C T
D F Z I A D T A E A U F Y E
I I L R N R H P N V R W G R
S E C E A E T G R D N N J A
P U R C H A S E S E I I E W
L Q T R N S T S C H T S W D
A I N C H N O I T C U D E R
Y T E S U B R O I I R P L A
S N C O Q P L N V A E F R H
N A C E X C H A N G E V Y I
```

54

FISHING SOCIETY

Whether you're hooked on fishing or just looking for some new **FRIENDS** with whom to **SHARE** your **INTEREST**, you might want to **JOIN** a local fishing **CLUB**. Sure, as a **MEMBER** you'll probably have to pay some **DUES**, but in the long run, the **ADVICE** you share and the helpful **TIPS** you receive will make it all worthwhile.

ADVICE	BASICS	DUES
AMATEUR	CASTING	EXPERT
ANGLING	CHARTS	FRIENDS
AWARDS	CLUB	GUIDE
BANQUET	CONTEST	HOBBY

HOW-TO
IDEAS
INTEREST
JOIN
LICENSE
MEETING
MEMBER
NEWSLETTER
POLES
SEMINAR
SHARE
SOCIAL
SPEAKER
TACKLE
TECHNIQUE
TIPS
TRIPS

```
D O T W O H O S S P I R T E
R U S J P G K V L G O G J R
E N E T F A N L N D R L T A
K Q T S R M L I C E N S E H
A O N S I A L A T B U L C S
E G O N E G H T I E K J H X
P X C O N R E C M C E W N N
S T P A D L E K A E O M I N
C E G E S E F T G B M S Q A
I U M W R T C U N M F B U W
S Q E I N T I I T I P S E A
A N K P N D L N V U O C U R
B A I D E A S K G D K J D D
Y B B O H H R U E T A M A S
```

LET YOUR HAIR DOWN

Did you ever stop to think about how many different ways you can STYLE your hair? Perhaps some of the 29 words in our list, all related to hair and its care, will provide you with some possibilites — enough, we hope, to keep you from ever having a bad hair day! Why not STREAK through the diagram and find them all?

BLEACH

BRAID

BRUSH

CLIP

COLOR

CURL

FROST

KNOT

PART

PERM

PLAIT

PULL

RINSE

ROLL

SCULPT

SHAMPOO

SHORTEN

STRAIGHTEN

STREAK

STYLE

TEASE

TINT

TRIM

TUCK

TWIST

WASH

WAVE

WIND

WRAP

```
V L C S S V C T A P C Y O O
K D N H A H N D Y D H B M W
V P I L C I O O H R G S N R
D H Y A T S O R F S G K O Y
P L E M R E P I T I A L P K
M L H T T B M R W E L Y T S
B U K R W R A P R I N S E M
M P K I F I H T M B N H A T
M P G M G R S M R D W D S S
O M N H K C U T H A L M E T
M I T O U O R U O S P V B H
O E H L H L B B T N A A H V
N C P G N O S M O W K W Y S
U T T C U R L G N A O E B T
```

Once you MEET the word list below, you will see that each entry contains the letter combination "ME." For additional puzzle fun, why not find some kind of TIMER so you can see how long it takes to find all 38 words.

ACME
AMEND
AMETHYST
AUGMENT
CAMEL
CAMEO

COMET
COMMENT
COMMERCE
DIAMETER
ELEMENT
EMERALD

EMERGE
ENAMEL
FAME
FARMER
GARMENT
HAMMER
HELMET
IMMERSE
MEAN
MEDAL
MEDIA
MEDIC
MEET
MELLOW
MELON
MEOW
MESH
MESS
METAL
METRIC
OMELET
REMEMBER
SEMESTER
TIMER
TORMENT
WOMEN

```
O D E C N A F H A M M E R M
C L E A E W B A E N M L M E
C H W M B B S D M R E E O O
D I C E L E I I R E T M M W
F A D O I A G E R R A E T A
I D N E M A B R I L L N E D
E T N E M M O C E E E T W M
R E T S E M E S T M E S S S
T E N M R M S R G A E Y O T
R E E E S M E U C N N H S E
E R M G E G A R M E N T U M
R I R L F N L F A R M E R O
T W O M E N W O L L E M A C
I N T D E H S E M E D A L L
```

BREAKFAST IN BED

Breakfast in bed makes any day seem like a special occasion. So lie back, relax, and enjoy your MORNING meal as you place a circle around each entry in the diagram below.

ANNIVER-
SARY

BACON

BAGEL

BUTTER

CEREAL

COFFEE

COOK

CREAM

EGGS

FRUIT

GARNISH

HONEY

JELLY

JUICE

MILK

MORNING

MOTHER'S
DAY

MUFFIN

NEWSPAPER

OMELET

PANCAKES

PREPARE

SAUSAGE

SUGAR

SYRUP

TOAST

TRAY

VALENTINE'S DAY

WAFFLES

YOGURT

```
S  B  E  V  W  M  D  T  R  U  G  O  Y  V
M  S  A  Y  R  A  S  R  E  V  I  N  N  A
O  V  M  C  U  A  F  G  L  L  S  R  B  G
T  C  O  E  O  C  O  F  F  E  E  A  I  L
H  M  B  T  C  N  T  J  L  P  G  M  R  I
E  A  D  M  B  I  T  E  A  E  A  G  O  R
R  R  S  O  U  H  U  P  L  S  S  Y  S  R
S  Y  A  R  T  F  S  J  F  G  U  G  E  Y
D  V  F  P  T  W  I  N  C  A  G  K  S
A  V  A  L  E  N  T  I  N  E  S  D  A  Y
Y  N  K  N  R  R  N  G  N  R  B  R  C  R
I  M  W  O  B  R  P  C  R  E  A  M  N  U
A  Y  E  N  O  H  U  H  U  A  T  G  A  P
K  L  I  M  P  C  M  J  E  L  L  Y  P  W
```

This puzzle is an **ELECTRIC** one as we've hidden many shades of the color blue, from **AQUA** to **TURQUOISE**, in the diagram below.

AQUA

AZURE

BABY*

BERYL

CADET

CERULEAN

COBALT*

CORNFLOWER

DENIM*

DUSTY*

ELECTRIC*

FRENCH*

INDIGO

LAPIS

METALLIC*

MIDNIGHT*

NAVY

NEON*

OCEAN

PACIFIC*

PASTEL*

PERIWINKLE

ROBIN'S-EGG*

ROYAL*

SAPPHIRE

STEEL*

TEAL

TURQUOISE

```
R N C Q I M O D C R U D W R
F R E N C H C Q U T L P G Z
Z L R R R O B I N S E G G E
L K U P U O S Y L R T A O F
E R L R C Z O A I L S Y L D
S T E E L F A W P B A B Y E
I F A W L W I U F P P T R N
O N N A O N N T T U H A E I
U G Y V K L L P C G N I B M
Q O I L L A F S I P A L R C
R G E D B W V N M Z V U A E
U N E O N S D E R Y Y D Q W
T S C I F I C A P O E Z S A
C Y O H M N C I R T C E L E
```

* *followed by blue*

WORDS WITH "ACT" IN THEM

In this ACTION-packed puzzle, test your reactions by trying to find all of the words containing the letters "ACT" hidden in the diagram below.

ACTION	INTACT	STALACTITE
ACTIVE	LACTOSE	SUBTRACT
ACTIVITY		
ACTRESS	PRACTICAL	TACTIC
ACTUAL	REACT	TRACTOR
ATTRACT		
BENEFACTOR		
CATARACT		
CHARACTER		
CONTACT		
CONTRACT		
DETRACT		
DISTRACT		
ENACT		
EXACT		
FRACTURE		
GALACTIC		
IMPACT		

```
C M U E M G T C A P M I A E
I O F T S N A U V E N T V T
T N N O C O U L T T T I C S
C R B T H I T I A R T A L E
A O E P A T T C A C E V A C
T T N L R C T C A R T B U S
X C E I A A T A U L F I T R
Y A F L C H Y T I V I T C A
P R A C T I C A L E C R A L
V T C L E A Y R T C X A X O
S S T N R E X A C T R E S S
A I O F T X T C A R T E D R
L D R T C A R T N O C L C Y
V V R Y I G F U E Y O N Y D
```

We all know that such landmarks as the Louvre Museum and the Eiffel Tower are in the city of Paris, France. But did you know that BLANCHE, IÉNA, and VENDÔME Squares are also pleasant sites in this City of Light? Search the puzzle to find all the squares listed below.

BALARD	CLICHY	GAILLON
BASTILLE	CONCORDE	IÉNA
BLANCHE	DE GAULLE	JUSSIEU
CHÂTELET	ÉTOILE	MADELEINE

```
F  P  T  U  P  P  T  E  R  N  E  S  E  N
S  T  R  E  S  I  V  R  A  P  O  T  O  G
D  H  F  T  R  T  G  H  V  R  O  R  A  A
M  E  L  L  I  T  S  A  B  I  E  I  O  S
N  A  B  U  A  V  R  O  L  D  L  C  M  O
O  T  U  Y  F  B  N  E  A  L  G  U  A  R
I  R  V  B  U  N  H  C  O  V  E  A  D  T
T  E  J  E  E  C  O  N  C  O  R  D  E  U
A  J  N  Y  N  R  D  E  G  A  U  L  L  E
N  C  I  A  T  D  T  R  H  M  E  E  E  I
O  S  L  U  N  B  O  O  A  T  J  L  I  S
E  B  O  U  O  V  C  M  A  L  N  I  N  S
D  A  R  E  P  O  J  H  E  E  A  A  E  U
O  Y  H  C  I  L  C  R  D  D  F  B  P  J
```

MAUBERT

NATION

ODÉON

OPÉRA

PANTHÉON

PARVIS

PIGALLE

PONT-NEUF

SORBONNE

TERNES

TERTRE

THÉÂTRE

TROCADÉRO

VAUBAN

VENDÔME

LOVELY LACE

Lace, which is usually made of cotton, linen, or silk, is a fine fabric or netting woven into ornamental designs. In the list below, you will find 28 varieties of this lace.

ALGERIAN

ANTWERP

BELGIAN

CHURCH

DIAMOND

ESCALIER

FRENCH

HONITON

HUGUENOT

LIMERICK

MADEIRA

MALTESE

MECHLIN

MENIN

MOORISH

NORMANDY

OYAH

PENICHE

POUSSIN

RIPON

RUSSIAN

SORRENTO

SPANISH

SWISS

TONDER

TRANSFER

TURKISH

VENETIAN

```
H O T N E R R O S S I W S E
O D U F K U E G N A K Y M S
N N H B S S F I Y N D A A D
I O S S P M S K L N I H L G
T M I Y R N N N A A S N T R
O A R I E D A M R I C P E G
N I O O W I R I K I Y S S M
D D O B T O T R R P P B E F
E B M E N H U G U E N O T R
R G N L A T H B C N G Y N E
Y E V G P O U S S I N L T N
V C A I Y N I L H C E M A C
T S P A N I S H C H U R C H
M E H N A K C I R E M I L P
```

FULL HOUSE

If you're hungry for Full House fun, we think this puzzle crammed with another 54 terms will SATE your solving appetite. When you're done, NONE of the letters in the diagram will remain uncircled.

ALLUDE
AMICABLE
ARGUED
ATTACK
AUDIBLY
BALLOON
BLEACHED
BLURB
BOOT

BRINK
CEDE
CHASM
CHIDE
CHILLY
COED
DATA
DIRE
EMBRACE

EXOTIC
HAZY
HOLY
LABOR
LACY
LEAGUE
LEARNED
LEVEL
LEVITY
MADLY
MARK
MIND
MYSTIC
MYTHOLOGY
NODE
NONE
ONSET
PROVISION
RABBLE
REQUISITE
ROIL
SATE
SEEN
SHOT
SIDLE
SQUID
TABOO
THIMBLE
TILE
TOPAZ
TOURS
TRENCH
TRIO
VACATIONS
VENT
WAYS

```
E D E H C A E L B A C I M A
V X D E N R A E L E A G U E
A E O D E O C V D Y L D A M
C T N T R I O E L D I S A B
A I A T I L E L B B A R R R
T S L D D C I M L T K U D A
I I L I H H W Y C A L O E C
O U U I C H A S M B B T U E
N Q D N I M Y T H O L O G Y
S E E N O I S I V O R P R L
E R B R I N K C A T T A A O
T H I M B L E V I T Y Z A H
```

PLANT NAMES PRECEDED BY "GROUND" | **63**

Most gardeners hate ground ELDER because its creeping underground stems spread so rapidly, but it does have its uses. At one time, it was grown and used to treat arthritis and gout. Find it and 30 other plant names that can be preceded by the word "Ground."

ALMOND

BIRCH

BURNUT

CEDAR

CENTAURY

CHERRY

ELDER

FERN

FLAX

GOLDENROD

GOLDFLOWER

HEMLOCK

HOLLY

JASMINE

JUNIPER

LAUREL

LEMON

LILY

MAHOGANY

MALLOW

MAPLE

NEEDLE

PINE

PINK

PISTACHIO

PLUM

RASPBERRY

ROSE

SWEET

THISTLE

VINE

```
J E K B E M D H G J D F N P
H D L S Y K H L A U R E L P
P F O T O J C S G L E U I D
C R E R S L M O O D M N N V
B R L R N I L I L Y K O I A
T U S C N E H E D M M N N P
Y R R E H C D T F E E C T D
L R W N A M A L L O W H N X
L E X T U M A H O G A N Y C
O P S A C T F C W G M G M R
H I W U L Y R R E B P S A R
P N E R Y F O I R F I D P S
V U E Y W P C B L R E D L E
J J T Y K K E N D C B P E F
```

DEPRESSION GLASS

Antique glass made in the 1920s and '30s is more commonly known as Depression Glass. It's transparent and primarily made in pink, green, yellow, and crystal. Some popular patterns are listed below.

ADAM

BARK

BLOCK

BUBBLE

CAMEO

CIRCLE

CUBIST

DAISY

DIANA

DORIC

FLORAL

FLORENTINE

FORTUNE

FRUITS

HOLIDAY

IRIS

LYDIA RAY

MADRID

NORMANDIE

OLD CAFE

PATRICIAN

PRETZEL

RING

ROXANA

ROYAL LACE

SHARON

SPIRAL

SYLVAN

VERNON

WINDSOR

```
M W N B M S P R E T Z E L E
N O R A H S T I K P K Y N W
Y O D H I F C I R O D U R K
W A S O X C X R U I T B R F
I I E L C R I C A R S U M B
E E N I T N E R O L F B I Y
C E L D G U A F T S I B U C
A R B A S Y N K A A E L T Y
L D H Y R O C N N C P E S U
L F I Z N O R M A N D I E Z
A X R R L E L K X V A L E O
Y A E B D M R F O D L N O V
O V A D I A N A R T K Y Z R
R V O U B C M L A R I P S H
```

FIELD GUIDE: HAWTHORNS

Hawthorns are thorny shrubs or small trees with fragrant white, pink, or red flowers and small, red fruits. How many can you dig up that have been planted in the grid below?

ALLEGHENY

APPLE

BARBERRY

BEAUTIFUL

BIGTREE

BLUEBERRY

DOTTED

DOWNY

DWARF

FIREBERRY

FROSTED

GOLDEN FRUIT

GREEN

LITTLEHIP

ONEFLOWER

PARSLEY

PASTURE

PEAR

RIVERFLAT

SANDHILL

SCARLET

SOUTHERN

TEXAS

THREEFLOWER

WEEPING

YELLOW

```
D P N U A V L E R U T S A P
W O L L E Y A F T Y I B S F
A A X Y Y R R E B E U L B B
R Y P I F B A R B E R R Y R
F P B I G T R E E E F S N R
S A N D H I L L W B N B W I
C R D G R E W O L F E N O V
A S E N D E L P P A D R D E
R L T I U F R T U E L E I R
L E S P E A R T T N O H Y F
E Y O E I O I T E I G T G L
T C R E C F O E C X L U U A
T H F W U D R V B W A O E T
T A L L E G H E N Y T S Y H
```

67

WELL-MANNERED

"Life is not so short but that there is always time enough for courtesy," Ralph Waldo Emerson tells us. This puzzle will help you mind your manners with this list filled with different terms for being POLITE.

AFFABLE

AGREEABLE

AMIABLE

ATTENTIVE

CIVIL

CORDIAL

CORRECT

COURTEOUS

COURTLY

DECENT

DUTIFUL

ELEGANT

FAIR

GALLANT

GENTEEL

GRACIOUS

LADYLIKE

MANNERLY

OBLIGING

POLISHED

POLITE

REFINED

RESPECTFUL

SUAVE

TACTFUL

URBANE

WELL-BRED

```
U R B A N E L E G A N T P A
E Y N L D G T N A L L A G M
P G R V E T N E C E D C H I
C E F E H E V I T N E T T A
U V K A S L T K G N R F W B
D A G I I P U N S I B U P L
U U L V L R E U E M L L S E
T S I C O Y O C A G L B U L
I C R O P E D N T H E E O B
F D E U T F N A H F W T I A
U A G R E E A B L E U I C F
L M U T R E F I N E D L A F
P O L L C O R D I A L O R A
C M Y Y T T C S T M B P G B
```

BRIGHT 'N' SHINY

BRIGHT and **BRILLIANT** could be two ways to describe our puzzle solvers. They are also two of the many synonyms for bright and **SHINY** that are hidden in the grid below.

AGLOW

BEAMING

BRIGHT

BRILLIANT

CANDENT

DAZZLING

EFFULGENT

FLASHY

FULGID

GLEAMING

GLINTING

GLOSSY

GLOWING

INTENSE

LAMBENT

LUCENT

LUCID

LUMINOUS

LUSTROUS

NITID

RADIANT

SHINY

SPARKLING

SUNNY

TWINKLING

VIVID

```
K T H G I R B G L O S S Y N
T N E G L U F F E U U H R L
H E S N E T N I O D S V A U
T D V I V I D R R A H M D C
C N B T F Y T I L V B T I I
D A A N N S G F G E H H A D
L C G I U P T N N L Z V N E
U B H L L N I T I G U H T L
M S Z G E L S S M L E F D B
I U Y C K A I K A O Z I O U
N K U R O O M R E W T Z G L
O L A G L O W I B I R M A V
U P T V M K S U N N Y V B D
S T W I N K L I N G O N L D
```

ACTORS WHO APPEARED ON TV'S BATMAN

Hidden below are 35 stars who appeared on TV's "Batman." Who can forget the sneering grin of The Joker as portrayed by Cesar ROMERO, or Burgess MEREDITH as The Penguin, with his affinity for umbrellas?

ASTIN (John)
BANKHEAD (Miss Tallulah)
BAXTER (Anne)
BERLE (Milton)
BUONO (Victor)
CARMEL (Roger C.)
CARNEY (Art)

COLLINS (Joan)
DUFF (Howard)
EVANS (Maurice)
GABOR (Zsa Zsa)
GORSHIN (Frank)
JOHNS (Glynis)
JOHNSON (Van)
JONES (Carolyn)

KITT (Eartha)
KRUSCHEN (Jack)
LIBERACE
LUPINO (Ida)
MCDOWALL (Roddy)
MEREDITH (Burgess)
MERMAN (Ethel)
NEWMAR (Julie)
PREMINGER (Otto)
PRICE (Vincent)
RENNIE (Michael)
ROBERTSON (Cliff)
ROMERO (Cesar)
RUSH (Barbara)
SANDERS (George)
SLEZAK (Walter)
THRONE (Malachi)
VALLEE (Rudy)
WALLACH (Eli)
WINTERS (Shelley)

```
V H J H K E O R E M O R I Z
T P T O P R E M I N G E R I
H Z R I H S U R E N N I E S
R C L I D N O S T R E B O R
O I A U C E S Z C D M N D E
N R F L O E R O A H E A S D
E F K I L S B E N W E O N N
L G S B L A H N M I S N R A
R E O E I K W A R N P O E S
E V Z R N T R O H E B U E T
B A C A S O G O D A T B L I
K N B C U H J W G C C X L N
M S R E T N I W L E M R A C
K I T T C A R N E Y T J V B
```

IT'S PORCELAIN!

Porcelain has long been a favorite collector's item for its great beauty. It was first manufactured by the Chinese in 618 A. D. Perhaps you're familiar with some of the porcelain types that are hidden below.

AMSTEL

BERLIN

BOEHM

BRISTOL

CAUGHLEY

CHAFFERS

CHANTILLY

CHELSEA

CHRISTIAN

COPELAND

DERBY

DRESDEN

EMPIRE

IMARI

LIMOGES

LOWESTOFT

MEISSEN

MINTON

NEW HALL

REGAL

ROCKINGHAM

ROSE

SAXON

SEVRES

SPODE

SWANSEA

VIENNA

WEDGWOOD

WORCESTER

```
F Y B E R L I N O X A S C I
Y B R E D O P S E L D H H S
P C N O T N I M L S A R E S
I H A I R L A A K F S R L E
R R D N B O H L F D V I S G
L I A R N W C E E E D W E O
A S A M E E R K S P O S A M
G T M N I S I R I R O S E I
E I S C K T D V C N W C B L
R A T G I O Y E L H G U A C
I N E H C F S N N G D H L O
P Y L L I T N A H C E H A K
M G L U E A E S N A W S C M
E W B R I S T O L B O E H M
```

SIX-LETTER U.S. RIVERS

Spanning the HUDSON River in New York, the George Washington Bridge is the busiest bridge in the world. The GWB opened in 1931, and it accommodated more than 5.5 million vehicles in its first year of operation (a lower-level deck added to the bridge was opened in 1962). Today, nearly 100 million vehicles use it each year.

ASHLEY

BRAZOS

CARSON

CLINCH

COOPER

COPPER

HUDSON

KANSAS

LEHIGH

MAUMEE

MOBILE

MOHAWK

NECHES

OCONEE

OWYHEE

PLATTE

POWDER

RAISIN

SABINE

SALINE

SALMON

SALUDA

SANTEE

SCIOTO

SEVIER

WABASH

WALKER

YADKIN

```
V D K S E N P M G H N B S S
K C S S T P R S O A I E A A
O L O N T V N P O B S L N L
E I T K A V M B E Z I N T U
A N O M L A S K S N A L E D
B C I H P O W D E R R R E A
N H C B R P H G I H E L B W
I I S W A L K E R E P P O C
K A N S A S E G M K O M V A
D W B K E B H U D S O N I R
A L A H U V A L E C C K T S
Y E C H N M I S E E H Y W O
M E E N O C O E H Y I S Z N
N W M Y G M G O R V Y V K I
```

Record companies are quick to react to the latest trends in music. It was no different back in the 1930s and 1940s, when big bands were the rage. If you dig out your collection of 78s, you'll probably see some of these labels.

AMCO

APOLLO

BANNER

BELL

BELTONA

CAMEO

CLEF

COSMO

CROWN

DEE GEE

DESIGN

EMARCY

FORUM

GENNETT

GRAND

GUILD

JEWEL

KING

LYRIC

MUSICOR

NORDIC

OKEH

OMNI

PATHÉ

REPRISE

RIVERSIDE

ROYALE

SAVOY

SENATE

TOPS

VARIETY

VARSITY

VOCALION

VOGUE

```
P R O C I S U M U R O F F M
O O I A W B P R N E L E E F
G M K V I D B O F Y W L O L
N S M G E N N E T T D C E A
N O H S Y R M I L K Y W M B
F C I K O D S O C T E C A B
D G W L V R L I E J O N C L
N S E N A T E I D K N N P U
A W K V S C R P U E V V A A
R R O L K A O L R G E O T V
G C E R V T Y V K I N G H E
H V Y Y C R A M E P S U E H
E P J P I O L L O P A E K E
L K N C I V E U C I D R O N
```

WORDS THAT BEGIN WITH "F"

The word list below contains 31 terms that begin with the letter "F." If you remove the "F" from the front of each word, you will create an entirely different word. However, each word is hidden in the diagram just as it appears in the word list.

FABLE	FEAST	FLAKE
FACTOR	FETCH	FLAME
FAIRY	FEVER	FLANK
FALLOW	FINCH	FLASH
FALTER	FLAIR	FLEDGE
		FLIGHT
		FLOCK

```
I  N  N  A  T  I  U  B  D  A  W  D  E  D
N  K  T  E  T  U  L  F  K  O  R  M  B  F
R  O  C  H  F  G  O  T  L  K  A  D  W  E
I  R  U  O  G  R  D  L  B  L  A  F  Y  T
B  O  E  W  R  I  A  L  F  R  A  N  K  C
Y  T  I  W  G  F  R  I  S  K  Y  Y  S  H
C  C  C  I  O  A  M  F  L  B  C  Y  S  C
S  A  R  E  D  L  O  F  L  D  B  O  O  N
C  F  F  F  F  T  F  L  I  G  H  T  L  I
E  D  E  L  F  E  V  E  R  W  R  A  F  F
E  G  U  A  A  R  C  D  F  S  E  Y  A  M
H  N  I  N  S  S  E  G  K  I  M  B  I  E
G  R  H  K  T  T  H  E  K  A  L  F  C  C
Y  K  R  N  T  L  G  C  D  E  C  M  Y  F
```

FLOSS

FLOUT

FLOWER

FLUNG

FLUTE

FOLDER

FRAIL

FRANK

FREED

FRIGHT

FRIGID

FRILL

FRISKY

FROCK

HUMAN TRAITS

It is basic to the unique human personality that each of us thinks, feels, and acts differently from one another. We all have our share of good and bad traits as well, and the degree of which these are expressed also differs from person to person. The grid contains human traits that are generally considered to be noble or highly admirable marks of character.

BRAVERY

CANDOR

CHARITY

COURAGE

COURTESY

DEFERENCE

DETERMINA-
TION

ENDURANCE

FAITH

FIDELITY

GENEROSITY

GENTLENESS

HONESTY

HOPE

HUMILITY

INTEGRITY

KINDNESS

LOVE

LOYALTY

MERCY

OPTIMISM

PATIENCE

PEACE

PITY

REVERENCE

SINCERITY

SYMPATHY

TACT

TOLERANCE

TRUST

```
G D Y T G E N T L E N E S S E
K L A C Y C C A N D O R L Y S
F O L D R N R D F V E I T M H
O Y D O E E U E H C C I M P U
Y A T K V R M T N O P A V A M
Y L O I A E B E O P N A F T I
T T N N R V R R P Y T E A H L
I Y C D B E T M T O T G S Y I
S E S N F R C I I K H A Y T T
O C T E U C R N M M M R T I Y
R L D S T G F A I T H U I L P
E T T S E R S T S S G O R E O
N M C T R N U I M P Y C A D K
E C N A R E L O T P V C H I N
G I P A T I E N C E E M C F S
```

BLOOMING FLOWERS

The first flowers to catch our eye in a garden are usually the showiest, more attractive ones, and two flowers that blossom in July, the IRIS and the LILY, are among the most beautiful and fragrant. See if you can sniff out the bouquet of blooming flowers planted in the grid below.

ALLIUM

AZALEA

BEGONIA

CARNATION

CORNFLOWER

COWSLIP

DAFFODIL

DAHLIA

DAISY

DOGWOOD

FOXGLOVE

GLADIOLA

GOLDENROD

HEATHER

HIBISCUS

HYSSOP

IRIS

JASMINE

LILAC

LILY

LOTUS

MAGNOLIA

ORCHID

PEONY

PETUNIA

POPPY

ROSE

SUNFLOWER

TULIP

VIOLET

```
F D A I S Y G P I L S W O C
Z O G H Y Y A Z V U I M A J
M G X P L R N E T B C R E D
U W P G R E W O L F N U S P
M O I A L W L H E A T H E R
P O D L I O H I T P Z N F O
Y D M O O L V I T E I A T S
D A Y I R F O E B M L M U E
H H L D L N J N S I U O L M
Y L I A Z R E A G I S U I S
S I L L O O J D L A R C P V
S A A G I C G L L M M I U S
O R C H I D A F F O D I L S
P E T U N I A I N O G E B O
```

PRODUCTS OF AFRICA

You might want to put on some cool clothing, because things are sure to heat up as you look for these 28 products of Africa, including DIAMONDS, RICE, and SUGAR.

BANANAS

BARLEY

BOATS

CATTLE

COCOA

COCONUTS

COFFEE

CORN

COTTON

DIAMONDS

FISH

GOLD

GROUND-
NUTS

HEMP

KAPOK (seed
fiber)

LACE

MILLET (grain)

PALM OIL

POTATOES

RICE

RUBBER

SALT

SHEEP

SISAL (rope fiber)

SUGAR

TOBACCO

VANILLA

WHEAT

```
F F P A V O A H T R G V C S
S K U L R U B B E R I C E H
I T B L F D P A L M O I L O
S A U I T R I N L L P C A I
A E S N L O S A I Y D O E Y
L H V A D B B N M C C L B Y
T W C V A N B A N O T T O C
U E L R A G U S C P N E A G
K P L A F R U O K C E D T W
R E K T P R N O R F O I S E
Y U C E T U P Y F G M R G K
K S E O T A T O P F F G N H
A H N S K I C T G M F E U U
S M V G W T F P V N O W I R
```

MUSIC MAKERS

You can tap your feet to the beat or just lose yourself in the beautiful sounds that the musical instruments in this puzzle provide.

BANJO

BELLS

BONGOS

BUGLE

CELLO

CHIMES

CLARINET

CONCERTINA

CORNET

CYMBALS

DRUM

FIFE

FLUTE

GUITAR

HARP

KAZOO

LYRE

MARACAS

OBOE

ORGAN

PIANO

PICCOLO

SAXOPHONE

SITAR

TROMBONE

TRUMPET

TUBA

VIOLA

VIOLIN

ZITHER

```
E E R D T B Y O L O C C I P
A O L Y R E D X K L J O S C
F B F D F U S P A L F N J B
M O U I L S M R N E Z R A M
A N F T U G I A Z C O S C B
S G O K T N G I R E L L H O
C O N C E R T I N A L O I V
V S A T O H O O B N C K M K
U A I Y E H H M E I E A E Y
V B P R A P Y J B L O J S I
T E N R O C M P E O G Z S R
K L P X D D S U Z I N U H I
M L A G U I T A R V I E B F
C S G G M I K S I T A R E B
```

"Ology," a suffix meaning "the study of," is derived from the Greek word *logos*, which means "word." Below are terms that when followed by "ology" become a branch of knowledge or a particular science.

AUDI

CARDI

CHRON

CLIMAT

COSM

DERMAT

ENTOM

EPISTEM

ETHN

GERONT

GRAPH

HEMAT

HIST

KONI

LIMN

METEOR

METHOD

MICR

MYTH

NEPHR

NEUR

NUMER

OCEAN

ORCHID

ORNITH

PETR

PHYSI

PROTOZO

PSYCH

RADI

ROENTGEN

SOCI

TECHN

TERMIN

```
L N R A I L R H A O O O P L
P O Z O T O R P C O L S I E
R R E H E R D L R U Y P P L
P H E T H N T O R C H I D D
Y C E Y N I T P H Y S I R P
L M C M M T A G P T I U I E
D D I R A H M G E Y E U L T
G L U M K T I M N N U M E R
G E R O N T L H I S T D N U
Y E P C S I C P D I N O K P
D U K E I E M A A R C C M M
U K P A T M U R R O Y O L S
Z U Y N T D G G E D A E S P
G T D L I Y H P C T I Y K M
```

Solve this puzzle about wallpaper and get a few ideas about home **DECOR**. A roll or two of colorful **PAPER** can liven up any room in the house. The list below will help you prepare for your next **PROJECT**.

BEDROOM

BORDER

COLORS

DECOR

DESIGN

FABRIC

FANCY

FLORAL

HALLWAY

HANG

KITCHEN

MATCH

MEASURE

METALLIC

MODERN

PAPER

PASTE

PATTERN

PLAID

PLAIN

PRETTY

PRINT

PROJECT

SCENE

SHAPES

SMOOTH

STRIPES

TEXTURE

VELVET

WASHABLE

```
R O B E D R O O M Y N B M W
C B U P L F G F C E G P E G
T P A B A B X N H D I A L P
H L T B U T A C R R S D N M
L A R O L F T H M E E E Y E
T I S T R I P E S M D C N A
C N T R K H T R R A D O P S
C M I G O A T V E N W R M U
K M N R L L E C N T H H Y R
E A Y L P L O T E X T U R E
H T I G V W A C C J O Y E D
J C S E P A H S S B O C P R
A H T A D Y D E H D M R A O
E L O E P O T W N E S S P B
```

WHAT'S THE SCORE?

In sports competitions, athletes give their all, hoping to emerge victorious. Find these 30 terms pertaining to scoring points in sports and you're sure to hit the BULL'S-EYE!

BASE HIT

BASKET

BIRDIE

BOGIE

BULL'S-EYE

CONVERT

DISTANCE

FINISH LINE

FIRST

GAME

GOAL

HAT TRICK

HOLE IN ONE

HOME RUN

HOOP

JUDGE

JUMP

KNOCKOUT

POINT

RINGER

SCORE

SERVICE

SHOT STONE

SMASH

SPARE

SPIKE

STRIKE

TARGET

TIME

TOUCHDOWN

```
E S I E H G G T E G R A T G
K C B B O G I E I E H E E R
I O I A M M T J R U O N K N
R R L V E F S U J A O O S R
T E B B R P I D O N P T A I
S P C P U E S G I K M S B N
N F O T N L S E C F C T W G
F I N I S H L I N E B O M E
V S V H N O R S I F D H N R
K S E E H T Y D E H K S W K
F I R S T F R I C Y P A N I
S G T A R I O U U L E M A G
V S H B B P O E K I P S U D
N E C N A T S I D L F C Y J
```

You may want to put on your thinking cap as well as a comfortable pair of solving SLIPPERS as you circle these articles of clothing.

APRON

BLAZER

BLOUSE

BOOTS

BOW TIE

CARDIGAN

CLOAK

COAT

DRESS

JACKET

JEANS

JODHPURS

KIMONO

MITTENS

NECKTIE

NYLONS

OVERALLS

PAJAMAS

PANTS

PARKA

PONCHO

SANDALS

SCARF

SHAWL

SHORTS

SKIRT

SLACKS

SLIPPERS

SMOCK

SNEAKERS

SOCKS

SWEATER

TOGA

TROUSERS

TUXEDO

```
S S E R D T Z X S A P R O N
J T A E I T W O B L A Z E R
L N R N N Y L O N S J R C N
P A S O D E X U T O A R L L
O P T T H A S B S O M P O O
H S O C K S L R R N A I A V
C H O T R O U S E R S G K E
N A B V U P W C K P O I R R
O W R S H E K A A T P M W A
P L E D A T S N E T T I M L
M M O T I M R K N F T I L L
E J E E O G C I S K C A L S
F R A C S A A Y K U A N O R
B C K E J E A N S S H A R C
```

ALL IN THE FAMILY

Tracing your family tree is an absorbing pastime that can also enable you to discover relatives you never knew you had. Find and circle the following terms that relate to finding your roots.

ANCESTRY

BACK-
  GROUND

BIRTH

BRANCH

CASTE

CLAN

DESCENT

DYNASTY

FAMILY

FILIATION

FOREFATHERS

GENEALOGY

HEREDITY

HERITAGE

HOUSE

LEGACY

LINEAGE

MENAGE
(household)

ORIGIN

PARENTAGE

PAST

PATRIMONY

PEDIGREE

RACE

SEPT

SOURCE

STEM

STOCK

STRAIN

SUCCESSION

TRIBE

```
U N O I S S E C C U S L T D
Y H E B I R T L I N E A G E
F L G E N E A L O G Y E E S
T B I R T H H I A L S R A C
L D Y M P T T C H U G H O E
M O N B A A Y E O I S C R N
M T O U I F R H D T D N I T
T R M L O E E E E Y G A G P
I P I H D R P M N C R R I E
C F R I I O G A E T A B N S
A L T T M F S K S N A R E G
S Y A Y R T S E C N A G M R
T G P N Y H N T S A P G E R
E C R U O S T O C K B U E F
```

THINGS TO STAND IN OR ON

For a change of pace you can stand in a BOOTH, on SKIS, or in an ELEVATOR as you solve this puzzle filled with 33 things that a person can stand in or on. If you're into golf, why not try it while standing on the GREEN?

BASE

BOOTH

BRIDGE

CURB

DAIS

DECK

DIVING BOARD

ELEVATOR

ESCALATOR

GREEN

HANDS

HEAD

HIGH WIRE

LADDER

LINE

MOUND

PATH

PLANK

POGO STICK

RINK

SCALE

SCOOTER

SHOWER

SKATEBOARD

SKATES

SKIS

SOAPBOX

STAGE

STAIR

STILE

STILTS

SURFBOARD

TOES

```
W H H K R O T A V E L E L K
L S T I L E M B S S I S W A
D B K O G B V L H A C C O X
T I R I O H S X O B P A O S
S P V E S B W D W R S L K S
S T L I T S M I E U E A E C
D E A A N O S M R C T T T A
U D P I N G O F V E A O B L
A P M V R K B C B K S R E E
I G O C P O G O S T I C K S
I N U R A G A L A D D E R F
H X N R I R I G G R N G F W
P T D K D N E E R G D A E H
X F L D E C K H L P A T H T
```

PALMTREES

"Down among the sheltering palms, oh HONEY, wait for me ..." begins an old Tin Pan Alley tune. And that rendezvous could be beneath any of the 28 species planted below.

BETEL

BROOM

CABBAGE

CHINESE FAN

COCONUT

DATE

DESERT

FANLEAF

FEATHER

FISHTAIL

GEBANG

GOMUTI

HEMP

HONEY

JAGGERY

LADY

LICUALA

MACAW

PALMYRA

PINDO

RATTAN

ROYAL

SABAL

SAGO

SUGAR

TALIPOT

TRAVELER'S

WINE

```
I N L N S Y Y V N T G F A B
J A B A Y T L Y A A H G J B
L C B R D V A I L N T G W E
J A Y A R Y M L A P E T A D
L L Y C M O V F U T O G A S
A U B O S J E M C P H G Y R
H H O C R S F M I W P S A P
U R O O E J E L L T I G I H
B F A N L E A F J D U N E F
W G I U E T T G E S D M E N
A H C T V Y H S G O P F O R
C A B B A G E C G E B A N G
A U B S R R R M L N R C F V
M S L E T E B D L M G Y N F
```

84

TROPICAL TREAT

Once you cut through a pineapple's rough shell, the FRUIT offers a TANGY burst of flavor and a SWEET, refreshing juice. This puzzle features 28 words related to the pineapple.

AROMA

CANNED

CHUNKS

CUBES

DESSERT

FOOD

FRESH

FRUIT

GARNISH

HARVEST

HAWAII

JUICY

LEAVES

PIECES

PLANT

PULP

RIPE

SALAD

SLICES

SNACK

STEM

SWEET

TANGY

TENDER

TOPPING

TROPICAL

VITAMINS

YELLOW

```
P J T D O V E F S I F E O R
T H O U S F R M O P N P Y S
S E P W R E E C S N R F N S
E N P U L P B H S E V A E L
V V I N L E E U D Y C I U J
R T N M H D Y N C K T I V P
A Y G N A T E K H R L R L F
H H S M E T S S O I A G D S
C I S E C E I P S P D A V F
J R W E V N I V Y E L L O W
M S M L R C A F N A R O M A
A E T A A F W N S O D T I E
W G G L P L A N T A P B V B
B N L C V C H M C H C W B C
```

86

BUZZ OFF!

The **HONEYBEE** is a social **INSECT** that communicates with its fellow bees by performing dance-like movements. There are three classes of honeybees: the female **WORKER** bees, the larger **QUEEN**, and the male bees, or drones. It is the queen and worker bees which have stingers, the drones do not.

ACTIVE
ATTACK
BEEHIVE
BEEKEEPER
BOLD
BUMBLEBEE
BUSY
BUZZING
COLONIES
DRONE
FARM
FLIGHT
FLYING
GROUP
HONEYBEE
HONEYCOMB
INSECT
JOBS
LITTLE
LOUD
NECTAR
ORGANIZED
POLLINATION

QUEEN
SMALL
SOUND
SPECIES
STING

SWARM
TERRITORY
WILD
WINGS
WORKER

```
S A S G N I W A C T I V E G
U T E R R I T O R Y U Y N N
E L E E L F L E R S T I E I
R M V D B O P A T K Z V C T
C R I D N E O P E Z E Y T S
L A H I E F L B U S Y R A M
K W E K A Z L B J O B S R A
A S E H K G I I M H R A F L
P E B T Q C N N G U F G I L
B I Y U M D A I A H B T O L
T C E S N I T T Y G T O H O
Z E N U T Q I J T L R G L U
N P O F D R O N E A F O C D
B S H T H O N E Y C O M B D
```

FA-LA THE LEADER

You'll be heading to solving nirvana with this LAVISH puzzle. Hidden in the diagram are 39 words that begin with either "FA" or "LA."

FABLE	FAITH	FATIGUE
FACADE	FALLACY	FAUCET
FACIAL	FALSE	FAULT
FACTOR	FALTER	FAUNA
FACTUAL	FARCE	LABEL
FACULTY	FATHER	LABOR
FAIRY	FATHOM	LADDER
		LADLE
		LADYBUG
		LAGOON
		LANCE
		LANTERN
		LAPEL
		LARIAT
		LASAGNA
		LASER
		LATCH
		LATER
		LATIN
		LATTER
		LAUGH
		LAUNCH
		LAUNDRY
		LAVISH
		LAYER

```
T  N  R  R  A  N  U  A  F  A  I  R  Y  R
L  A  O  E  O  V  Y  F  S  Y  H  M  E  R
U  I  C  O  Y  T  L  U  C  A  F  T  E  E
A  E  G  E  D  A  C  A  F  B  A  T  R  D
F  A  C  T  U  A  L  A  S  L  T  P  O  D
L  T  I  N  E  L  B  A  F  A  I  Y  B  A
A  A  D  F  A  C  I  A  L  H  G  U  A  L
D  R  V  F  H  L  U  M  F  B  U  N  L  A
Y  P  L  I  P  C  F  A  L  T  E  R  A  D
B  F  A  L  S  E  T  A  F  A  R  E  B  L
U  Y  P  R  E  H  T  A  F  I  U  T  E  E
G  U  E  I  O  I  R  M  L  R  Y  N  L  H
D  H  L  M  N  C  H  T  I  A  F  A  C  C
U  L  A  S  E  R  I  A  L  L  Y  L  V  H
```

AND SOMETIMES "Y"

Grammar teaches that the vowels are "A, E, I, O, U, and sometimes Y." This is a "sometimes Y" puzzle, as all the words contain this letter used as a vowel.

COMPLY

CYPRESS

DECRY

DEFY

DEIFY

DENY

DYNAMIC

ENZYME

FLYLEAF

GLORIFY

GYRATE

HYBRID

HYENA

HYPHEN

JULY

LULLABY

LYRE

MULTIPLY

NYLON

PAPYRUS

PSYCHIC

PURIFY

PYREX

PYTHON

RELY

RHYME

SPRY

TYING

TYRO

UNIFY

```
R N R O O Z G D P L S P G J
L G O Z R L E P A U P M U U
P F Y L O F N A O L R L Z N
D E C R Y T Z R E L Y I O A
R C I M A N Y D N A L H F F
H F P Z E T M L L B T P B Y
Y F D H S S E R P Y C F F C
M T P I U O G P P I I L L J
E Y X R R N N A H Y T Y E S
H U O X Y B I C E G R L R G
U C O M P L Y F I E D E U U
S L T X A S T H Y E N A X M
H B X G P P G B N H P F B A
L N J B Y A D Y L Y N Z H C
```

STAR MAPS

The star **MAPS** we're focusing on in this puzzle won't guide you to famous Hollywood mansions; instead, they help astronomers navigate the **UNIVERSE** by mapping out the **COSMOS** in minute detail.

ASTRONOMY

BACKYARD

CHARTS

CLOUDS

COMETS

COSMOS

DATA

DEGREES

ECLIPSE

GALAXY

HEAVENS

LIGHT

LOCATE

MAPS

MEASURE

MILKY WAY

MOON

OBSERVE

ORBIT

PATHS

PATTERNS

PLANETS

POSITIONS

SCALE

SCIENCE

SEASONS

SOLAR
  SYSTEM

STARS

TELESCOPE

UNIVERSE

```
S  E  G  T  H  E  A  V  E  N  S  N  O  S
C  L  I  G  Y  P  T  I  B  R  O  P  N  T
N  A  P  V  B  S  H  T  A  P  L  Y  A  X
E  C  L  I  P  S  E  G  C  P  A  X  G  M
R  S  C  I  E  N  C  E  K  W  R  A  N  E
U  E  R  M  O  O  N  H  Y  B  S  T  T  A
S  E  V  E  C  I  S  K  A  T  Y  S  Y  S
A  R  W  R  V  T  L  C  R  R  S  E  N  N
E  G  S  Y  E  I  O  O  D  D  T  R  M  S
M  E  T  N  M  S  N  O  S  A  E  S  D  L
D  D  A  E  M  O  B  U  C  T  M  U  X  I
U  L  R  O  M  P  R  O  T  A  O  G  W  G
P  K  S  Y  X  A  L  A  G  L  C  O  Y  H
U  L  C  A  K  E  P  O  C  S  E  L  E  T
```

WORDS AFTER "GOOD"

You'll have a good TIME searching for all the "good" words below, so be a good SPORT and start the hunt for EVENING, TASTE, YEAR, and other words that can be preceded by "good." Good LUCK!

CHANCE

CHEER

EVENING

FELLOW

FOR-NOTHING

FORTUNE

FRIDAY

FRIENDS

GRIEF

HEARTED

HUMOR

IDEA

INTENTIONS

LOOKING

LUCK

MANNERED

MORNING

NATURED

NEWS

NIGHT

SAMARITAN

SENSE

SHOW

SIZED

SPEED

SPORT

TASTE

TEMPERED

TIME

TURN

WILL

WISHES

WORD

YEAR

```
K R E T S A T P S R N S Y L
F E G E U U W H G N O A S C
C E N U T R O F G S D M H Y
C S I Z E D N Z D I T A U P
E H N R W A D N R O N R O H
M O E O G O E F A C Y I K P
L W V E I I R D E R U T A N
T H E A R T E D Y M D A G V
D W T F O R N O T H I N G N
E O V F E O N E W S I T M O
E L D P P P A F T K P D L Z
P L M K P S M H O N N L E O
S E H S I W M O R N I N G A
T F G K C U L U L W R U Z T
```

An important detail to keep in mind when planning a wedding is the rings. If the bride and groom choose to have gemstones in their rings, they need to decide what kind of cut they want. Gems are cut into various shapes to bring out each stone's individual beauty.

ANTIQUE

BAGUETTE

BEVEL

CALF'S HEAD

CUSHION

EMERALD

EPAULET

FRENCH

HEART

HEXAGON

HONEYCOMB

KEYSTONE

KITE

LOZENGE

MAGNA

MARQUISE

OLD-MINE

OVAL

PEAR

PENTAGON

PORTUGUESE

RONDELLE

ROSE

SCISSORS

SPIRAL

SQUARE

STAR

STEP

TRIANGLE

WINDOW

```
M L E V E B A S P I R A L H
W O D N I W M O T K A Q E E
V Z F N N P L O L E E X L X
K E Y S T O N E C D P X L A
Q N D L A R E M E Y M C E G
W G A M K T V U E E E I D O
T E E R A U Q S Q S S N N N
N T H T G G I H R I E O O E
O Q S I T U N O C P T G R H
I Z F A Q E S A A N A N A Y
H V L R V S U U R T E Q A E
S L A A I E L G N A I R T I
U M C C V E H E A R T I F Y
C Q S W T O P R Q B K S F T
```

TOOLS FOR THE JOB

Your pencil will be the right tool for this job as you PLOW your way through the diagram below and HAMMER away at the word list by finding the names of 29 handy tools. Now, get to work!

ANVIL	PULLEY	SICKLE
BLOWTORCH	RAKE	SPADE
BUZZ SAW	SCISSORS	TROWEL
CALIPERS	SCREWDRIVER	WINCH
CHAIN SAW	SHOVEL	WRENCH
CHISEL		
CLAMP		
CROWBAR		
DRILL		
FILE		
HAMMER		
HATCHET		
JACK		
LATHE		
PICK		
PITCHFORK		
PLIERS		
PLOW		
PRUNER		

```
P A P I K S P A D E F L S F
I M O W H P S N Z W K R S R
C L A O U R T M S D K C R R
K B V L K Y U R R R Z E E
T E L K C I S I O E E J P N
L E S I H C L F W W M I I U
Y E H T A L H D S D E M L R
H L V C I C R A C L P L A P
H C R V T I P I I W I N C H
R R N I V A D F S N C K O Y
Y A P E L Z H T S O S C N Y
M K R L R D C R O W B A R O
B E B L O W T O R C H J W E
H M U Y Z W W A S S Z Z U B V
```

Constellations (groups of stars) are imaginary things that astronomers, farmers, and poets have created over the past 6,000 years. The true purpose of constellations is to help us find our way around the sky. As the sun makes its yearly revolution, the path it follows is known as the ecliptic. The stars surrounding the ecliptic are called the zodiac constellations.

ANDROMEDA

APUS

AQUARIUS

AQUILA

ARIES

CANCER

CAPRICORN

CEPHEUS

CETUS

CRATER

CYGNUS

DORADO

FORNAX

GEMINI

HERCULES

HYDRA

INDUS

LIBRA

LUPUS

LYRA

ORION

PAVO

PEGASUS

PISCES

PUPPIS

SAGITTARIUS

SCORPIO

TAURUS

VIRGO

```
I  V  I  R  G  O  L  H  P  O  E  S  C  A
A  E  X  N  R  O  C  I  R  P  A  C  B  N
C  E  A  Y  D  S  P  S  B  R  Q  E  A  D
H  C  N  L  D  U  P  U  D  R  U  P  R  R
L  Y  R  A  I  R  S  Y  P  S  A  H  H  O
D  P  O  A  O  U  H  V  M  P  R  E  D  M
Y  N  F  V  R  A  Q  E  P  X  I  U  P  E
I  S  A  G  I  T  T  A  R  I  U  S  X  D
C  P  U  Q  O  I  P  R  O  C  S  L  G  A
A  S  A  S  N  D  E  O  A  R  U  C  Y  P
B  U  C  I  A  T  A  N  S  P  N  L  E  U
H  T  M  P  A  G  C  R  U  P  G  N  E  S
S  E  I  R  A  E  E  S  O  V  Y  D  O  S
G  C  C  O  R  G  O  P  Q  D  C  S  V  H
```

Although it is a fast-paced capital and the largest city in Ireland, Dublin remains compact and accessible to visitors. Its cathedrals, colleges, pubs, and friendly natives give the city a distinctly old-European feel. Search for some of Dublin's streets below.

BAGGOT
BOYNE
CAMDEN
CLARE
COLLEGE
COPE
DAME
DAWSON
D'OLIER
DRURY
DUKE
ERNE
FADE
FENIAN
FLEET
FOWNES
GRAFTON
HARRY
HATCH
HERBERT
HOLLES
HUME
KILDARE
KING

LEESON
LEINSTER
LOMBARD
MERCER
MERRION
MONTAGUE

MOUNT
NASSAU
SHAW
STEPHEN
TRINITY
YORK

```
K K F L E E T K F C A I D F
N O S E E L P Y I S W A H S
C E K C N E T O G N W O W C
H U U E T I R M C S G Y D A
D C Y G N N A N O I R R E M
U I T I A S U N E T A R H D
A Y R A O T M O O B F A D E
S T E P H E N G M L T H S N
S D B M R R G O C N O U B Y
A R R C A A L E M L N M T O
N U E M B D H K L B A E K B
R R H D O L I E R L C R I N
Y Y U R F I S E N W O F E E
A R C N T K A H M Y W C G E
```

BUILDING PARTS

This puzzle highlights some components that are used in the construction of buildings. There are 30 terms for you to find.

ABUTMENT

APERTURE

BATTEN

BEAM

BRACE

BRACKET

BULWARK

CAPSTONE

CASING

CHIMNEY

COLUMN

CROSSBAR

DECK

FACADE

FASCIA

FIRE WALL

FIXTURE

GIRDER

GUTTER

HINGE

INSULATION

LATCH

MOLDING

MUNTIN

PANEL

PIPE

RAFTER

RAILING

TIE ROD

TRIM

```
W E B Y X R R R E T T U G T
L T I H L G R H N I T N U M
M I P C L F R A I L I N G W
R E K R A W L U B D O E L N
A R L C W P M K L S C M O D
F O A E E I S O C A S I N G
T D T K R L M T R E T O E D
E P C T I E W B O A D E R X
R P H W F N R D L N R N U C
E Y I X Y A B U T M E N T O
M G M P C P S O T T D N R L
L A N K L N I C T X R F E U
C R E I I P R A I M I D P M
S T Y B H C B A N A G F A N
```

In New York City, to go through the TURNSTILE, you need to pay the FARE with a METROCARD. Some trains run LOCAL and others EXPRESS, and if you need information about how to connect to another TRAIN, each STATION has at least one large ROUTE MAP. You'll be on SCHEDULE if you discover all 28 terms associated with a subway system.

AGENT

BOOTH

BRIDGE

COMMUTER

CONDUCTOR

DOOR

ENGINEER

EXPRESS

FARE

LINE

LOCAL

METROCARD

PLATFORM

RAIL YARD

RIDER

ROUTE MAP

SCHEDULE

SEATS

SHUTTLE

SIDING

STANDEE

STATION

STRAPHANGER

TOKENS

TRAIN

TUNNEL

TURNSTILE

WINDOW

```
T L C O M M U T E R U N L H
W O A O I K X L E N N U T R
B P E C B R I D G E D O T P
G A K R O T C U D N O C O D
B M W T S L X S S B O E K R
T E M N B F S R S E R U E A
S T R A P H A N G E R G N C
C U O D U I R R L E R O S O
T O F T L C E U E S I P W R
O R T Y E E D N A T S O X T
B L A B Y E I X A G D K E E
E R L I H G R T X N E N U M
D C P C N D S S I D I N G C
A I S E A T S W X L X W T L
```

ESTATE HOUSES

A hacienda can refer to an ESTATE whose expanse of land is used for ranching or farming, or to the estate's main HOME. We're highlighting the splendor and majesty of Mexican haciendas in this puzzle.

ALCOVE

ALTAR

ANTIQUES

ARCHES

ARTWORK

BUILDINGS

CARPET

CHAPEL

CORRIDORS

COURTYARD

ENTRANCE

ESTATE

EXTERIOR

FURNITURE

GARDENS

GATE

GROUNDS

HEIRLOOMS

HOME

INTERIOR

LOBBY

LOUNGE

MEXICO

PORTRAITS

POTTERY

ROOMS

SALONS

WINDOWS

```
A L C O V E I Y Y V D D K A
S O G L I N T E R I O R Q R
A U A W A Y C A E U O A U C
V N T Y S N B G T W S Y W H
C G E H A N R B T R M T B E
H E O R B O E R O M O R U S
A O T X U U A D P L O U M T
P N M N S T I A R T R O P A
E R D E L R I L S A O C S T
L S Q A R Y U N D L G H N E
O V Q O E X T E R I O R O P
N O C I X E M I M U N B L R
A N T I Q U E S S O F G A A
R S L V A H W I N D O W S C
```

HOW ARE YOU FEELING?

97

Moods are funny sometimes. One day you can feel **BLAH** and **BLUE**, and the very next day, you're **CAREFREE** and **JOLLY**. You'll be **HAPPY** when you've placed a circle around the following "moody" adjectives. **EXCITED?** Well, then, get started!

BLAH	LAZY	PRETTY
BLUE	LONELY	SILLY
BORED	LOST	TIRED
CAREFREE	PENSIVE	WELL
EDGY	PLAYFUL	WONDERFUL
ELATED		
ENERGETIC		
EXCITED		
FINE		
FOOLISH		
FREE		
FRISKY		
FRUSTRATED		
FUNNY		
GOOD		
GREAT		
GRUMPY		
HAPPY		
JOLLY		

```
C N P B L U F R E D N O W S
T J M N D O I J H O P L C I
K E O G O O D P Y L E N O L
K V E L K J W E L L X G U L
Y D I D L N V U R Y C Y S Y
M S E E G Y F W T I I F B L
H A Y T I Y D T T A T L L S
C F Y A A H E E R F E R A C
F C R L O R G V R N D R H X
C U P E P R T I C O B C G L
L P N N E O S S C L B C Y A
O I D N X K O N U L S A C Z
F J E R Y M L E G R U M P Y
E A C B H H A P P Y F T G P
```

99

TO WHAT "END?"

You haven't reached the end of your solving, but you have come upon a list which every word contains the letters "END."

ADDEND

AMEND

ASCEND

ATTEND

BLEND

CONTEND

DEFEND

DEPEND

DESCEND

ENDEAR

ENDLESS

ENDURE

EXTEND

FENDER

FIEND

GENDER

LEGEND

OFFEND

PENDING

PRETEND

RENDITION

SLENDER

STIPEND

SURRENDER

SUSPEND

TENDENCY

TREND

VENDOR

```
P O B G A V G T F Y B M N I
U X R M E M E R I L G E O P
L N B N D N E P E D S R I R
C E D O D D D N N S C A T U
T O I E N B D E D Y S E I C
R D N E P I T S R U N D D D
P C F T R X S E S T R N N P
Y F D P E N D I N G E E S
O X Y N T N A N I F C T R P
D E S C E N D L E S S T T S
L P S R N G D D A P T A U D
I L R E D N E L S T S V F R
U U P C P X N L N E D U Y A
S G S B S S D C N X L B S X
```

A FEW OF MY FAVORITE THINGS

For your enjoyment, we've filled this puzzle with 28 things that can comfort you.

BATH

BREEZE

CANDLES

COCOA

COFFEE

FAMILY

FRIENDS

HAMMOCK

HUGS

KISS

MASSAGE

MOONLIGHT

MUSIC

PILLOW

RAINBOW

RECLINER

ROBE

SAUNA

SHADE

SHAWL

SHOWER

SLEEP

SLIPPERS

SMILE

SOFA

SUNRISE

SUNSET

VACATION

```
D Z S V R P B H S T O T A S
V K N O I T A C A V C C S A
S K B L F M F V H W H R N K
H E L P M A S S A G E U Y N
A O L O M S E L D N A C G E
W R C I S U M D I S W S Z S
L K L R M N W L A P V D W I
C Y R A O S C H E H P N R R
A U T I U E Z E E R B E K N
D O G N R T L B D E W I R U
C B C B S S L W A O F R V S
B M O O N L I G H T T F F E
F O Y W C K I S S K H W O I
O V D E B S R O I A V E G C
```

Here are 34 terms that can be preceded by the word "dry" to form new words or phrases.

BATTERY

BULK

CELL

CLEANING

COUNTY

DOCK

EYED

FARMING

FOOTING

GOODS

HOLE

KILN

LAKE

LAND

MEASURE

MILK

MOUNTING

NURSE

OFFSET

PLATE

POINT

RENT

ROASTED

SALT

SEASON

SHOD

SINK

SOCKET

SPELL

SUIT

TOAST

WALL

WASH

WELL

```
P N H O M W E L L L T Y O Y
F L S O T I L A A E R N Y
D R A M F N L K W N H S R M
H I W T T F E K C O D Y W Y
R G L L E P S A L T R C E D
D O L Y E O R E P Y O T O E
T O E T C G U G T R N N H W
T D S K N N N B C E L L A W
W S E N L I K I R T Y O B P
Y T A T T M O U N T I N G D
U T S O S R S P N A E B B K
A N O I T A H U E B E U L L
L F N A E F O P I K M L W F
B K O M W C D R E T P K C D
```

COURTROOM CAPER

"Perry Mason" was television's most successful and longest-running LAWYER series of the 1950s, with Raymond Burr starring as the popular defense attorney. In the 1990s, "Ally McBeal" was a hit for Calista Flockhart, who portrayed Ally, a Boston TRIAL attorney who was confident in the courtroom but neurotic about her personal life. Some of the legal terms used by these TV counselors-at-law can be found here.

APPEAL

BAIL

BENCH

BOND

CASE

CHARGE

CLERK

COUNSEL

COURT

DEFENDANT

EVIDENCE

FACTS

FILES

HEARING

JUDGE

JURY

JUSTICE

LAWYER

OATH

PLAINTIFF

PLEA

PROSECUTOR

QUESTIONS

RIGHTS

RULING

TESTIMONY

TRIAL

VERDICT

WITNESS

```
S V L C I I A S R I G H T S
S V E E O H J R U L I N G V
W D C R C V S U L I A B J M
G N L N D O W W R D P B U A
R T E S T I M O N Y S V D E
Q B R O T U C E S O R P G M
E U K N N E F T A H L R E C
J C E R O E S T E A A E L P
U S N S D S H A I H E Y L Y
S S O E T B R N C F P W T Y
T N F C D I T S L Y P A R B
I T A N N I O T R I A L U V
C F O G F W V N A M Q N O J
E B E F F I L E S N U O C W
```

102 LET'S GO TO "D" MOVIES!

We think you'll be "D"-lighted to solve this puzzle filled with 35 "D" films. We've included a wide range of films, from drama in *The DEEP*, to Disney cartoon fun in *DUMBO*, and horror in *DRACULA*. Search for these and other film titles which start with "D."

DAKOTA
DALLAS
DAMES
DANIEL
DARK (The)
DAWNING (The)

DECEIVERS (The)
DECEPTION
DEEP (The)
DEFIANCE
DELIVERANCE
DEMON

DERBY
DESIRE
DESTINY
DESTRY
DETOUR
DILLINGER
DIMPLES
DINER
DINO
DIVA
DIXIE
DOGMA
DONDI
DRACULA
DRAGNET
DRAGON-
  SLAYER
DREAMER
DRESSER (The)
DRIVER (The)
DRUMS
DULCY
DUMBO
DUNE

```
U S D E S I R E M A E R D I
D M R D L D U G N C D R B P
O U R E Y A L S N O G A R D
B R N C V N N A U I M E R B
M D L E L I R L E U N E U I
U U C P T E E U E I S W D S
D T D T V L G C D S O N A Y
E I X I D I N A E N O L R D
R S L O M A I R I D L U K E
O E G N I P L D R A G N E T
D M V F W U L P D K A Y O O
A A E I E O I E Y O V M M U
O D Y B R E D E S T I N Y R
Y R T S E D B D D A D K C Y
```

104

FLOOR ART

When it comes time to tear up and replace the old carpet, why not use your imagination and let the floor be your canvas by decorating with fancy linoleums or unusual coverings, such as BAMBOO. Or, if you have them, you can EMBELLISH CEMENT floors with PAINT or STAINS.

BAMBOO

BORDER

BRIGHT

CEMENT

CERAMIC

CHECKER-
   BOARD

COLOR

CORK

DECORATE

DESIGN

EMBELLISH

FINISH

FLOOR-
   BOARDS

GRID

HUES

INLAY

LAMINATE

LINOLEUM

PAINT

PAPER

PATTERNS

POLISH

SEAL

SHADES

STAINS

STONE

STRIPES

TEXTURE

TILE

TINT

VIBRANT

VINYL

WOOD

```
P Y A V T A P L C A U N K M
U A T T L E P O L I S H I D
N L P N X A L M H T F D I L
I N O E I O M S R L T R O Y
P I O M R A I I O S G A B N
A V B E U L P O N H O O R I
S W M C L E R T N A R B I V
T L A E S B L C A D T R G N
O I B R O W U O E E V E H S
N M P A T T E R N S L K T H
E C R M N Y U K B I A C U W
N D F I N I S H T G L E O O
S C T C K S T A I N S H F O
F E R U T X E T A R O C E D
```

Any building, be it a house, restaurant, or an office, requires the efforts of many people to make the finished product. Some of those who would likely be involved are listed below.

ARCHITECT

BRICKLAYER

CARPENTER

CONSTRUCTION
(worker)

CONTRACTOR

DECORATOR

DRYWALLER

ELECTRICIAN

ENGINEER

GLAZIER

LANDSCAPER

LATHE
(operator)

MACHINE
(operator)

MARBLE
(setter)

MASON

MECHANICAL
(engineer)

OPERATING
(engineer)

PAINTER

PAPER-
HANGER

PIPE (fitter)

PLASTERER

RIGGER

ROOFER

WELDER

```
A R C H I T E C T Z L R H D
R E L L A W Y R D M A S O N
W T E N G I N E E R C L C P
P N M L N A C G P P I O L U
L I C A E O L N I P N C U B
A A O L R C L A P S A D R O
S P N A H B T H T R H I L P
T R T D H H L R P H C R M E
E O R N S K U E I K E E A R
R O A K E C N P L C M I C A
E F C T T A A G R I Z H T
R E T I E O Y P B C O A I I
I R O R R E D L E W W L N N
C N R U R I G G E R I G E G
```

OOPS!

It might be hit or MISS locating these 28 synonyms for the word MISTAKE in the diagram. If you make an ERROR along the way, no need to worry… there's plenty of time to right your WRONG.

BLUNDER

BOBBLE

BOO BOO

BOTCH

DEFECT

ERROR

FALLACY

FAULT

FAUX PAS

FLAW

FLUFF

FUMBLE

GAFFE

GLITCH

GOOF

LAPSE

MISDEAL

MISDEED

MISHAP

MISPLAY

MISPRINT

MISS

MISTAKE

OMISSION

OVERSIGHT

SLIP

TYPO

WRONG

```
O R U M D U B O B B L E K M
N V X X Y C A L L A F T M V
D H C T O B L S U F C C P M
E P P F N A S C A N N E F F
E T K C E I B G O B D F L E
D H G D M M R I O U P E L W
S G S L M I S P L A Y D R E
I I P Y I S Y Y S L M O L H
M S B V I T A A A I N B N E
C R O M Y A C P S G M I Y M
S E O S S K S H X U F W W N
K V B R E E A F F U L F I X
F O O G R P I L S F A U L T
V V O S I E H T X M W F V N
```

106

BIRDS OF CHINA

China, the most populous country in the world, also has a large population of birds. While some of the birds in our list can be found in other countries, all of them are found in China.

ALBATROSS
AVOCET
COUCAL
CRAKE
CUCKOO
CURLEW

DRONGO
DUNLIN
FORKTAIL
GADWALL
GARGANEY
GRANDALA

HARRIER
HOOPOE
IORA
KITE
KNOT
LINNET
MERLIN
MESIA
MONAL
NILTAVA
PARAKEET
PETREL
PIPIT
PITTA
RAIL
ROLLER
SCOTER
SKUA
TEAL
TERN
TESIA
TWITE
WREN
YUHINA

```
V D R O N G O R V C T A E F
O K P C P N R H T L E R F F
A A A E T Y G A D W A L L V
T R V I T T E N N I L N U D
T O P A S R R N L D B Y O V
I I K I T E E K A R A P C M
P C W G T L T L S G T L Y T
Y O M E R L I N H C R I A E
R U O D L O W N A E O A N E
M C H A A R T H I O S T G K
B A A I E K U R K P S K E A
M L S N N I R C O O S R C R
T E C O V A U K S O K O N C
M P T P H C K W Y H R F M M
```

NAME THAT TOWN

The town of GARY, Indiana, was built on fill brought from the bottom of Lake Michigan. It's also the birthplace of Michael Jackson, the "King of Pop," who returned to his boyhood home on June 11, 2003 to receive the key to the city. Locate 30 towns in the Hoosier State that can also be people's names.

ALEXANDRIA

BRADFORD

CLAYTON

CLIFFORD

CRAIG

DEXTER

ELIZABETH

FLORENCE

GARY

GEORGIA

GERALD

HOMER

JASPER

JEROME

KENNETH

LAMAR

LAWRENCE

LUTHER

MILTON

OLIVER

OTIS

OWEN

QUINCY

RANDOLPH

SHIRLEY

STANLEY

VERNE

VICTOR

WILFRED

WYATT

```
W  I  L  F  R  E  D  K  E  S  B  D  I  K
Q  Y  Z  C  W  A  C  L  H  R  Q  M  A  E
C  L  A  Y  T  O  N  N  A  L  M  A  Y  N
L  A  A  T  Q  O  M  D  E  R  I  Y  K  N
I  M  O  J  T  U  F  L  O  R  E  N  C  E
F  A  T  L  Y  O  I  U  D  L  W  G  Y  T
F  R  I  H  R  Z  V  N  R  K  P  A  E  H
O  M  S  D  A  E  A  I  C  I  R  H  L  K
R  R  B  B  G  X  H  R  C  Y  E  E  N  D
D  E  E  V  E  S  A  T  M  T  M  M  A  A
K  T  V  L  E  I  V  O  U  N  O  O  T  N
H  X  A  I  G  R  O  E  G  L  H  R  S  M
D  E  H  B  L  K  N  E  W  O  H  E  U  U
D  D  G  M  T  O  R  E  P  S  A  J  N  R
```

Many of the words that we use in our everyday speech have their origins in foreign languages. Since the 17th century, the Dutch language has been a linguistic "cousin" of English. We've listed 34 terms whose meanings were derived from the Dutch.

BOOR

BOWERY

BUMPKIN

CLAPBOARD

COLESLAW

CRANBERRY

CRULLER

DRILL

DUCK

DUFFEL

EASEL

FOIST

FURLOUGH

HOCK

JIBE

LANDSCAPE

MAELSTROM

PICKLE

PINKIE

PRAM

SANTA CLAUS

SAWBUCK

SCOW

SERIF

SKIPPER

SLED

SPLIT

STIPPLE

TACKLE

TRAWL

WAFFLE

WAGON

YACHT

YAWL

```
K Y A C H T B H F I I C Y S
S C R O R M O R T S L E A M
C P U E M Y O M U I D P W T
O I K D W D R A O B P A L C
W C H G U O L R U F G C O L
A K B F D C B P E O Y S W L
F L F N A T O G N B Y D U I
F E S T I P P L E D N N S R
L S N L G K A P E L O A E D
E A P R E P P I K S W L R K
S S P B L D K M W B L W I C
A J I T Y N P B U U I A F O
E J F O I S T C R B P R W H
E Y W P E L K C A T T T U I
```

There are nearly 100 bays in the islands of Great Britain and Ireland. In Scotland they are called firths or lochs, and in Ireland many are known as loughs.

BALLIN-
  SKELLIGS

BLACKSOD

BROAD

BROOM (Loch)

CLYDE (Firth of)

DROGHEDA

DULAS

FALMOUTH

FISHGUARD

FORTH (Firth of)

FYNE (Loch)

HERNE

LAXFORD (Loch)

LONG (Loch)

LORN (Firth of)

LUCE

NEWPORT

PADSTOW

PEGWELL

PORT ISAAC

RED WHARF

SAND

SLIGO

START

ST. AUSTELL

ST. IVES

SWILLY (Lough)

TARBERT (Loch)

TRALEE

```
Y X W C T H I D D G H M U S
R L V D T R O P W E N A B G
R R L R R S A Y O E R R V I
W R O I K O A T T L O N G L
U F A C W I F N S A L U D L
I W A D C S I X D R L U C E
S L L L E T S U A T S A A K
B D Y V M H H S P L A C X S
A D I L E O G I L S H R F N
E T V N Y E U O I M N P M I
S T R E B R A T R E O F K L
R E D W H A R F H D Y O P L
H N S A U O D D P N O R R A
F H K O P E G W E L L K Y B
```

MULTIPLICITY

All the listed terms below can be used when describing multiple items or people. Go through the puzzle and gather up the GROUP of 35 words.

ARMY

BAND

BEVY

BROOD

CAMP

CASE

CAST

CONVENTION

CREW

DUET

EIGHT

FAMILY

FIVE

FLOCK

FOUR

FRATERNITY

GALAXY

GANG

GROUP

GUILD

HERD

MANY

NINE

PACK

SCHOOL

SEVEN

SORORITY

SQUADRON

SWARM

TEAM

THREE

THRONG

TRIBE

TRIO

TWIN

```
R W U P X X E E O E Q R U Q
G H D C M W Y H T O V D O W
N D E T E A M L R H E I Q C
C N L R P V C Y I N S O F I
S A C I D T X T O M W R C X
Y B S B U A H I D P A C K W
S E T E L G T R U T R F Q L
G C N A V N M O E Q M P I R
T H G I E E R R T E Y V E B
Q K Y V N G N O R H T F R R
H C N F V I G S C H O O L C
Q O A I T S A C P U O C F S
C L M Y W C N O R D A U Q S
L F W P V T G T G R P O T N
```

IN BLACK AND WHITE

The most readily identifiable characteristic of the DALMATIAN is its short white coat with black spots. And what side does the Dalmatian have the most spots on? The *outside*, of course! The puzzle below is filled with items that are usually black, white, or both.

CHALK
CHESS SET
CLOUD
COAL
CROW
DALMATIAN
DICE
DOMINO
EBONY
ESKIMO DOG
FROST
GOOSE
HOLSTEIN
KEYBOARD
LICORICE
LILY
MASK
MILK
NEWSPAPER
OLIVE
PANTHER
PENGUIN
PEPPER
POLECAT

RAVEN
SALT
SKUNK
SMOKE
SNOW
SUDS

SURF
SWAN
TIRE
TUXEDO
WHALE
ZEBRA

```
M U R M R T M K L V P X B S
Z N I U G N E P W H A L E U
U L R E P A P S W E N I O D
K R Y P P I X Z S I T L A S
N E V A R T O K E S H Y K W
U P Y K Y A I T E B E D L A
K P A B Z M S R Y A R H I N
S E O P O L E C A T I A C P
E P D D O A K K L L T Y O F
C S O H E D R S O T A N R O
I G O V U X C D A M I O I B
D N I O T S U R F M S B C W
A L L U G Z N T O T H E E I
O C H A L K Z D Z W O N S S
```

HAPPY THANKSGIVING!

Every year on the fourth **THURSDAY** of **NOVEMBER**, Americans take a moment to give thanks for the blessings of **FOOD**, **FAMILY**, and **FRIENDS**. Solve this puzzle by finding all the Thanksgiving terms listed below.

APPLES

BREAD

CORN

CROPS

DINNER

FAMILY

FEAST

FOOD

FOOTBALL

FRIENDS

GRAVY

HARVEST

HISTORY

HOLIDAY

MEAL

NATIVE
   (Americans)

NOVEMBER

PIES

PILGRIMS

PLYMOUTH

POTATOES

PRAYER

REUNION

ROAST

ROLLS

SALAD

STUFFING

THURSDAY

TRADITION

TURKEY

VEGETABLES

YAMS

```
Y A D S R U H T C R T S D H
Y F R I E N D S N R L M T R
R L C S R L E H A R V E S T
O L C O M O B D O O F A A C
T A C R T A I A A P P L E S
S B R A O T Y P T L P P F O
I T T K I P R L Y E K R U T
H O U O P E S M I R G L I P
P O N F Y N O V E M B E R R
I F L A F U O U D D A Y V O
E F R I T I N O A T A F G A
S P R H D I N N E R O L L S
N G V O O A V G R A V Y A T
M H L N U I Y E B T Y B L S
```

TEXAS PLACES WITH MEN'S NAMES

Texans have honored some men by naming towns and cities after them. From the Spanish explorer **DE SOTO** to the mysterious **FRED** (Flintstone?... Astaire?), try and find all 28 names.

ALEXANDER

ALFRED

BARRY

BENJAMIN

BRYAN

CLAY

CLYDE

DALE

DE SOTO

DUMAS

EDDY

ELROY

EMORY

FRED

KENT

KYLE

LEROY

MASON

MAXWELL

MORGAN

NOLAN

O'BRIEN

PORTER

REAGAN

SHERMAN

SIDNEY

TROY

YANCEY

```
B B T N A Y R B F O N Y E P
U X R O O N E Y J M B N R O
B S G R W N D C O W A C I R
B D T D J D U E N B R N J T
P A E A E W M N R A R S H E
Y P M O R G A N K F Y I S R
E I O P L L S X O T O S E D
N Y R C O G L R U D U D F N
D B Y N L C H E A M N W M K
I E O E L Y K R W A A M R H
S T R G Y E D W X X G S T Y
M O L F T S H E R M A N O O
Y X E I L C L A Y A E M P N
P H M E L A D A E K R F C X
```

"C" FOODS

If you're the designated cook for your household, then this puzzle is right up your alley. A selection of "C" foods for your pantry is hidden below.

CABBAGE

CAKE

CANDY

CARP

CARROT

CATFISH

CELERY

CEREAL

CHEESE

CHERVIL

CHICKEN

CHICORY

CHILI

CHOCOLATE

CHOP SUEY

CHOWDER

CINNAMON

CLAMS

CLOVES

COCOA

COCONUT

COFFEE

COLD CUTS

COLE SLAW

COOKIES

CORN

CRAB

CRACKERS

CUCUMBER

```
C A K E P E C H S P S A H C
C E R E A L W E E R R S L M
N C A F O H V A E F I A S K
F A H F O O N K L F M Y C U
Y R C O L D C U T S N R U G
L R C C P A P A E S E E H C
I O O O R S C T M N V L V H
V T R C R R U I N O B E O O
R F E O I N R E B M U C U C
E M D A O H K B Y A A W H O
H A W C B C C M F N R I N L
C O O K I E S C D N L C C A
S C H H W D F Y C I S C C T
A Y C E G A B B A C V E S E
```

"T" TALK

They speak **TAGALOG** in the Philippines, **TAMIL** in southern India and Sri Lanka, and **TUAREG** in the African Sahara. However, you don't have to say a word as you circle this selection of lesser-known languages and dialects beginning with the letter "T."

TAAL

TAGALOG

TAGULA

TAHITIAN

TAJIKI

TAKELMA

TALAMANCA

TAMIL

TATAR

TAVGI

TAW-SUG

TELEUT

TELUGU

THRACIAN

TIBETAN

TIGRE

TIGRINYA

TINO

TIPURA

TOCHARIAN

TODA

TONGA

TUAMOTU

TUAREG

TULU

TUNGUS

TUPI

TURKISH

TURKOMAN

```
U A R U P I T R E D A A H P
J W H T K G Y N A D G G T H
O N A I R A H C O T S N G S
T N J B U L C T D T A O T I
V A I E G G D N E U L T U V
T V S T A G U L A A T A R V
A I Y A Y C E L G M N K K E
V R M N Y U B A E O A E O Y
G B T T T N T E Y T I L M Y
I U U U H S I K R U T M A W
P L I M A T H R A C I A N T
U Y V G W R O Y G N H B S J
T R T I G R E P G I A U O H
P H T A W S U G N U T E I E
```

AMAZON TOUR

Take a JOURNEY into the JUNGLE as you circle the words in this puzzle, which are all related to the beautiful and MYSTERIOUS Amazon RIVER. Feel free to EXPLORE the WILDLIFE as you NAVIGATE your way down the 4,000-mile river — just don't forget your MAPS!

ANDES

ANIMALS

BANKS

BRAZIL

CLIMATE

COAST

COURSE

CRUISES

CULTURES

CURRENT

DEPTH

EXPLORE

FISH

JOURNEY

JUNGLE

LARGE

MAPS

MYSTERIOUS

NATURE

NAVIGATE

PERU

RAIN (forests)

RIVER

SAIL

SHIP

SOUTH (America)

TOUR

TRAVEL

VILLAGES

VOYAGE

WARM

WATER

WILDLIFE

```
U E S R U O C C T R Y H G R
C X E A T Y U N L A R G E D
D P S I H L E T A G I V A N
C L I N T R D N I T I S F P
C O U U R O S S R R U J Y U
O R R U E B U A K U U R D U
A E C D S F O L I N O O E B
S E G A L L I V G R A J T P
T F I P D Z R L N N E B O X
C L I M A T E D D E P T H G
Y H R R S V T E J L F P A P
S A B M A P S L A M I N A W
W S Y R V O Y A G E S W K Y
B H T U O S M L N R H Y E K
```

STREETS OF HONOLULU

Honolulu, Hawaii, is often called the Crossroads of the Pacific. Since 1794, when British Captain William Brown sailed into Honolulu, it's been a major trading center. It was also an important strategic location for U.S. military operations during World War II. Today, much of Honolulu's economy is based on tourism. Your MISSION is to see if you can spot 30 of its streets.

ARCHER
AUAHI
AVON
CHAPIN
COOKE
CORAL
CURTIS
DREIER
EMILY
FREELAND
GREEN
LANA
LISBON
MATLOCK
MERCHANT
MILLER
MISSION
PROSPECT
PUNCHBOWL
QUEEN
QUINN
REED

RICHARDS
SOUTH
SPENCER
THURSTON

VICTORIA
WARD
WILDER
YOUNG

```
N W T N W N S D R A H C I R
C H A P I N N H V C A P H E
E I H A U A W O Q U I N N E
Q H T A L N N G S R K V A D
Q W C E T K C O L T A M E L
F A E T V N U H B I I K B B
V R P T H T A Y B S O R S T
F D S U H U I H S O I E C L
R E O P R R R I C E W L O S
N G R E E N O S N R M L R M
C N P D H N T P T E E I A R
R R L O C C C V L O E M L O
E I L D R E I E R G N U O Y
W S G V A V V D R S L Y Q B
```

118

AUCTION ITEMS

If you're hunting for a bargain, the auction is where the action is. From **ANTIQUES** to **WATCHES**, you can find almost anything you're looking for and then some. Here is a list of items that you might come across at these shopping meccas.

ANTIQUES

ARTWORK

AUTOMOBILE

BOOKS

CANDLESTICKS

CHAIRS

CLOCKS

DESKS

DOLLS

FLATWARE

FURNITURE

HARDWARE

JEWELRY

LAMPS

LINEN

MACHINERY

MIRRORS

PAINTINGS

PENDANTS

POTTERY

QUILTS

RINGS

RUGS

SILVER

TABLES

TAPESTRY

VASES

WATCHES

```
S Q W L A M P S C L O C K S
E E L I B O M O T U A L G F
L R S M C F J H N L B N Q W
B U A G A D S E U Q I T N A
A T F W N C T W T G U N T
T I J B D I H Y N E W J Q C
Y N P F L R R I R A L K A H
Y R T S E P A T N E D R E E
R U L V S P N H Y E T N Y S
U F L A T W A R E W R T E A
G I A S I K K E O V A Y O P
S G Y E C M I R R O R S V P
Q D E S K S K O O B C T N U
D O L L S R I A H C K P B T
```

COAST TO COAST

A **MANGROVE** is any one of various coastal or aquatic tropical trees or shrubs that grow in large colonies, providing a habitat for young fish and shrimp. You'll find it in a **SWAMP**, a **MARSH**, a tropical river **MOUTH**, and the puzzle below — which also includes other coastal features.

ANCHORAGE
(a place to
anchor)

BANK

BAYOU

CAPE

CHANNEL

COVE

CREEK

DELTA

ESTUARY

FJORD

GULF

HARBOR

HAVEN

HEAD

INLET

LAGOON

LANDING

LOCH

MANGROVE

MARSH

MOUTH

NARROWS

PENINSULA

POINT

PORT

PROMONTORY

SOUND

STRAIT

SWAMP

```
J A D J C F K E Y P H T M F
G H H E A E U N V D R L B E
I O P A E T S H A O F L U G
Y A U R V W L K P B C S G A
C O C D O E K E L F G A C R
H B O R R M N T D Y Y B S O
A N R O G I O D E R T S W H
N A H G N I D N A L S K A C
N C V S A M O U T H N R M N
E O U P M W T O I O B I P A
L L O C H S A S A O R O R Y
A K Y G E F J O R D D Y E P
H L A H A R C W T N I O P B
S K B I D L S H S R A M O G
```

TAKE A HIKE

Load up the car or truck with family and friends and get ready to go on a camping or hiking trip, but first make sure you have everything listed below.

BACKPACK

BANDAGES

BANDANA

BEACON

BEDROLL

BLANKET

BOOTS

BOWLS

BUG SPRAY

CAMERA

CELL PHONE

FIRST-AID KIT

FLASHLIGHT

FOOD

FORK

GLOVES

JACKET

KNIFE

LANTERN

LINIMENT

MAPS

MATCHES

RADIO

RAINCOAT

RATIONS

ROPE

SOCKS

SUNSCREEN

TARP

TENT

TOOL KIT

WATER

```
I F I R S T A I D K I T L A
J R O F M E F I N K D F I M
T P T O E F G S N O I T A R
E Y T E D C M A T C H E S A
K C A P K C A B D G B T U D
C D O R T N E M I N I L N I
A G C W P N A L E K A M S O
J L N B O S H L L R A B C L
Y O I C A S G O B P A E R L
F V A S A N O U S R H F E O
G E R L K T D T B A I O E R
B S F W O C L A N T E R N D
P V C O P I O F N E F K P E
D P F B O O T S W A T E R B
```

CAN YOU HEAR IT?

Here's a noisy puzzle that can be solved silently. All the words hidden in the diagram are types of sounds. SNAP your fingers, CLICK your pen, THUMP your feet, and circle away!

BANG

BARK

BLAST

BOOM

BUZZ

CHIME

CLANG

CLATTER

CLICK

CLINK

CRACKLE

CRASH

DRONE

FIZZ

GURGLE

HISS

HOWL

JINGLE

PATTER

PEAL

PURR

RATTLE

ROAR

RUMBLE

RUSTLE

SIZZLE

SNAP

THUMP

TOOT

WHEEZE

WHINE

WHIR

```
M H M G C I I P T K F R Z Z
Z U I P Z J A W A O R F Z W
T K H S C N F F B T E A U H
M D P Z S E I U R H T W B G
W I U S D N M P P H T E N C
S L G N A B U I U I A A R R
S P M U F R T M H B L A S T
M E N O R D P M Z C C F G F
G A E L O G E E E K C I L C
W L L H E B L Z L N L I R H
S L T O O T Z E B G I W A G
E E S J T I Z E M S N H O W
K O U A F F I H U E K I W H
N C R A S H S W R O A R J D
```

GODS ON GREEK COINS

Just as our currency states "In God We Trust," the ancient Greeks also relied on their deities to back their funds. Here's a list of gods found on ancient Greek coins.

AGATHODAIMON	ASKLEPIOS	EROS
APHRODITE	ATHENA	HADES
APOLLO	BAKCHOS	HEKATE
ARES	DEMETER	HELIOS
ARTEMIS	DIONE	HEPHAISTOS
		HERA
		HESTIA
		HORUS
		HYGEIA
		ISIS
		KASTOR
		KORE
		KYBELE
		NIKE
		POLYDEUKES
		PTAH
		SARAPIS
		ZEUS

```
N G C S N K B P M M K D R T
E M A P O L L O H O R U S T
U E B H E I C T H E S T I A
P R N P O K P K T L K O M H
O I A S Y G I E I N S A E Y
L K R B U R M N L I M T T G
Y B E P Z E R O S K I S R E
D L S R D S Z I S D S B A I
E P N O M I A D O H T A G A
U E B T I U T R A S R K A H
K U T S Z L H D A E N C Y E
E O H A T P E O H P B H O I
S H R K A S N H H B I O P R
E U H E P H A I S T O S D M
```

IT'S TIME

Don't waste another **MOMENT** . . . simply start solving this puzzle which is filled with words relative to **TIME**. And remember the words of Benjamin Franklin who wrote, "You may delay, but Time will not."

AEON

ANNUM

CENTURY

CYCLE

DATE

DECADE

EPOCH

FORTNIGHT

FUTURE

GENERATION

HOUR

MOMENT

MONTH

PAST

PRESENT

QUARTER

SEASON

SECOND

SEMESTER

SESSION

SPAN

STAGE

TENURE

TERM

TIME

TRIMESTER

WEEK

YEAR

```
W T R D D Q P L H H R M C G
C C O K N U K E E W R A E Y
Q E S S P A N R U P Q W M K
U L N E M R U K F N Q L I Y
Y C U T M T T Y P Q E O T O
F Y D R U E D N R K S R T Y
D C O F D R S K E E I H A K
S E A S O N Y T S M G K F A
E H C O P E A S E I O W M O
C C H A W D I S N R M M R A
O H S T D O T T T D U U D Y
N T G E N E R A T I O N K C
D M H M R O A G D H U N E W
Y Q M M F N M E N O E A O T
```

YOU "RR" RIGHT

This **CURRENT** puzzle contains 29 terms that feature the letter combination "RR." **BURROW** through the maze of letters to uncover them all.

ARRANGE

BARREL

BLURRY

BURROW

CARROT

CORRECT

CORRODE

CURRENT

EARRING

ERRATIC

FERRET

FLURRY

FURROW

HERRING

MARRY

MIRROR

NARRATE

NARROW

PARROT

QUARRY

SCURRY

SORROW

SPARROW

TERRACE

TERRAIN

TERRIER

TORRENT

WARRANT

WARRIOR

```
Y Y S N D B W Q T I U S E W
D S I T W R U T N A P T F F
C O R R O D E R E A A O I R
S R F R R R B I R R C R M L
G R Q N R L R R R O R R G R
Q O O A U T O A U R W A N C
U W C R F W N W C C E P I A
A E R R R G Y E A O D T R N
R Y O O E T N A R R A W R P
R R R W L D G N I R R A E M
Y R R U C S S R R E O I H A
T U I B A R R E L C H T O R
B L M U F E R R E T H G E R
W F C S C D B I T F U N B Y
```

WORDS AFTER "HOT"

Since it's the time of year for hot WEATHER, we've filled this puzzle with 37 words which can be preceded by, or are otherwise related to, the word "hot." Can you find them all?

BATH

BREAD

BROTH

CAKES

CHOCOLATE

COAL

COCOA

COFFEE

COMB

EMBER

FIRE

FLAME

FOOD

FOOT

FUDGE

HEAD

HOUSE

IRON

LINE

MEAL

OVEN

PEPPER

PLATE

POTATO

PRESS

SAUCE

SAUSAGE

SEAT

SHOT

SPOT

SPRING

TAMALE

TEMPER

TODDY

WATER

WEATHER

WIRE

```
Y T W C D D V E U V L F T T
I P L A O C E H U A L I D O
U Y L R T L I N E L F T E O
O Y B A A E D M I R O N I F
P V F M T B R O T H B D L I
E B A F O E G I S E K A C R
G T T G P C H F W F M T T E
A E A P E N E V O E E L M H
S M E L T G A O C O C B O P
U P S T O D D Y U B E U K R
A E R N P C C U Y R S F A E
S R E I S C O F F E E V E S
B H Y M N R E H T A E W H S
E D V P E G B Y C D R N O I
```

Make your **MARK** as an expert solver by looping the 41 words hidden in the diagram. Each one can be preceded by the word "water" to form a new word or phrase.

BALLET	COLOR	GAUGE
BEETLE	COOLER	HEATER
BIRD	COURSE	HEMLOCK
BISCUIT	CRESS	HOLE
BUCK	FALL	LEVEL
BUFFALO	FOWL	LILY
CHESTNUT	FRONT	LINE
		MAIN
		MARK
		MELON
		METER
		MILL
		MOCCASIN
		PIPE
		PISTOL
		POLO
		SHED
		SPANIEL
		SPOUT
		SPRITE
		SYSTEM
		TABLE
		TOWER
		VAPOR
		WHEEL
		WINGS
		WORKS

```
B A L L E T I R P S P R W P
C U I E N O L E M O K F T M
H N F S V W C L L A D R I B
E S S F L E L O E B I O O R
S G W K A R L O K S A N E W
T N U R O L O C T Y R T L E
N I S A C C O M F S V U N R
U W U M G L U V P T I O O K
T U R C M H E A T E R P M C
F C R E S S N E M M A S Y U
U A H E T I D P H V I W I B
E E L T E E B I M W S L P B
F O W L H N M P S D L I L Y
H V N S T A U H S D A L W K
```

Risotto is a popular dish in many restaurants these days. Arborio RICE is cooked slowly in BROTH, with grated CHEESE and other ingredients added towards the end of cooking. In Sicily, however, it is prepared with BEEF and CHICKEN livers and stuffed into rice balls which are then fried in OLIVE OIL. Whet your appetite as you circle the words about this Italian treat.

ARTICHOKES	RICH	SHRIMP
BASIL	SAFFRON	SIMMER
BEEF	SALT	TOMATO
BROCCOLI	SAUTÉ	WATER
BROTH		
BUTTER		
CARROTS		
CHEESE		
CHICKEN		
CORN		
CREAMY		
FISH		
GARLIC		
HERBS		
ITALY		
LOBSTER		
MUSHROOMS		
OLIVE OIL		
ONION		
PARSLEY		
PEPPER		
RECIPES		
RICE		

```
S E P I C E R H P C P R S V
A S K N A M T V G G A B R N
S A F F R O N S S R R T N L
O U F K R O L F T E S L P P
H T M B O I C I H P L T M C
I E A U T L C S V P E M I H
K A R M S H I H R E Y L R O
N O I N O H L S I P O H H S
I P C K R T R T A C F I S K
C H E E S E A O C B K I L O
W S T N T L G O O P M E Y M
S A L T Y C R E A M Y R N E
W L U H S B N R E T S B O L
R B E E F U R R R K F C Y A
```

128

GIDDYAP!

The art of riding and handling a HORSE dates back thousands of years. As the skill developed, aids were created for riding comfort and easier maneuvering. Can you GALLOP through our list of equestrian terms?

BOOTS

BRIDLE

CANTER

CINCH

CROP

DRILL

FILLY

GAIT

GALLOP

GIRTH

GROOM

HORSE

JODHPURS

JUMP

MARE

MOUNT

PACE

PATH

REINS

RIDER

SADDLE

SNAFFLE

SPURS

STABLE

STALL

STIRRUPS

TRAIL

TROT

```
Y C B U D N F S L I A I H S
I C F A I I T S H S O N T B
G S R C N J R T G T T I A G
D D O O G U C E H S R U P S
U A E B P D E C T R A I L N
N M L H J R N A U L L T G A
C O D E A I L P P J M U N F
S O I M C L S B M A A E E F
J R R P O L L A G U T F H L
N G B E H U A D D O J G Y E
J B O O T S N P R D I L A F
H B R E I N S T A B L E F M
C S R U A L A P R I D E R N
E H E H E T L C F I Y I P I
```

LIGHTS

You can shed some light on this particular puzzle by trying to SPOT the 32 types of lights we've obscured in the diagram. Don't be in the dark any longer, begin your SEARCH now!

ANCHOR

BLINKER

BOUNDARY

CANDLE

CEILING

COURSE

ELECTRIC

FIXED

FLASH

FLOOD

FOOT

GREEN

HEAD

HIGH

LAMP

LANDING

LIME

MOON

NEON

NIGHT

PILOT

POSITION

RUNWAY

SEARCH

SIDE

SIGNAL

SPOT

STAR

STOP

STREET

TAIL

TRAFFIC

```
L K N U Y A S N H H F O O T
Y S B L E T E S G C K Y R R
A D Y E O E A S I G N A L E
D N D P R L R I H D F W W U
N E K G F O C T L F E N L D
F O X N L T H G I N C U B R
D N W I O L B C E K K R W C
D O O L F O I L N L A M P F
W S I I I R M E I A X X O F
B P H E T M D S L N W O C U
N O R C F I E R M D K H U S
N T E E R T S U I I N E T X
O L N Y R L B O U N D A R Y
E M B M D W U C P G R D C S
```

131

PERFECTLY PLAID

There's a timelessness to plaid which keeps it always in style. And with unlimited PATTERN designs, it's easy to experiment with lovely plaids.

ACCENT

ATTRACTIVE

BASKETS

BEAUTIFY

BOXES

COVERLET

CRAFTS

CREATIVE

DECORATION

DINING (room)

DISPLAY

EMBELLISH

FABRIC

FESTIVE

HOLIDAY

HOUSE

LIVING (room)

MANTEL

NAPKINS

PAPER

PATTERN

PRESENTS

RIBBON

SACK

SKIRT

STOCKINGS

TABLECLOTH

TARTAN

THROW

```
T  R  I  K  S  S  O  B  G  T  S  F  Y  E
E  M  A  N  T  E  L  I  S  N  A  F  H  S
D  X  K  F  O  A  N  O  B  B  I  R  C  U
K  C  A  S  C  I  S  V  R  T  H  V  U  O
Y  R  L  C  K  N  T  I  U  N  H  L  I  H
C  A  E  V  I  T  C  A  R  T  T  A  S  L
B  N  L  K  N  M  E  E  R  H  O  I  H  C
T  A  P  P  G  B  T  O  R  O  L  U  O  R
G  A  S  R  S  T  O  O  Y  L  C  V  L  E
N  I  E  K  A  I  W  X  E  W  E  E  I  A
I  P  A  P  E  R  D  B  E  R  L  G  D  T
N  I  I  C  E  T  M  G  L  S  B  L  A  I
I  A  S  T  N  E  S  E  R  P  A  T  Y  V
D  N  A  T  R  A  T  F  E  S  T  I  V  E
```

MARTIAL ARTS

Discipline, training, and tradition are all part of the ageless sport of martial arts. Most originated in the Orient and combine movement with philosophy. Find 30 types of martial arts below.

CHIEN

GOJU-KAI

GULAT

HARIMAU

HO-JUTSU

HOP GAR

HSING-I

IAI-JITSU

JIU JITSU

JUDO

KALI

KARATE

KEMPO

KENDO

KUNG FU

KYUDO

LATHI

NAHA TE

PA-KUA

SAVATE

SHIAI

SIKARAN

SUMO

TAEKWONDO

TAE KYON

TAI CHI

TANG SOO DO

WADO RYU

WING CHUN

WU SHU

```
H H W U S H U S T I J I A I
U U E F N A R A K I S F G J
D A T S L S E U U F G N U K
T E A O A K L J Y N R K L T
A G H H W V I K R R J E A S
N C A O A T A E K Y O N T L
G J N J S R K T I E P D N H
S D U U A D U M E S M O A T
O D A T H T J A R N H P A W
O R E S A C O A M E A I O E
D K Y U D O G O J I C H A I
O U K M L P A N P H R T L I
P A E O O N C D I C O A P H
P O O H S I N G I W K L H T
```

TASTY TEMPURA

Tempura is best known as a **JAPANESE** method of deep-frying fish and **VEGETABLES**. It actually was first prepared by 16th-century missionary Saint Francis Xavier as a tasty alternative to meat dishes, which were forbidden on certain holy days.

ASPARAGUS

BATTER

BOWL

BROWN

CHOPSTICKS

COATING

CRISP

CUISINE

DIPPING

DRAIN

FLOUR

FRIED

GINGER

GOLDEN

JAPANESE

LIGHT

LOBSTER

OYSTERS

PAPRIKA

PEPPERS

POTATO

SALT

SCALLOPS

SHELLFISH

SHRIMP

SOY SAUCE

TARO ROOT

VEGETABLES

```
F Y W A B B R O W N I M N G
V K T P S R E P P E P B N C
L E S E N A P A J C O I H U
T H G I L V S S U T O P I
M H A E A K I R P A P H M S
I R S D T L M R O S V U I I
D U P I Y A E C T Y T U R N
E O A P F G B I R O J E H E
I L R P N L C L O S T V S D
R F A I P K L R E T S B O L
F I G N S L O E A S A B R O
M W U G W R W B H V L T G G
J I S C A L L O P S T A O J
O Y S T E R S N B C R I S P
```

GETTING OFF TO A GOOD START

Looking for a light bite? Try a **BAGEL** with **BUTTER** or **CREAM CHEESE**. If **BACON** and **EGGS** is more your style, we've got that too in this list of breakfast offerings.

BACON

BAGEL

BISCUIT

BREAD

BUNS

BUTTER

CEREAL

CHEESE

COCOA

COFFEE

CREAM

CROISSANT

CRULLER

DANISH

DOUGHNUT

EGGS

FISH

FRUIT

JELLY

JUICE

MILK

MUFFIN

PANCAKES

POTATOES

PRESERVES

ROLL

SAUSAGE

SUGAR

SYRUP

TOAST

WAFERS

WAFFLES

```
N T M C V C U D T U A A A O
U C U A R P O I A L A B W V
Y W F J E U U F Y L L E J W
D R F J G R L L F S S V S D
H T I H F Y C L A E R E C N
J T N P V S B H E V E R O W
P U D A N I S H D R F V C C
T O I N S I C B R E A D O H
O K T C F S W A Y S W G A B
A L U A E J I C R E T T U B
S I I K T L L O R R G N A S
T M E E Y O K N R P S G F G
S A U S A G E E T C E C S M
G O F D C Y S S E L F F A W
```

Some anglers tie flies themselves to save money, but most do it because they're "hooked" on the sheer pleasure of catching a fish on a homemade work of art. Hidden below are 31 names of flies specifically designed for catching trout.

ALDER FLY

BEAST

BIBIO

BUZZER

CARDINAL

CORIXA

EMERGER

EXOCET

FIREBALL

GNAT

GOLDIE

GRENADIER

HACKLE

JANE

JEZABELLE

KEHE

LEECH

MARIA

NYMPH

OLD NICK

PEARLY

PRIEST

QUILL

RENEGADE

SEDGE

SPIDER

TADPOLE

VIVA

WAGGY

ZUGBUG

ZULU

```
B E A S T F G N A T U T S X
I R C E H U B H L L A A P U
B R E D B T E Y U J I D I C
I L R G S B U Z Z E R P D E
O Z U E R L H S I L A O E G
V Z I E N E Y R K L M L R A
P R H O G E M G D E L E V J
P E I D L O G E G B N I A I
K L A N I D R A C A V N U E
H K C R D F N X D Z W L N Q
H C E E L Y F I R E B A L L
R A G Y M Y E R C J J E I Z
V H O P H R Q O U K J M C S
D E H Z Y T E C O X E T F Y
```

STREETS OF MUNICH

Munich's annual festivals attract many tourists, especially its famous 16-day Oktoberfest. Here are some of the streets found throughout Germany's third largest city, the colorful and popular Munich.

ARCIS
ARNULF
BAADER
BARER
BAYER
BLUMEN
BRIENNER
BRUDER
DIENER
EINSTEIN
ELISEN
GOETHE
HACKEN
HANSA
KARL
KEFER
KIRCHEN
KLENZE
LAMMER
LEOPOLD
LILIEN
LUDWIG
LUISEN
MAFFEI
MARS
MOZART

MÜLLER
OCCAM
OTTO
RESIDENZ
ROSEN
SEIDL

TROGER
TÜRKEN
UHDE
UHLAND
VERDI
WEIN

```
S I A C B L U M E N T T B N
B M U L L M S R E D U R B A
A A A C C U E S E W E I N B
Y F A F R L I P Z N Z G T A
E L S D F L D S N N E S O R
R U L I E E L E E E O I L E
O N E H C R I K D N I A D R
T R O G E R C N I I M L M O
T A P I B A A E S M D O I M
O S O W H L Z K E T Z R A L
M N L D H N O R R A E C E H
P A D U E D H U R F C I H V
N H R L N E H T E O G S N F
B G K S L R A K Z I Z N S P
```

DOROTHY'S HOMETOWN

Based on L. Frank Baum's children's book, the 1939 film *The Wizard of Oz* tells the story of Dorothy, a Kansas farmgirl who, after being hit on the head during a tornado, is transported to a land filled with colorful characters and adventure. However, Dorothy came to learn that "There's no place like HOME." Search for the following cities and towns from Kansas, Dorothy's beloved state.

ADMIRE
BARNARD
BELVUE
COATS
DELIA

DWIGHT
ENSIGN
EUDORA
FOWLER
FRANKFORT

GLADE
HOME
IDANA
INGALLS
JARBALO
JEWELL
KEATS
KIOWA
LAMONT
LEONA
MAIZE
MULBERRY
NATOMA
NORTON
OBERLIN
PAOLA
POMONA
QUINTER
RAMONA
ROSALIA
SEDAN
SELMA
THAYER
TRIBUNE

```
G L A D E A H L S Y K R G L
Q Z N S Z T R O F K N A R F
A R O D U E R J C A W P E Y
V O M U L B E R R Y A N T F
J S A D B W Y J P O M O N A
S A R E E O A M L E S T I N
T L Q L K R H A A E N W U A
A I L I B N T F D O O J Q D
E A O A O N O R M W H N N I
K W L T G W A A I A I G A C
A O R F L N L D R B I G R O
E O B E R L I N E S U Z H A
N O R A M O T A N S R N E T
B W B E L V U E M O H A E S
```

ALL WORN OUT

Spring is in the air and it's time to put away all of your winter BOOTS, GLOVES, PANTS, and TIGHTS, and make space in your closet for CULOTTES, open-toed SHOES, SHORTS, and T-shirts!

APRON	SHORTS	TIGHTS
ASCOT	SKIRT	T-SHIRT
BELT	SLACKS	TUNIC
BERET	SOCKS	TUXEDO
BLAZER	SUIT	VEIL
BLOUSE	SWEATER	VEST
BOOTS		
CAFTAN		
CAPE		
CLOAK		
COAT		
CULOTTES		
DRESS		
FROCK		
GLOVES		
GOWN		
JACKET		
JEANS		
JUMPER		
KIMONO		
PANTS		
ROBE		
SARI		
SASH		
SCARF		
SHAWL		
SHOES		

```
I G L O V E S U O L B N B K
C H N J P T A D K F T E F S
C L S C N L R S R A R B D E
D K O A U E I K K E V O O L
W S P A S B B C T E P R C O
H W I S K V U A I A B M T K
I N I C C L E L G N P I U G
B L A O O W I S H O U R L J
B O O T S H I R T S W T O O
R D T J F R A C S R C N O N
V E R E Z A L B S H O E S D
S X I A P S C V M M A H G A
P U K N C A P F I L T W S C
G T S S J A C K E T N X L J
```

All of the ballroom dances below were popular during the reign of Queen VICTORIA of England (1837-1901). In this list you'll notice the word *"valse"* is used in two entries. That's the German word for "waltz," and it was customary to use it in Victorian times. Try to find all the dances hidden in the diagram.

ARCADIAN

BARN DANCE

BERLIN (The)

BOUNTY (The)

BRONCO (The)

CAMELIA

CARLTON (The)

CORONATION

ESMERALDA

FROLIC

GALOP

KOSKA

MIGNON

NIAGARA

PALATIVE

PATRIA

POLONAISE (The)

RACKET

RIPPLE

SLOW VALSE

UNION DANCE

VALSE MINUET

VELETA (The)

VERSA

VICTORIA

YORKE (The)

```
P A L A T I V E L E T A I G
B O U N T Y V E V E R S A M
C L L T E U N I M E S L A V
C W V O C S N O C N O R B R
I O A I N U L N T P M V D A
L M R R A A A A I L E M A C
O Y C O D D I I V A R I L K
R M A K N L R S R W G A Y E
F I D O R A O F E T O A C T
B G I S A R T W K L A L R G
A N A K B E C I R I P P S A
U O N A E M I F O G G P P C
V N K Y V S V P Y N N K I F
W N I L R E B R E V V W N R
```

MAKE MINE MARCASITE

Much of the marcasite in today's jewelry is really **PYRITE**, also known as fool's **GOLD**. In addition to being used for adornment, pyrite has commercial importance in the manufacture of sulfuric acid. Go digging for 29 minerals found in North America.

ACMITE	INESITE	RUTILE
ADAMITE	JADEITE	SPINEL
AUGITE	KERNITE	TALC
AZURITE	PYRITE	TOPAZ
BARITE	REALGAR	ZOISITE
BAUXITE		
BERYL		
BISMUTH		
BORAX		
BORNITE		
CALCITE		
COPPER		
CRYOLITE		
CUPRITE		
EPIDOTE		
GALENA		
GOLD		
GYPSUM		
HALITE		

```
M S P E T I R A B O R A X B
Y P P Y E T O D I P E S A B
K T I I R Y I L S A C U Z A
E E O C N I R O M X G S D R
R T Z P U E T G U I G A N Z
N I I S A P L E T I M C A E
I E E L C Z R E H I L R T J
T D G B O R N I T E Z I P C
E A Y S U Y R E T I S I O Z
R J N A Z U R I T E C P D N
M O I E T M X C N I P L Z X
C B N I L U L I J E L X A C
E B L U A A L Y R E B A Y C
T E I B T N G Y P S U M H D
```

SUPER BOWL MVPs

In a stunning upset, Super Bowl XXXVI saw the underdog New England Patriots defeat the St. Louis Rams 20-17. On the final play of the game, Adam Vinatieri kicked a 48-yard field goal to give the Patriots their first-ever world championship. New England quarterback Tom BRADY was named the game's MVP. An interesting fact . . . linebacker Chuck HOWLEY of the Dallas Cowboys is the only player from a losing team to have garnered this award.

AIKMAN (Troy)
ALLEN (Marcus)
ANDERSON (Ottis)
BILETNIKOFF (Fred)
BRADSHAW (Terry)

BRADY (Tom)
BROWN (Larry)
CSONKA (Larry)
DAVIS (Terrell)
DAWSON (Len)

DENT (Richard)
ELWAY (John)
HARRIS (Franco)
HOWARD (Desmond)
HOWLEY (Chuck)
LEWIS (Ray)
MARTIN (Harvey)
MONTANA (Joe)
NAMATH (Joe)
PLUNKETT (Jim)
RICE (Jerry)
RYPIEN (Mark)
SCOTT (Jake)
SIMMS (Phil)
SMITH (Emmitt)
STARR (Bart)
STAUBACH (Roger)
SWANN (Lynn)
WARNER (Kurt)
WILLIAMS (Doug)
YOUNG (Steve)

```
Y D A R B G P F V I P S C D
N R R A T S K N H B I I W T
O S T A U B A C H R T W O B
S G M N W M M A R T E E I R
R W C A A O O A E N E L L A
E H A T I R H K R H E Y V D
D O H N F L N R M T T O C S
N W Y O N U L W N I I U B H
A L B M L N A I K M A N C A
N E I P Y R K B W S S G A W
H Y D A N O N R I R I C E V
N B W E F R O O B E M V R H
A L R F N O S W A D M M A E
E S Y U G T C N U U S I F D
```

HOLY MACKEREL!

Florida's coast is home to many saltwater fishes, including the black MULLET, MARLIN, POMPANO, red SNAPPER, SNOOK, and TARPON. Get ready to reel in the 32 species swimming in the diagram below.

ANCHOVY

CARP

DRUM

FLOUNDER

GROUPER

GRUNION

HADDOCK

HAKE

HERRING

KINGFISH

MACKEREL

MARLIN

MULLET

PERCH

PIKE

POLLACK

POMPANO

PORGY

SAILFISH

SALMON

SARDINE

SHAD

SHARK

SMELT

SNAPPER

SNOOK

SOLE

SWORDFISH

TARPON

TROUT

TUNA

WAHOO

```
F  R  T  S  O  L  E  K  A  H  D  T  P  C
S  G  W  W  H  N  H  M  U  R  D  K  L  T
T  R  E  P  P  A  N  S  E  W  G  I  E  C
R  U  Y  I  S  A  R  D  I  N  E  N  R  H
G  N  G  K  E  W  N  K  I  F  R  G  E  L
N  I  R  E  P  U  O  R  G  P  L  F  K  Y
O  O  O  F  O  K  R  R  E  P  P  I  C  F
K  N  P  L  Y  E  K  R  D  A  H  S  A  S
H  O  F  R  H  V  C  C  S  F  N  H  M  S
T  M  O  W  A  H  O  O  A  I  I  E  S  T
R  L  A  N  U  T  D  H  L  L  L  S  U  Y
O  A  L  C  S  L  D  R  C  T  L  I  H  E
U  S  P  O  M  P  A  N  O  N  F  O  K  E
T  E  L  L  U  M  H  N  E  C  A  R  P  V
```

142   "H" MINNESOTA CITIES

Minnesota is a big state, the 12th largest in the nation. So you figure a state that size must have more cities than just Minneapolis and St. Paul, right? Well, here's a list of other Gopher State cities, and these are just some of the ones that begin with the letter "H."

HALLOCK

HALSTAD

HANCOCK

HANSKA

HARMONY

HARRIS

HASTINGS

HAWLEY

HAYFIELD

HECTOR

HENDERSON

HENDRICKS

HENNING

HERMAN

HERON LAKE

HIBBING

HILLS

HILLTOP

HINCKLEY

HOFFMAN

HOKAH

HOLDING-FORD

HOPKINS

HOUSTON

HOWARD LAKE

HOYT LAKES

HUGO

HUTCHINSON

```
H N Y D A I S H E N N I N G
A A B L N L K G A K S N A H
R M T E L O H C N N Y L N R
R R A I H R S A O E C O H S
I E H F U S A R L L T O L N
S H O Y T L A K E S L S C I
K O H A C N C K U D T A F K
C F E H H N A O I P N A H P
I F C C I L H N N O H E D O
R M T H N S G N I T S A H H
D A O O S F W Y E L W A H U
N N R H O W A R D L A K E G
E E G R N H I B B I N G T O
H Y D Y N O M R A H A K O H
```

144

MUSTACHE BASH

Growing a mustache is usually a man's way of making a fashion statement; however, for some men it can have a practical use as well. A mustache can DISGUISE a weak UPPER LIP or help BALANCE the FACE by drawing attention away from a prominent NOSE or receding hairline.

BALANCE

BEARD

BRISTLES

BRUSH

CAMOU-
FLAGE

COMB

CURL

CURVE

DISGUISE

FACE

FALSE

FU MANCHU

GROWTH

HAIRS

HANDLEBAR

HEAVY

MOUTH

NOSE

OVER-
GROWN

SCRATCHY

SHAPE

SHAVE

SINISTER

SMILE

THICK

THIN

TRIM

UPPER LIP

WALRUS

WAVY

WAXED

WHISKERS

```
W  I  U  O  E  Y  O  Y  L  F  A  L  S  E
A  E  Y  P  R  V  V  D  I  N  R  F  V  L
N  O  S  E  P  A  H  S  W  U  T  A  M  I
R  G  O  I  W  E  B  O  C  G  H  F  T  M
T  R  I  M  U  H  R  E  T  S  I  N  I  S
C  O  M  B  O  G  I  L  L  H  C  L  H  F
U  W  A  L  R  U  S  S  I  D  K  D  U  B
R  T  W  E  G  H  T  I  K  P  N  M  E  D
V  H  V  C  V  S  L  H  D  E  A  A  N  H
E  O  H  N  W  U  E  H  M  N  R  I  H  B
W  H  H  A  I  R  S  E  C  D  H  S  U  K
P  G  X  L  W  B  Y  H  C  T  A  R  C  S
T  E  G  A  L  F  U  O  M  A  C  G  Y  D
D  M  X  B  P  K  T  O  V  K  F  L  H  B
```

TAROT TALK

Tarot cards are any set of 22 cards bearing pictures of certain tradition-al allegorical figures. Used in fortunetelling, the pictures on the cards represent the various FORCES, VIRTUES, and VICES of man. Claimed to have originated in China, India, or Egypt, their true origin remains obscure.

CHARIOT

DENARII

EMPEROR

FOOL

FORCES

FORTITUDE

FORTUNE

GAMES

HANGMAN

HERMIT

JUDGMENT

JUSTICE

KING

KNAVE

KNIGHT

LOVERS

MAGICIAN

MOUNTE-
BANK

PAGE

PENTACLE

PRIESTESS

STAR

SUIT

TEMPERANCE

VICES

VIRTUES

WANDS

WORLD

```
S J C W O R L D J H N C V M
E T M C N L H U E A U V G D
C N K O M C S E I N D H F C
R E U N U T M C R G A J V F
O M L T I N I S M M L R V B
F G P C R G T S D A I I I K
E D E R A O H E B N R T E I
L U V M I T F T B T A E M N
F J E R C J N S U A K W P G
B S A T E M P E R A N C E F
I H V I C E S I P E A K R F
C E D U T I T R O F V J O G
T B N S F M A P A G E O R G
E P S M S B R T D J L C L B
```

TRAVELING THROUGH TENNESSEE

If you want to visit **BRAZIL, CUBA, INDIA, LEBANON,** or **WALES,** you needn't go abroad — just go to Tennessee! Find these and the names of 32 other small Tennessee towns hidden below.

ADAIR

BRAZIL

BUCKEYE

CHEROKEE

CUBA

CURVE

DOYLE

DUCKTOWN

DYER

ELKTON

ERIN

GIBBS

GOIN

HENRY

INDIA

LADDS

LANE

LEBANON

LONE OAK

NEVA

NIOTA

NUTBUSH

OCOEE

OLD HICKORY

ONLY

RED ASH

RODDY

ROME

ROVER

SEWANEE

SHILOH

SPIVEY

TROY

VALE

VINE

WALES

WHEEL

```
W A L A N E N R E V O R G H
T A E M O R D I L C Y L N O
G O L D H I C K O R Y S D L
V Z Y E W N N E O T D B E I
A A O H S H E D Y L A B P H
L A D D S V B U Y E V I P S
E D B A R U N C L B K G R W
E B D U I W B K W A T C A W
A E C A C R T T A N L I U D
R V H S A O H O U O D L Y B
W R E Z N S E W A N E E D R
G O I N E K N N I E R N D A
D L E E K O R E H C B I O A
A K Z T R O Y W P K T V R L
```

DISPLAYING AFFECTION

You don't have to be confined to conventional forms when it comes to displaying your photographs. Instead of hanging photos on walls, try resting framed photos on shelves. Or if you do HANG them, why not ARRANGE them in geometric patterns? Another creative way of displaying your favorite images is to make a mobile out of them.

ALBUM
APARTMENT
ARRANGE
BABY (picture)
BEDROOM

BUREAU
CHILDREN
COLLAGE
COUPLE
DESK

DINING ROOM
DISPLAY
FAMILY
FOYER
FRAME
FRIENDS
HALLWAY
HANG
HOME
HOUSE
LIVING (room)
MANTEL
MATTING
OFFICE
PHOTOGRAPH
PICTURE
PORTRAIT
RELATIVES
SHELF
SNAPSHOT
TABLE
WALL
WEDDING (picture)

```
P R E Y O F L E H S L U I F
M E R U T C I P T A B L E D
A L B U M N B O Y L I M A F
Y A W L L A H A F M O P F W
D T K C B S L B T F C G R F
E I I Y P P E B M O I T A N
S V N A S D G A L W N C M N
K E N I R G N L B E S C E E
C S D O N T A U M D D I S R
O H O I E G R T K D N U U D
U M V L E E R O U I E G O L
P I V M A A A O P N I N H I
L U O U P H O T O G R A P H
E H M A T T I N G M F H F C
```

CAPES OF ALASKA

NEWENHAM Cape, located in southwest Alaska, is an extremity of a small peninsula that was formed by rugged mountains. Uncover the following 28 capes contained within Alaska's 45,000 square miles of water. The best thing about an armchair sailing expedition is that you can't get seasick!

ALITAK

BEAUFORT

CHICHAGOF

CHINIAK

CORWIN

DARBY

DENBIGH

DOUGLAS

ETOLIN

GRANT

GREIG

IGVAK

IKOLIK

KUMLIUN

KUTUZOF

LISBURNE

MANNING

MOCHICAN

NARROW

NEWENHAM

NOME

PANKOF

PEIRCE

SAGAK

SEAL

SENIAVIN

SIMPSON

WOOLLEY

```
M L C D P A N K O F N D P A
G M O V Y E L L O O W B F L
N A R R O W B G M Z B N I I
I T W O L U A E O U O S R T
N R I K K H U V A T B F F A
N K N A C S A L G U O D C K
A A G I D P E N R K F N Y O
M A H N E W E N U B R O B T
S C C I N D E I I I D S R N
T E E H B T B K R A L P A T
H N A C I H C O M C V M D N
B H A L G N I L O T E I U B
W F F R H A W I V K U S N K
G R E I G V A K Z I S P H T
```

148

We value those who keep us company, encourage us in our endeavors, and help us enjoy our leisure. This puzzle is dedicated to all the people who stand by us.

ABETTOR

ADVOCATE

ALLY

ANGEL

BACKER

BROTHER

BUDDY

CHAMPION

CHUM

COHORT

COLLEAGUE

COMPANION

COMRADE

CONFEDER-
ATE

CONFIDANT

CRONY

DEFENDER

FAMILIAR

FELLOW

FRIEND

HELPER

INTIMATE

PARTISAN

PARTNER

PATRON

PEER

SISTER

SUPPORTER

```
D D S C L M R E K C A B M R
P C R E H T O R B O S W C N
R O T T E B A V N H A O A B
E U C L D I M O G O M S P U
T H H A L L R P F R I E N D
S T A I N T I M A T E D E D
I U M Y A L N D R R O U Y
S A P P D B E A W W T D G T
F W I P V W P G D N L N A H
E F O C O M P A N I O N E G
C R N L C R O N Y A F L L R
M Y L L A U T Y V A P N L S
Y E R E T A R E D E F N O C
F D E F E N D E R M U H C C
```

"Z" SEARCH

Prepare to be AMAZED as we DAZZLE you with this SNAZZY PUZZLE. There are 34 six-letter words hidden below in which the letter "Z" appears at least once, and it's up to you to ZIGZAG through the diagram and find them all. Now that's nothing to SNEEZE at!

AMAZED	SNEEZE	ZENITH
AMAZON	TWEEZE	ZIGZAG
AZALEA	WIZARD	ZITHER
BAZAAR	ZANILY	ZODIAC
BLAZER	ZEALOT	ZOMBIE
BLINTZ		
BRONZE		
BUZZER		
CHINTZ		
COZILY		
DAZZLE		
ECZEMA		
ENZYME		
FIZZLE		
FREEZE		
GAZEBO		
GEEZER		
GLITZY		
GUZZLE		
MIZZEN		
NOZZLE		
PUZZLE		
QUARTZ		
SNAZZY		

```
Y Q B L I N T Z Y Q F G B C
Z I T H E R B O G L A R A H
Z O B N T N R M G Z I A Z I
A E D E O I O B G O D N A N
N A A I A Z N I E B Z M A T
S R W L A N Z E E E A Q R Z
Y L I Z O C E L Z Z U G P F
R I Z Z U T Z E E A U H R P
E R A O Y Z E D R G N E U M
Z M R E I N N T W E E Z E H
A D D F S D Z O L Z Z U O D
L G L I T Z Y A E L Z Z A D
B N E C Z E M A E R I S U Y
T M A Z A L E A C M M Y I B
```

HIDDEN "ORE"

Be a word miner as you plumb the depths of the diagram below for the hidden words that all contain the letters "ORE." We promise you won't be BORED!

ADORE

ANYMORE

BEFORE

BORED

CHORE

DEPLORE

ENCORE

EXPLORE

FLOORED

FOLKLORE

FORECAST

FOREGO

FOREIGN

FOREMAN

FORENSIC

FOREST

FOREVER

HONORED

HUMORED

IGNORE

IMPLORE

JAMBOREE

MAJORED

MOREOVER

OREGANO

PORE

SCORE

SNORE

SPORE

STORE

SWORE

SYCAMORE

THEOREM

TOREADOR

```
T H U V E R O N G I E P S F
S K E O N N S D F M X E P O
A S O R A S C L D U P A O R
C D W G M N O I M P L O R E
E E E O E O G L S C O R E S
R R R R R P I D N R D V T
O O O E O E O O E G E R E E
F M D L F M T F R R A R R P
B U A A K H Y F O E O O O J
O H D J E L V N J N H F F F
R E V O E R O M A C Y S E P
E C R N B H O F M O E P H B
D E P L O R E T E R O T S J
M S U J A M B O R E E J W K
```

A RIVER RUNS THROUGH IT

Adventurous vacationers may want to take a river journey on the RHINE. This famous river flows from the Swiss Alps to the North Sea, passing grand castles, quaint medieval towns, and lush vineyards. Listed here are 31 of the world's longest rivers.

AMAZON

ARGUN

ARKANSAS

COLORADO

COLUMBIA

CONGO

DANUBE

DNIEPER

GANGES

HUANG HE

INDUS

IRTYSH

LENA

MACKENZIE

MEKONG

MISSISSIPPI

MISSOURI

MURRAY

NELSON

NIGER

NILE

OHIO

ORINOCO

PURUS

RHINE

RIO GRANDE

URAL

VOLGA

YANGTZE

YUKON

ZAMBEZI

```
C Z Z D R Y E N I H R M Y E
N B B M I S S O U R I Z E U
V U E Z T G N A Y S O H H S
A R E G I N D U S A G L O V
M A C K E N Z I E N R D D Y
A L O L M U S Z A I A R S C
Z S S R A S A U C R N K U E
O O G E I M H B O T D K R M
N G L P B N E L N Y E O U A
A I P E M B O K G S I I P T
N I Z I U C D C O H D E K T
E I N N L Y U K O N U G R A
L D A D O S E G N A G V L V
T D O L C U B U P T B R M Z
```

HERE'S LOOKING AT YOU, KID

Hidden in the diagram below are 31 different terms meaning "YOUNG-STER" or "young person." However, you don't have to be young in years to enjoy this puzzle . . . just young at heart!

ADOLESCENT

BABY

BOBBY-SOXER

CHICK

CHILD

CHIT

COLLEEN

FLEDGLING

GAMIN

GIRL

INFANT

JUNIOR

JUVENILE

LADDIE

LASS

MAIDEN

MINOR

MISS

NIPPER

PRETEEN

PROGENY

SHAVER

SLIP

SMALL FRY

STRIPLING

TEENAGER

TEENY-BOPPER

TODDLER

URCHIN

YOUNGSTER

YOUTH

```
P A V R O I N U J X Y O J N
E T E E N A G E R N T E I U
M E M L A D O L E S C E N T
M A I D E N C G X H F F E V
F T S D Y U O C O L L E E N
A J S O D R E T S G N U O Y
H C U T P A S A Y Y X E U R
C T H V R R L Y B R A K R F
H K T I E I I O B H O E C L
I C N V T N P D O A P N H L
L I A C E P I L B P B D I A
D H F L E D G L I N G X N M
S C N R N B T N E N L A S S
L R I G A E N I M A G Y G J
```

MAKE UP YOUR MIND!

In a 1966 Top-10 hit, the Lovin' Spoonful posed the musical question, "Did You Ever Have To Make Up Your Mind?" Well, we know you won't waver or waffle as you seek out this group of verbs denoting steps in decision making.

AFFIRM

AGREE

APPRAISE

ASSESS

CHOOSE

CONCLUDE

CONCUR

CONFER

CONSIDER

DECIDE

DEDUCE

DEEM

DETERMINE

ELECT

EVALUATE

FIGURE

GUESS

INDUCE

INFER

JUDGE

MULL (over)

MUSE

OPINE

PONDER

REASON

REVIEW

RUMINATE

SETTLE

SOLVE

SUM UP

THEORIZE

THINK

```
I N D U C E R U G I F E R C
A G A A O H U W E I V E R P
N F O G N A M R Z A K S D R
P P P R C G I I L N U A E R
S O I E L T N U I M I F E E
Z S N E U W A H U N N F N D
S E E D D T T P V I N I E I
S T Z U E I E T P O M R L S
E O L I G R C T C R C M T N
S V L W R O U E E G A O T O
S A S V N O D T D I G I E C
A A T C E L E E C H O O S E
E S U M H D D H E J U D G E
F R E A S O N K T M U L L R
```

154 PLANTS PRECEDED BY "STAR"

"Follow the stars to find your way" is old advice for navigators. Whether you're solving on land or at sea, you're sure to find your way to the 28 hidden trees, plants, and flowers, all of which are preceded by the word "star."

ANISE

APPLE

BEGONIA

BLOOM

CACTUS

CHICKWEED

CORN

DUCKWEED

FLOWER

FRUIT

GLORY

HYACINTH

IPOMOEA

JASMINE

LEAVED GUM

LIGHTS

LILY

MAGNOLIA

PEPPER

PHLOX

PINE

PLUM

PRIMROSE

ROOT

THISTLE

TULIP

VIOLET

WORT

```
N P F B E F E T Y E V W O C
A L I L Y M J S R I O U A E
F D V F O U D V O S P C N K
D F E O T W E L L R T I X T
B H L E A V E D G U M O H V
X B P I W T W R S S L I K P
W H P S B K K H A H S P R E
V C A B E O C J P T U L I P
S I O E G T U I L N F U F P
O N T R O W D E H I T M R E
F X A O N M H Y E C G X U R
L J R A I L O N G A M H I B
E S I N A H I P A Y C B T S
O O W Y X P X M I H T D N S
```

156

COLORADO CROSSROADS

In 1893, Katharine Lee Bates wrote the words to "America, the Beautiful" after seeing the majesty of Colorado from the summit of Pikes Peak. Listed here are 39 small towns of the Centennial State.

ANDRIX
ARAPAHOE
AULT
BARTLETT
BAXTER
BEULAH
BONANZA
CARR
CENTER
COWDREY
CREEDE
DOWD
FALCON
GENOA
HEBRON
HOEHNE
HOYT
IDALIA
JAROSO
LA VETA
LOG LANE
NUNN
OTIS
OVID
OXFORD
PANDO
PAOLI

PAONIA
PINE
PINON
REDMESA
ROMEO
RUSH

SHAW
SIMLA
SWINK
TYRONE
YAMPA
YUMA

```
O C O A N U C I N J C B C J
C O W D R E Y N O C L A F X
X O N T N A N D R I X X T W
M S Y T T A P M B N R T L W
W O E E A Z P A E D E E R C
H R V B N N A P H L D R H L
Y A T N O A I M T O M G M K
L J L N K N L R Y V E W H N
Y Y U U O O A G R N S H O S
O U A N E B D I O K A X N Y
V X M M D B I A N L F B P E
I L O A P O D I E O T I S E
D R U S H A W G R R A C N I
V A L M I S Z D E N I P H W
```

WORDS MEANING "JOIN"

There are many ways to join things together. You could use any of the methods below to AFFIX something permanently or temporarily. For now, just SECURE a quiet place and COMBINE all your solving skills to UNITE the letters in the puzzle below.

AFFIX

ANCHOR

ANNEX

APPEND

ATTACH

BIND

BLEND

BOND

BRIDGE

CEMENT

CHAIN

COMBINE

CONJOIN

COUPLE

DOVETAIL

ENTWINE

FASTEN

FUSE

GRAFT

HITCH

KNIT

LACE

LINK

LOCK

MERGE

MOOR

SECURE

SPLICE

STAPLE

SUTURE

UNITE

WEAVE

WELD

```
L H V X E N N A P H W X T E
G F O G O V F P V L U I X G
W K R P F D A P S J N F T N
S E C U R E W E C K W F R L
M C S O L T M N W M A A K E
B E K P L E G D I R B S F L
C D A M C O M C G O B T O P
E T I D M D T E T O J E D U
S W R K U R L M C M N N N O
R U N O E N R E N I B M O C
H I T C H A I N W G L M B C
L M A U H C A T T A E P J J
R L O I R B N O E C N R S C
X G D O V E T A I L D N I B
```

TYPES OF CONTAINERS

The list below contains 32 words that all represent some kind of container.

ALFORJA

BURETTE

CALATHUS

CANNIKIN

CIST

COSTREL

CRUSE

CUCURBIT

DOSSER

FIRKIN

GABION

GALLIPOT

GROWLER

JORUM

KYACK

KYLIX

LOTAH

MATRASS

MAUND

MAZER

NOGGIN

PIGGIN

POTICHE

PUNNET

QUAICH

RUNDLET

SEIDEL

SKEEL

TASS

TAZZA

TERRINE

TOBY

```
C A L A T H U S H O U Z C L
A E T H J O R U M L A Z K R
N Z N C E K P E T T E R U B
N Z Z I C C F I R K I N I X
I U O A R Q B E L L D W S J
K L Y U T R S L M L O S C S
I K S Q U S E K E A A T A J
N E Z C O D Y T E R Z G A N
O H U D I L N M T E T E J H
G C A E I I P A S L L S R S
G I S X G C M U I W T O O R
I T U G Q G X N C O T K F C
N O I B A G H D B R N R L J
F P U N N E T Y J G S S A T
```

CARBURETOR PARTS

The parts list for a two-barrel carburetor contains 96 items. If you do your own cleaning and rebuilding, you'll not only save money, but will most likely encounter the 32 terms listed here.

AIR HORN

BALL

BOWL VENT

BRACKET (upper)

CLIPS

COVER

DIAPHRAGM

FILTER

FLOAT

GASKETS

JETS

MAIN BODY

NEEDLE

NUTS

"O" RINGS

PEDESTAL (primary)

PINS

PLUG

PUMP

RODS

ROLL PIN

SCREWS

SEAL

SEAT

SHIM

SLEEVE

SOLENOIDS

SPRINGS

THROTTLE (body)

VALVES

VENTURI

WEIGHT

```
F I L T E R F S P I T Y P G
E M H H E N V E P O H S M A
U V D R D E D M B R G A U S
S D I O N E L O S I I U P K
H J E T S D W R A N E N N E
Y L U T E L L A B G W I G T
M R A L V E G O F S P T U S
I L N E R O D S V L E R L W
W P N R S Y J M L K O H P E
S T U N O S I O C E S A P R
I D I A P H R A G M E F T C
F P L I S F R D R B V V A S
E P L V D B V I K C O V E R
M C M O S E V L A V G T S V
```

CAN IT

Remember Aunt Bee Taylor from TV's "The Andy Griffith Show"? It seems she was always canning fruit or making preserves to enter in the county fair. Here are 37 terms associated with the art of home canning.

AIRTIGHT
BLANCH
BOIL
BROTH
CANNER
CANS
CLEAN
COOK
COOL
COVER
DRAIN
FILL
FRESH
FUNNEL
GASKET
GLASS
HEAT
KETTLE
LIDS
LIQUID
MASON JAR
PACK
PEEL
PRESERVE
PRESSURE

PROCESS
RINGS
SEAL
SELECT
SKIN
SORT

STEAM
SWEETEN
SYRUP
TURN
TWIST
WATER

```
B L A N C H L E E P U R Y S
V I N R C L A T R Q R E K D
D Q B B L A I E I M Y U W H
N U O I D E S D L S C W E N
E I F R E S H E S T E A M I
L D A M U P H S Q P T T N K
B T U R N R R S R H C E V S
H S E A D E I O G E G R K H
G V E J N S C I L A V E T E
I L C N N E T E E W S O R T
C K A O S R S G N I R K C D
O C C S I V I E N B Q O E R
O Y S A S E W F U S O O L T
L Q R M P B T U F K W H A R
```

TAKE A CLASS

It's never too late to learn something new . . . perhaps ACTING, KARATE, or SCUBA DIVING! You could also take a COMPUTER course to help you keep up with the ever-changing technology. Here is a list of classes you might want to sign up for. Don't forget that each line is a separate entry.

ACTING	CHESS	DRAWING
BALLET	COMPUTER	DRIVING
CARVING	COOKING	FLYING
CERAMICS	DESIGN	GOLF
		GUITAR
		JUDO
		KARATE
		KNITTING
		LANGUAGE
		PAINTING
		PIANO
		REAL ESTATE
		RIDING
		SCUBA DIVING
		SEWING
		SINGING
		SKATING
		SKIING
		SWIMMING
		TENNIS
		WRITING

```
W J U E C A R V I N G M S B
R R T R C O O M I M J K A V
J N I A Y N O M K G A L M S
U O E T A R A K N T L W G E
D G N I I K S I I E I Y N W
O I P U Y N V N T N S G I I
T B V G R I G A T C G N T N
G E G I R E T S I N G I N G
S U N D N S T M N J V Y I I
C V I N E G A U G N A L A S
U D W L I R F I P U H F P E
B H A C E S W I M M I N G D
A E R C H E S S F L O G U Y
R I D I N G A G N I T C A I
```

MOTORING THROUGH MISSISSIPPI

As the birthplace of Elvis Presley, TUPELO has to be the best-known small town in Mississippi. The state has many other towns with charm and appeal for visitors. Motor through 41 towns in the Magnolia State.

ALCORN
ALLIGATOR
ARCOLA
AVON
BOBO
CANAAN
CLARA
COMO
CROWDER
DARLING
DERMA
DREW
EDEN
ENON
FREENY
GOSS
HOT COFFEE
KEWANEE
KOKOMO
LEAF
LELAND
LENA
LOGTOWN
MAGNOLIA
MIDNIGHT
MONEY
MOSS

ONWARD
PETAL
POND
RED LICK
REFORM
SOSO
THORN

TUPELO
UNION
VALUE
VELMA
WADE
WEBB
ZAMA

```
A N R O H T V G N W C H V R
S H R B M U N D N O P U E C
O B O O W P Z G M I V D L A
S B N T C E N O N Y L A M M
O E W H C L K S L I R R A A
Y W A G G O A S C A E O A Z
S A R I K G F K S D A T M D
M S D N L T L F L E L A N D
M R E D W O R C E D O G O R
H R C I A W N N A E C I I E
S S O M H N A G F N R L N W
G H U F K W E D A V A L U E
O L A T E P F L E M B A N G
D F P K N R G V F R E E N Y
```

BACKYARD RETREAT

If your home is your castle then your backyard must be the royal grounds. Take a relaxing stroll through the word list, and search for items that might be found in a backyard.

ADIRONDACK (chair)

BENCH

BOCCE (court)

BUG SPRAY

CITRONELLA

CROQUET (set)

DECK

FEEDER

GARDEN

GAZEBO

GRILL

HAMMOCK

HORSESHOES

HOSE

HOT TUB

LANTERN

LIGHTING

LOUNGE (chair)

PATIO

PLANTER

POOL

RADIO

SHED

STEAMER (chair)

SWING SET

TABLE

THERMOME-TER

TIKI TORCH

TRELLIS

UMBRELLA

```
B B R A I F E I B U T T O H
U M B R E L L A E L B A T A
G O R E M A E T S H E D S M
S B D T A E E G Q N N H B M
P E W E G U H O A H C W O O
R Z P M Q N I S O R H B C C
A A D O A D I R O N D A C K
Y G R M A L S T R L H E E S
Z C A R L E I E H O L K N H
P O U E S K T E S G N I W S
G O R H I N C E Y H I A R D
F T O T A M E G N U O L E G
W E A L L E N O R T I C E O
S Q P A T I O I P M K B B M
```

Technology has enabled television news crews to keep audiences well informed with **COVERAGE** of local and worldwide events as they are happening. Now join us as we uncover this puzzle about **LIVE** news.

AIRPORT

ANSWER

AUDIO

CAMERA

CAMPAIGN

COURT

COVERAGE

ELECTION

EVENT

FEATURE

GAME

HEARING

HELICOPTER

HIGHWAY

INFORM

INTERVIEW

LIVE

LOCATION

MICRO-
  PHONE

POLICE

QUESTION

RACE

RESCUE

RULING

STORY

TEAM

TRAFFIC

TRAVEL

TRIAL

UPDATE

VERDICT

VIDEO

```
W S T O R Y H I G H W A Y D
G G R N R E W S N A P L W R
S A U O E H E C I L O P A L
H M L I M V L Q R C H C I G
L E I T N A E G A R E V O C
A L N C R O E T E E E V W A
I E G E R O I T H S F I E M
R V M L Y O P T M C E D I P
T A E E N O P R S U A E V A
C R H R C O O H I E T O R I
F T U I D F I N O A U O E G
H L L O N I Q D D N R Q T N
T E A I C G C P U C E E N S
H Y F G S U U T R A F F I C
```

BRACE yourselves, solvers, as hidden below are 28 items found in rooftop constructions. If you don't CURB your appreciable skills, we know you'll be done in no time at all!

BEAM

BOARD

BOLT

BRACE

CORNICE

CUPOLA

CURB

DOME

EAVES

FRAME

GABLE

GAMBREL

JOIST

KING POST

M ROOF

OGEE

PURLIN (rafter support)

PYRAMID

RAFTER

RIDGEPOLE

SHINGLE

SKYLIGHT

SLATE

TAR PAPER

THATCH

TILE

VANE

VENT

```
S E U R T F J P A V P G S L
K R Y M V O A N D J D E P A
Y I E C A B G U O D V U P T
L D N P V E J E M A R F H O
I G A G A M B R E L B A G B
G E V C P P O E I C T L O B
H P E I C O R N I C E L T B
T O Y Y F O S A H A E S B R
U L D R E L I T T L I C V A
R E T F A R M O G O O O I C
K N N T O M Y N J P T H I E
A I E B V M I Y C U R B G F
A K V A M H U D O C H V F T
F T S K S Y K T S P S U D K
```

BREAD

Prepared a variety of ways all over the world, bread has often been called "the staff of life." PITA bread is from the Middle East and has a pocket for filling. Long, crusty loaves of bread are native FRENCH and ITALIAN varieties. What's your favorite?

BANANA

BRAN

BRIOCHE

CARROT

CHALLAH

CHEESE

CINNAMON

CORN

CRANBERRY

DATE NUT

FRENCH

GARLIC

ITALIAN

OATMEAL

ONION

PEASANT

PITA

POTATO

PUMPER-
NICKEL

PUMPKIN

RAISIN

SODA

SOURDOUGH

WALNUT

WHEAT

WHITE

ZUCCHINI

```
B O Y R R E B N A R C S L L
C Z D H H P O T A T O A E B
R G A Z A M P B U L E K U B
I A T E A L B N R M C N A N
N R E N A I L A T I S R B S
I L N P E A S A N T O O O H
H I U I W G O R H H U C D T
C C T T K A E M H C R A H A
C B R A N P N B H N D R B E
U P M A M O M E Z E O R K H
Z K N U I R E U S R U O Z W
G A P N H S R M P F G T D A
B N O P E T I H W L H G P T
H R D F C D W N T N M Z F H
```

SCUBA ADVENTURE

The acronym SCUBA stands for "Self-Contained Underwater Breathing APPARATUS." You don't have to be a diving expert to take part in an undersea odyssey, as many warm-weather vacation spots offer licensed instruction for the beginner. Set ADRIFT and find 32 terms associated with this popular activity.

ADRIFT

APPARATUS

ASCENT

BORE

BOTTLE

BUDDY

CURRENT

DESCENT

DIAPHRAGM

DRY SUIT

EDDY

FINS

GAUGE

HITCH

HOOKAH

HOSE

KELP

LEEWARD

MASK

MOUTHPIECE

NEAP TIDE

REGULATOR

RUN OUT

SCUBA

SEAWARD

SPEAR GUN

TANKS

TIDE

VALVE

VEST

WET SUIT

YOKE

```
E R O M K V E S T A R W A U
H V A M N U Y D D U B V Y Y
G G Y G P H M S I R O H G C
T A C A E W O N W T C N R U
A T D R Y S U I T T P L U R
N C O H C G T F I R D A P R
K B B P R V H H E R G L E E
S U T A R A P P A N E G T N
T W E I Y L I W E K U N H T
S P G D D V E G M L E G A S
S C D T N E C S A C T S K Y
M E U S L W E T S U I T O N
K W P B T C O E K Y G K O H
S E A W A R D L W L E E H B
```

THREE-RING FUN!

P. T. Barnum and his partner, James A. Bailey, made the American circus a popular and gigantic spectacle, the so-called Greatest Show on Earth. Can we have a DRUMROLL, please, as you search for these sights and sounds that can be found in and around the BIG TOP?

ACROBAT

AERIALIST

BALLOONS

BEARS

BIG TOP

BLEACHERS

CAMELS

CLOWNS

COTTON CANDY

CURTAIN

DRUMROLL

HIGH WIRE

HOT DOGS

JUGGLER

LADDER

LEAPS

LIONS

MAKEUP

PARADE

PEANUTS

PONIES

RINGMASTER

ROPES

SEALS

SOUVENIRS

SWINGS

TENTS

TIGERS

UNICYCLE

ZEBRAS

```
J A E C W C D B B I G T O P
U E L H U V A A G N S T E A
G R C O V N L M G R B M O R
G I Y T I L M Z E B R A S A
L A C D O Y S H L L Z K O D
E L I O N S C R T E S E R E
R I N G M A S T E R A U U S
I S U S E R C T I G M P T H
W T N L S R E N A R I N S L
H U B W S E E D O B E T E U
G N E L O V I L D T O R D E
I A A A U L L N I A T R U C
H E R O H R C Y O T L O C G
S P S G N I W S E P O R C A
```

Speaking of space, each word hidden in the puzzle below can be preceded by "space," or is otherwise related. See if you can find them all.

BIOLOGY

CADET

CAPSULE

CENTER

CRAFT

CREW

FLIGHT

HEATING

LATTICE

LAUNCH

MARK

MEDICINE

OPERA

ORBIT

PLATFORM

PORT

PROBE

SCIENCE

SHIP

SHOT

SHUTTLE

STATION

SUIT

TIME

TRAVEL

VEHICLE

WALK

WOMAN

WRITER

```
U B P E F S C D W V O F W F
N A P S V E U H H E B O R P
E H L O P C B I N H K K L I
H E A T I N G I T I B R O M
C G T I L E C C O C F N A E
N U F E C I T T A L R N E M
U T O R D C W P I E O A N U
A C R E W S S G T I L G F E
L H M T L U H I T S K W Y T
I I P N L T R A V E L O E I
T C F E D W T U R U D M G U
W R M C A S L U R E D A B V
I U O L M S M S H I P N C K
E C K P E P N W K S H O T P
```

A TO Z

The SUBJECT of this puzzle is quite simple: Each of the words in the list begins with a different letter of the alphabet, from A to Z.

ABANDON

BROCADE

CONIC

DELTA

ELOPE

FASHION

GARLIC

HOUND

INDIAN

JUMPER

KATYDID

LEMON

MOSQUITO

NOMADIC

OILSKIN

PICKAXE

QUEENLY

RODEO

SUBJECT

TRUCK

UNTOWARD

VARNISH

WINDOW

XENON

YODEL

ZODIAC

```
K O Y P I C K A X E J G D G
E Y O X E E C B D L Y S T F
Z U D E O U K A T Y D I D J
U Y E N D D C N C E K A H R
K K L O N O L D E L T A S W
V C P N R O R O J X K O I Y
P W U B E A I N B E C N N S
R G R R W E N H U C D O R E
E R A O T I U Q S O M M A M
P P T R K N I Q W A J E V C
M N O S L D X T D R F L I E
U Q L L H I A I H O U N D F
J I V T E A C A I D O Z C A
O X U M H N I P G C Z D I D
```

Pin beading is so EASY...no glue, needle, or thread is needed, just a STRAIGHT PIN inserted through a bead and into a CUSHION to create a lovely design. The CRAFT was developed in the 1800s when mass production reduced the cost of straight pins.

ANGLE

ATTACH

BATTING

BEADS

BORDER

COMPLEX (designs)

CRAFT

CUSHION

DECORATE

DIMENSION

DIRECTION

EASY

ELEGANT

EMBELLISH

FREEHAND

GEOMETRIC (shapes)

HOBBY

INSERT

INTRICATE (patterns)

MEASURE

OVAL (box)

PADDING

ROUND (box)

SIMPLE (designs)

SQUARE (box)

STRAIGHT PIN

SWIRLS

SYMMETRICAL (design)

```
I N S E R T B O R D E R H N
E G N I T T A B T N L A V O
F R E E H A N D F O E G E Q
W O U N M D R S A I G T S E
X U P S Q B L O R T A S Y L
H N C C A R E R C C N Q M P
C D I O I E C L I E T U M M
A U C W M R M R L R D A E I
T S S N I P T H G I A R T S
T D D H H N L E A D S E R P
A A N O I S N E M I D H I M
O E B Q A O N M X O R V C X
B B N E L G N A M N E T A I
Y S A E P P A D D I N G L S
```

A SAILOR'S VALENTINE

A sailor's valentine is a **WOODEN, SHALLOW BOX**, often **OCTAGONAL**, that forms the frame for a symmetrical seashell mosaic. The name of the box derives from the habit **SAILORS** had of purchasing them in the **CARIBBEAN** as gifts for their loved ones back home.

ANTIQUE

BEACH

BORDER

CARIBBEAN

CASE

COLLAGE

COLLECT

COMPLEX

CRAFT

DELICATE

GIFT

ISLAND

MESSAGE

MOTIF

MYTH

OCTAGONAL

PATTERN

PORTRAITS

PURCHASE

REVIVAL

ROMANTIC

SAILORS

SCENES

SEASHELLS

SHALLOW BOX

SOUVENIR

SYMBOLS

WOODEN

```
H H C R A C E G A L L O C D
A C A E Q U O N M O T I F M
U A I V Q A C L S Y T F W U
D E L I C A T E L N T M I S
T B T V E X A S A E A H X G
F N S A R S G M Y B C D O S
A D A L H I O N P M N T B C
R X I E Y R N Q R A B O W E
C E L G B A A E L E R O O N
A L O A F B L S V D T F L E
S P R S T H I G E U H T L S
E M S S T I A R T R O P A F
U O N E D O O W A A L S H P
N C R M W G P U R C H A S E
```

It's said that good things come in small packages. This puzzle is comprised of words that represent small quantities that are often just enough to fit the bill.

A BIT

A DAB

A DASH

A DRAM

A DRIBLET

A DRIP

A FLECK

A GRAM

A JOT

A MINIM

A MITE

A MOLECULE

AN IOTA

A NIP

A PINCH

A SCANTLING

A SCRUPLE

A SHADE

A SHADOW

A SMACK

A SMATTER

A SNATCH

A SNIP

A SPECK

A SPRINKLE

A TAD

A TINGE

A TRACE

A TRIFLE

A WHIT

```
E R C J I P A A A D R A M G
A D O R E I D E F O T P S A
A C A S P R I N K L E I S T
E M L H I D M E B L E N G O
G H O B S A H O N L I C A I
N N L L R A M S F P C H K N
I E I G E D H I A R E K N A
T K A L T C R B T D C M H S
A W H I T T U H L E A I C H
P M E A A N E L P U R C S A
M I N I M A A S E U T N T D
N S N A S M A C K L A I P O
A P L A A J O T S G K E B W
A F U I R B I F B A D A T A
```

"M" VERBS

Here are 32 verbs, all beginning with the letter "M." Can you MANAGE to find them all?

MAGNIFY	MOCK	MOTIVATE
MAINTAIN	MODERATE	MOVE
MAKE	MODIFY	MUMBLE
MANAGE	MOISTEN	MUSTER
MANDATE	MOLLIFY	MUZZLE
MARK	MONITOR	MYSTIFY
MATCH		
MEANDER		
MEASURE		
MEDDLE		
MEDIATE		
MEDICATE		
MELT		
MEND		
MERGE		
METE		
MIGRATE		
MIMIC		
MINISTER		
MOAN		

```
L K O M E D C H H C T A M D
T E K E T E M R M M U R U Y
K G K T G M M O V E E Y Z M
V A N A O M O N T D R E Z E
M Y N R E T S I N I M G L A
D A F G C O E A S A V D E S
M O D I F Y E T G T D A M U
D K M M T M N N A E E A T R
T I E O T S I I M R N N B E
M O L L I F Y A H D E I E T
E G E Z Y A O M A R K D Y S
N M E D I C A T E N E C O U
D M U M B L E R O T I N O M
F B I O Z F M T U G C V K M
```

The ancient art of bonsai produces beautifully pruned MINIATURE TREES that symbolize man's deep respect for the forms of nature. In addition to the popular EVERGREEN specimens, bonsai extends to the cultivation of shrub species, flowering trees, and even fruit trees. Circle the following words pertaining to this plant-lover's HOBBY.

AZALEA	CHERRY	GROW
BAMBOO	EVERGREEN	HOBBY
BRANCHES	FOLIAGE	JUNIPER
CEDAR	FORM	LEAVES
		MINIATURE
		MOSS
		PINCH
		PLANTS
		PLUM
		PRUNE
		ROOTS
		SEEDLING
		SHAPES
		SPIRAL
		TINY
		TRAIN
		TREES
		TRIM
		TRUNK
		TWIST
		WIRE

```
W G A B U P F C Z B A M O E
D T B A M B O O U P K I A S
F U S H Z A Z A L E A V E S
N T O I C G G A L I N P Z D
I I H M W N N S I T A U T T
A N I A R T I N Y H M G R R
S R Z Y S A L P S E I U E P
T F G B R T D F L P N P E I
F O M B W R E E Z K I Z S H
O R O O T S E H C N A R B M
K M R H S W S H U Z T N A U
F G T B I S S J C E U J N L
H Z I R G N S E O W R I J P
O N E E R G R E V E E E H A
```

RHYME TIME

175

We BESTOW upon you the 34 terms BELOW that rhyme with the letter "O." We KNOW you'll GLOW after finding them all!

ALTHOUGH

BANJO

BELOW

BESTOW

BUFFALO

BUNGALOW

CAMEO

COCOA

CROW

DEPOT

DOUGH

ELBOW

FLOW

FOREGO

GLOW

HELLO

INDIGO

JUMBO

KNOW

LIMBO

MISTLETOE

OBOE

PISTACHIO

PLATEAU

PORTICO

SHOW

SNOW

STOW

STUDIO

THOUGH

THROW

VOLCANO

WINDOW

YELLOW

```
C J K F L O W N U E H W S N
C P I N D I G O L A F F U B
A T I J W L C B L Y U J I A
M F U S O I O L L E H M V N
E K O B T W N Y O L B I B J
O W M R S A A D T L W S H O
G I O W E E C P O O H T V N
L P D L B G L H N W P L J O
O O U U A A O K I C L E V G
W O R H T G V D O O R T D A
O B O E L S N C H G U O H T
N M A L T H O U G H U E W T
S U V O F A D J B G J V N N
R J W B S P P S H O W P R P
```

177

176

SWEETS FOR THE SWEET

Here's a very tasty treat for all you solvers with a sweet tooth. Just be warned, we are not responsible for any dental bills that may result from completing this puzzle! Remember that each line is a separate entry.

BROWNIES

BUBBLE GUM

CAKE

CHOCOLATE

COBBLER

COOKIES

DANISH

DOUGHNUT

FROSTING

FUDGE

HONEY

ICE CREAM

ICING

JELLY BEANS

LICORICE

MINTS

MOLASSES

NECTAR

NOUGAT

PASTRY

PEANUT BRITTLE

PUDDING

SHERBET

SODA POP

SUNDAE

SWEET ROLL

SYRUP

TAFFY

TART

WAFERS

```
Y D N J P O P A D O S E M N
R O E C A K E G F H U O E K
T U A O T U N A E P L C S T
S G D O L L O R S A T R R S
A H N K F B B B S A E A E Y
P N U I G E U S R L T I F I
U U S E T N E B B I N A A C
R T D S Y S I B B W T M W E
Y A A D C H O C O L A T E C
S F N L I C O R I C E A L R
N F I Y M N B N F U D G E E
A Y S O G I G P E J D U U A
E U H S B J E L L Y T O G M
B O W R R T E E W S T N I M
```

TREES OF THE PHILIPPINES

Do you know what a BAGO, DANLI, and LANETE are? Only after doing some research did we discover that they're names of trees native to the Philippines. We've hidden these and 32 others below for your solving pleasure.

ACLE

AGOJO

ALMACIGA

ALMON

AMUGIS

ANONANG

ANUBING

APITONG

ARANGA

BAGO

BANUYO

BATAAN

BATETE

BATINO

BAYOG

BETIS

BITANGHOL

CALUMPIT

CAMAGONG

DANLI

DITA

IPIL

LANETE

LAUAN

LUMBAYAO

MABOLO

MALAPAHO

MANCONO

MARANG

MAYAPIS

MOLAVE

SAGING

TANGUILE

TINDALO

YACAL

```
R L D J E J B H N G O Y A B
Y A C L C D T O B A T E T E
S C C B L N A G N I U M B T
I A O P O J N L P I M A R I
G Y G M H O G M M A T Y L S
U M L I G L U M B A Y A O T
M A D A N L I O A G C P B I
A L M E A G L N N N I I R N
T A N C T O E O A M C S G D
C P D J I E T G N A N O N A
G A N U B I N G U R H V N L
J H U A P A Y A B A N U Y O
O O G A R I P I L N O A B I
M O L A V E O J O G A T I D
```

178

Boston dates its beginning from September 17, 1630. Named after a town in Lincolnshire, England (which was the original home of many of the Puritan leaders who founded the city), it was the largest British settlement in the Colonies. The capital and largest city in Massachusetts, the names of some of Boston's suburbs are featured in the list.

ACTON
AVON
BELMONT
BEVERLY
BROCKTON
CAMBRIDGE
CANTON
CHELSEA
CONCORD
DANVERS
EVERETT
LEXINGTON
LINCOLN
LOWELL
LYNN
MALDEN
MEDFORD
MELROSE
MILTON
NAHANT
NEEDHAM
NEWTON
NORWOOD
PEABODY
REVERE
SALEM
SUDBURY
WALPOLE
WALTHAM
WESTON

```
D L N E W T O N O T L I M W
P O N L E X I N G T O N M A
Y W Y O U C K I F L B A E L
D E L O P L A W D R D H L T
O L R K B E L M O N T A R H
B L E G S U S C B D Y N O A
A Y V L E R K C N R L T S M
E V E R E T T E U O I R E A
P H B V O C E B C C T D I H
C P N N S R D N A N F C G D
T A O S E U I N T O H F A E
D V P V S L T I R C L R D E
A W E S T O N D O O W R O N
B R C E N E D L A M E L A S
```

STREETS OF BELFAST

Founded in 1177, Northern Ireland's capital, Belfast, is a major commercial and industrial city. It is one of Great Britain's most important ship-building and repairing centers, as well as the seat of the Queen's University of Belfast, Belfast COLLEGE of Technology, and the Union Theological College. See if you can spot 29 of its streets in the diagram below.

AGNES

ALBERT

BERLIN

BRIDGE

CANMORE

CARRICK

CASTLE

CLIFTON

COLLEGE

CONWAY

CRIMEA

DONEGAL

FREDERICK

GROSVENOR

HIGH

HOWARD

LEESON

MIDDLEPATH

NELSON

NORTH

OXFORD

ROSS

ROYAL

SERVIA

SYDENHAM

WARING

WELLINGTON

WESTLINK

YORK

```
D W P E F K W E X S X W E H
R A C A H R L A Y O R A T G
A L B E R T P M N I L R E B
W C C A S M A Y Y K O I L I
O O L A E H L P H N A N S V
H N C A N M O R E I E G O O
T W E E G X I V Y L G V T F
R A D L F E S R N T D H K M
O Y W O S O N O C S I D C L
S G R E R O T O S E R V I A
S D N G S F N K D W B E R M
C G E E I K C I R E D E R F
A W E L L I N G T O N F A R
K L C O L L E G E K Y V C M
```

181

FALCON is the common name for members of the *Falconidae*, a family of long-winged birds of prey that are closely related to the HAWK. They range in size from the 6 1/2" falconet to the 24" gyrfalcon. In flight, falcons can swoop hundreds of feet at speeds of up to 200 miles per hour to capture their quarry!

CROW
DOVE
DUCK
EAGLE
FALCON

FINCH
GOOSE
GULL
HAWK
HERON

LARK
LOON
MAGPIE
ORIOLE
PARROT
PELICAN
PIGEON
PLOVER
PUFFIN
RAIL
RAVEN
ROBIN
SPARROW
SWALLOW
SWAN
SWIFT
TEAL
TERN
THRUSH
TURKEY
WREN

```
S D A U E K N G H B N F O P
U E O N K V C L A E T T N C
O Y I Y S H I R W L R E D U
I N S K B W S V K G V O R P
U V E I O N W U K A V T N N
A H H R S W Y I R E V O L P
T H C I W C K Y S H E D N R
B N N M A G P I E G T L N P
P T I M L M L B I K O U A A
U N F B L O S P A R R O W V
F H B I O W M K I L R U S V
F K A N W R N O C L A F T E
I R D P S S L F B U P R S M
N A C I L E P P C G D G K A
```

IBSEN'S WOMEN

Henrik Ibsen's 19th-century heroines often seem to reflect the problems of today's women. For example, NORA Helmer of "A Doll's House" escapes from her unhappy marriage to establish her own individuality as a person. Uncover Nora and 33 other female characters from Ibsen's plays.

AASE
AGNES
ALINE
ANITRA
ASTA
BETTY
BOLETTA
CHRISTINA
DINA
ELLA
ELLIDA
FANNY
FRIDA
GUNNHILD
HEDDA
HEDVIG
HELEN
HELGA
HILDA
INGRID
IRENE
JULIA
KAIA
KARI

LONA
MAIA
MARTA
MARTHA
NORA

REBECCA
REGINA
RITA
SOLVEIG
THEA

```
M C H R I S T I N A J F N T
M H J R A D O E J A T R A M
A S U B A E L L I D A C F T
N N L G A E L I V K C N R R
O T I H H Y O S H E D V I G
I H A T T E L O B N I Y D D
A J N T R A D E S E N G A A
M S E H A A R D N N G U N Y
Y B T E M E I E A N R N G B
E S A A G N R F N O I A L L
A F I I G I H O O O D N U G
B A N R T L R E L L A N U A
K A H A B A E E I J K J I Y
F O U K B A R H H R I E C M
```

IT'S A MYSTERY

The investigation is about to begin, and you're the chief DETECTIVE who must solve the plot. Can you find all 38 terms that often serve as mystery elements? No search warrant is required for this puzzle.

ALIBI
AUNT
BODY
BRIBE
BUTLER
CLOCK

CLOSET
CLUES
COOK
CRIME
DETECTIVE
DOCTOR

EVIDENCE
FINGERPRINTS
GARDEN
GUESTS
HOUSE
HUSBAND
KNIFE
LAWYER
LETTERS
LIBRARY
MAID
NEPHEW
NIECE
NOTE
PARTY
POISON
POLICE
ROPE
SCENE
SUSPECTS
TRACE
UNCLE
VICTIM
WIFE
WILL
WITNESSES

```
N K N V T W I T N E S S E S
B O D Y R M W N E G T L T E
I Y T R A P N E I N C S H U
S T Y E C N E D I V E P O L
E D E R E M I R C U P C U C
U L E S A B P A G O S H S N
D O C T O R R G L C U E E R
U W E N E L B I M S S P S C
K P I G U C C I B R H O M L
T O N L A E T A L E G R A O
M I O W L C N I W T V W I C
F S R C I D U K V T Y F D K
W O O V B F A Y R E L T U B
G N K N I F E M R L V A Y T
```

WHILE YOU'RE AWAY

If you're planning on taking a vacation soon, you may want to consider hiring a house sitter, someone to basically baby-sit your RESIDENCE while you're away. Responsibilities can range from the simple, like watering PLANTS and retrieving mail, to the slightly more demanding, such as feeding PETS and lawn MAINTENANCE. In return, the house sitter gets a place to stay for free.

APARTMENT
ARRANGE-MENT
BENEFITS
CARETAKER
CHORES
CONDO-MINIUM
COST
DAYS
ESTATE
GARDEN
HOME
INDIVIDUAL
MAINTE-NANCE
MANSION
MONTHS
OCCUPY
OWNER
PETS
PLANTS
PROPERTY
RESIDENCE
SECURITY

SERVICE
SUMMER (home)
TEMPORARY
TERM

TOWN HOUSE
WATCH
WEEKS
YARD

```
M F O C C U P Y R E N W O C
T E R M N T H R C E P W S H
T A T I U R O A O H M L O O
E P Y A N I R W T P C M S R
M A I N T E N A N C E T U E
P R V G T S C I E H I R A S
O T D A Y S E N M F O S T W
R M K R K S O O E O P U C Y
A E O D K I N N G D D T S I
R N V E S T E P N P I N L E
Y T E N H B P L A N T S O C
R W A S R Y S E R V I C E C
F M D R A Y T I R U C E S R
I N D I V I D U A L H U N F
```

CAPRICORN QUALITIES

December 22 to January 20 marks the period of Capricorn, the tenth sign of the zodiac. The symbol for Capricorn is the Goat. Capricorns are **DEVOTED** to making every aspect of their lives a success. They are also very **LOYAL** and **PRACTICAL** individuals. Find the qualities for this sign in the diagram below.

AMBITIOUS

CALM

CAREFUL

CAUTIOUS

CLEVER

CONFIDENT

DEFT

DETACHED

DEVOTED

DISCIPLINED

EARNEST

FAIR

HUMOROUS

IMPARTIAL

KEEN

LOGICAL

LOYAL

PATIENT

PRACTICAL

PRUDENT

RATIONAL

RELIABLE

RESERVED

SERIOUS

SHREWD

STABLE

STRICT

STRONG

```
S T R O N G R I D O D U Y I
I W C T D T N E D I F N O C
W M L I S I T E S T A B L E
G U P V R A F C L E V E R T
E P R A C T I C A L R M G P
S E K H R P S D C S I V D R
H S E S L T N E I T A P E U
R D E I U A I E G V F L V D
E G N R W O N A O E B O O E
W E I R I N I O L A U Y T N
D F K S U O I T I B M A E T
P C A R E F U L U T L L D V
T S E N R A E S V A A F E T
Y H U M O R O U S L C R P A
```

OREGON COUNTIES

Oregon, nicknamed The Beaver State, was admitted to the UNION on February 14, 1859, making it our nation's 33rd state. It is the ninth largest in the U.S. and has a total of 36 counties, most of which will be found in the diagram.

BAKER

BENTON

CLACKAMAS

CLATSOP

COLUMBIA

COOS

CURRY

DESCHUTES

DOUGLAS

GILLIAM

GRANT

HARNEY

HOOD RIVER

JOSEPHINE

KLAMATH

LAKE

LANE

LINN

MALHEUR

MARION

MORROW

MULTNOMAH

POLK

SHERMAN

TILLAMOOK

UMATILLA

UNION

WALLOWA

WASCO

WHEELER

YAMHILL

```
W H G T U M B A K E R Y K B
O B I Y A M H I L L G O A U
R E L E E H W B A C O O S M
R N L N G O E M M M U E A V
O T I R S O K U A P T R M S
M O A A Y D A L T U I J A C
D N M H W R L O H O O L K W
T O S L T I A C N S G O C O
G I I H T V S W E U C N A U
R N I A E E H P O S T A L C
N U M I D R H D A L Y R C E
C U R R Y I M W L K L O P M
M U L T N O M A H E N A L W
T R U E H L A M N Y I N W U
```

WORDS PRECEDED BY "AIR"

Take a deep breath and SPEED through this puzzle. It lists 43 words that can be preceded by the word "air" to form new compound words or phrases.

BASE	COACH	FIELD
BORNE	CONDITION	FLEET
BRAKE	COOL	FOIL
BRUSH	CRAFT	HOLE
CASTLE	CREW	JACKET
CELL	CUSHION	LIFT
CHAMBER	CYLINDER	LINE
		LOCK
		MAIL
		MASS
		PASSAGE
		PLANE
		PLANT
		POCKET
		PORT
		PRESSURE
		PROOF
		PUMP
		RAID
		RIFLE
		SHAFT
		SHIP
		SICK
		SPEED
		SPRING
		STRIP
		TIGHT
		VALVE
		WORTHY

```
T R P K K P M U P L A N T A
E T E K C A J R V A L V E R
S E G B I S E D F I E L D D
A K W L M S I W H O T E S M
B C W S S A M E C S I W V A
L O O U R G H R A O U L A S
I P R N K E O C O P O R T N
F E T N D T L O C K I L B O
T T H D E I E A D G S R T I
V F Y K E N T E N A L P T H
D A A S H H E I L O E L L S
V R I H G P R O O F I C E U
B C K I S P R E D N I L Y C
K J T P S P N L E I R R H U
```

IT'S IN THE CARDS

A baseball card's VALUE is determined by its age, CONDITION, and rarity. ROOKIE cards of famous players and cards that contain errors or flaws are also highly valued.

AUTOGRAPH

BUBBLEGUM

CARD

CAREER

COLLECT

CONDITION

EDITION

GRADE

HITS

HOME RUNS

MINT

NUMBER

PHOTO

PITCHER

PLAYER

POSITION

PRICE

RARE

RECORD

ROOKIE

SEASON

SERIES

SETS

SHOW

STATS

TEAM

TRADE

VALUE

VINTAGE

WRAPPER

YEAR

```
B O N E A T E A M M T P H U
P Y D V R C C E G A T N I V
M E V M H A I P D R O C E R
E A I C I C R O S I A P S S
K R E Y A L P S T E T D G Y
H H R R S R L I I M I I E S
W P E T L P D T H U W R O Y
S E A S O N B I C G R W E N
R T E R O R H O M E R U N S
S T T C G O T N H L L U I D
S N R U B O S C K B M L N B
H I Y A H K T O E B W S O L
O M E P D I S U E U L A V C
W R A P P E R R A B P V E O
```

CHEESE, Peas, and Chocolate PUDDING is a story of a little boy who wouldn't eat anything but these three foods. He is offered a lamp chop, a COOKIE, and ICE CREAM, but he only wants cheese, peas, and chocolate pudding. Perhaps one of the desserts listed below is your favorite.

AMBROSIA

BROWNIE

CAKE

CANDY

CHEESE

COBBLER

COMPOTE

COOKIE

CORDIAL

CRUMBLE

CUSTARD

DOUGHNUT

DUMPLING

ÉCLAIR

FRUIT SALAD

ICE CREAM

JELLY

MERINGUE

MOUSSE

PASTRY

PUDDING

SHERBET

SORBET

SOUFFLÉ

SUNDAE

TART

TRIFLE

TURNOVER

```
W O H V Y T R I F L E V H M
H E S E E H C M M A L S R O
S L N J J U A F D R F L F U
P B T K S E G N M S F R T S
P M N T R T U N H G U O D S
U U A C T S D E I I O V I E
D R E V O N R U T R S J C A
D C I K R B P S M J E L L Y
I O N B E E A O L P A M R T
N M W T T L L R J I L T C C
G P O A A A M B R O S I A W
C O R D I A L E B A N K N L
U T B G H R V T P O E H D G
S E I K O O C G G B C I Y E
```

AQUARIUS TRAITS

January 21 to February 19 marks the eleventh sign of the zodiac, Aquarius, represented by the symbol of the Water Bearer, a figure pouring water from an urn onto the earth. Aquarians like to follow a course of action until it's completed. They are also OPEN and accepting where friendships are concerned. Reel in 28 ATTRACTIVE traits that describe Aquarians.

ACTIVE

ALTRUISTIC

ASTUTE

ATTRACTIVE

BRIGHT

CHEERFUL

CLEVER

CONTRARY

CREATIVE

DILIGENT

FRIENDLY

GENIAL

GENTLE

HONEST

IDEALISTIC

INDEPEN-
DENT

INTUITIVE

INVENTIVE

LIVELY

LOYAL

NOBLE

OPEN

ORIGINAL

REFINED

SENSIBLE

SENSITIVE

SMART

TOLERANT

```
T C L E V E R A O T F T S Y
L O P D C I T S I U R T L A
A N L O L H O N E S T A T C
Y T E E V I T C A S T T M L
O R C V R U U L F N R L A S
L A B I I A C R E A T I V E
U R R T T N D C R N V E N
F Y I I I S N T F E E L S
R V G S O E I E G F G L B I
E A H N P V L L V I I Y O B
E E T E E T R A A N L R N L
H L D S N Y L D N E I R F E
C N B E T U T S A D D Y M H
I P G B S R L A N I G I R O
```

BACKGAMMON

Although backgammon became highly popular worldwide in the late 20th century, excavated relics and literary references show backgammon-type games were played thousands of years ago in the ancient civilizations of Persia, Greece, Rome, and the Far East, making it the oldest known game in recorded history. Hidden in the puzzle below are terms pertaining to this enduring game.

ACE POINT

ANCHOR

BEAR OFF

BLACK

BLOCK

BLOT

BOARD

DICE

DOUBLE

DROP

GAMMON

INNER TABLE

MID POINT

MOVE

OPPONENT

OUTER TABLE

PLAY

PRIME

RACE

REENTER

ROLL

SCORE

SHUT OUT

STRATEGY

TRIPLE

WHITE

```
G U A F P R I M E E T I H W
T N E N O P P O R U N W Y U
N D O N L U V E O C I N M D
I Y I O I K T T C O O O Y K
O R N C H N U E S B P G W O
P I N U E H V L R K E V O M
D D E E S C B P P T C V R O
I K R L B B A I A G A A O P
M G T O B E A R O F F B L B
L N A V P U T T O L B A L B
N R B M U S O F A H Y O S E
D S L O M E A D I L C M W I
C Y E R G O G D O K C N R C
M U T T O B N N F B I I A F
```

VACATION VERBS

Thinking of taking a vacation? Whatever your mood, whatever your preferences, you're bound to find an activity in the list below that will strike your fancy. Whether you're ready to TRAVEL or content just to RELAX and READ a good book, we hope the possibilities suggested here will help you to have a good time!

BIKE

CAMP

CANOE

CLIMB

DANCE

DINE

DOZE

DRINK

DRIVE

FISH

FROLIC

HIKE

HUNT

PLAY

RAFT

READ

RELAX

REST

RIDE

ROMP

SHOP

SIGHTSEE

STROLL

SURF

SWIM

TOUR

TRAVEL

VISIT

```
P R A P T D A P D I N E F M
C A M P S R R B Y F K F D X
I V K M O W T A R I F W D K
C Z V F H H I U B N U D S N
F Y A U C S S M P L A Y L U
I M N P E V I R D M H F R H
S T R O L L V G R U O T F M
H M V Z C I E M H B V R X R
M M G Z M E I D T T O A V V
L H S T K I O A I L S V T V
T Z W I G Z K N I R D E S P
Z X H D E C V C A X A L E R
U L T F G L E E K C E F R A
S C C G D F O L K F R B T L
```

Author Ernest Hemingway lived in France for several years, and was quoted as saying "Wine is the most civilized thing in the world." So, let's make a toast...to the beautiful red wines of France. *À votre santé!*

AUSONE

BANDOL

BARET

BELAIR

BROUILLY

CAHORS

CANON

CHINON

CORNAS

FIEUZAL

FIGEAC

FITOU

FLEURIE

GAZIN

GIVRY

GRAVES

LATOUR

LOUDENNE

MARGAUX

MEURSAULT

MEYNEY

MONTHELIE

MORGON

NENIN

OLIVIER

PALMER

PAVIE

PÉTRUS

RULLY

SAVOIE

TALBOT

TROTANOY

```
G S S I X T O B L A T E O T
C R M D E I L E H T N O M H
R O A B F O N U E N I Z A G
U H R V D N O N A C L Y I C
L A G N E I O V A S X V H E
L C A D A S F L E U R I E F
Y B U L U S M A O Y N U O S
L O X A S M X T L O R L E R
L A N H U M I O N P I C E M
I V Z A R F O U M V A M D E
U S A U T F V R I E L V G Y
O T M M E O N E G A E F I N
R Y T M P I R I P O B G Z E
B A R E T V F T N E N I N Y
```

MAKING THE CUT!

193

Use your pencil as a CHISEL to CHIP away at the word list below which contains 40 terms that can be used to describe ways of cutting something.

BISECT
BITE
CARVE
CHIP
CHISEL
CLEAVE
CLIP
CROP
CURTAIL
DICE
DIVIDE
FELL
GASH
HACK
LACERATE
MINCE
NICK
NOTCH
PERFORATE
PIERCE
PRUNE
PUNCTURE
QUARTER
REAP
REND
RIVE
SCARIFY

SCISSOR
SCORE
SCRUB
SHAVE
SHEAR
SKIVE
SLASH

SLICE
SLIT
SNIP
SPLIT
SUNDER
TRANSECT

```
F P F M P O R C I S G K F Y
D O Y E A H E A N K C A H P
I Y S F L D S I E I S H S I
C R K T I L P S N H R L K H
E E U V A R E D N U S I I C
T N I S R R A S V P H A V T
I D H T O L A C E R A T E E
B P L C L I P R S N Y R V H
I E S E T P F U E H U U E A
S C I S S O R B E T A C U R
E I D N R I N U C A R V E R
C L E A V E H N N E G A E Y
T S T R Y Q U C I E P A U Y
I E L T H P H P M M G L S Q
```

194

IRELAND'S COUNTIES

The island of Ireland is divided into two separate countries which encompass four historical provinces that are further divided into a total of 32 counties. At 84,288 square kilometers (32,544 square miles), it is about the size of South Carolina and would fit in Texas a little over eight times! The names of Ireland's counties are listed below.

ANTRIM

ARMAGH

CARLOW

CAVAN

CLARE

CORK

DERRY

DONEGAL

DOWN

DUBLIN

FERMANAGH

GALWAY

KERRY

KILDARE

KILKENNY

LAOIS

LEITRIM

LIMERICK

LONGFORD

LOUTH

MAYO

MEATH

MONAGHAN

OFFALLY

ROSCOM-
MON

SLIGO

TIPPERARY

TYRONE

WATERFORD

WESTMEATH

WEXFORD

WICKLOW

```
C H T U O L E I T R I M M Y
K L C D H N N I L B U D O D
I O I L T M P W T Y R O N E
L O Y M A P I O R N Y W A R
K O L A E R D R G E A N G R
E W L R M R E O T I W V H Y
N D A H T K I S N N L G A U
N R F T S C R C W E A S N C
Y O F A E O A O K N G U E X
S F O E W R L M A R M A G H
U X H M L K F M S I O A L M
R E Y O C D R O F G N O L S
V W W I B E T N R D G L D S
V L W G F X K I L D A R E T
```

DAY-CARE CENTER

In today's society, more and more **PARENTS** are working, so finding **QUALITY** alternative **CARE** for their children is a fact of life. A good day-care center will provide a friendly and warm environment that will help the child develop mentally, physically, socially, and emotionally.

BLOCKS

BOOKS

BOYS

CARE

CENTER

CRAFTS

DIRECTOR

ENROLL

GAMES

GIRLS

GOALS

GROUP

INDOORS

INFANTS

LEARNING

LICENSE

LOCATION

MEALS

MUSIC

NURSERY

PARENTS

PLAY

POLICIES

PRESCHOOL

PROGRAM

QUALITY

READING

REGISTER

REST

STAFF

TASKS

TODDLERS

TOYS

```
T S S R E T N E C N E D R S
R E T S I G E R S U E I P N
O I N K G F N S T N E R A P
B C A O N F B I B H E E A Q
Y I F O I A S O D S B C F C
T L N B N T Y T C A L T I Q
I O I I R S A H F L E O I L
L P D N A C O C O A C R C M
A L L D E O P R O G R A M S
U A D O L S N G B L O C K S
Q Y O O L E S L A O G S L Y
N N U R S E R Y E M A A N O
M T I S D R E S T T E H M T
P G R O U P N Q K M U S I C
```

CARNIVAL GLASS PATTERNS

The 28 terms in the word list below are all types of carnival glassware patterns. What we'd like you to do is use your EAGLE eyes to scan the diagram and circle them all. We think this is a PEACH of a puzzle, don't you?

ACORN

BUTTERFLY

CHERRY

COSMOS

DAHLIA

DEER

EAGLE

FERN

FLUTE

GRAPE

HERON

HOBSTAR

HOLLY

ILLUSION

IRIS

KIWI

LOUISA

MIKADO

PEACH

RIPPLE

ROBIN

ROSES

RUSTIC

SCROLL

SUNFLOWER

SWAN

SWIRL

TEN MUMS

```
Y S P G N W R G D P Y E O I
M R K O S W S A D T N A A B
W E R S F E I A T A N K L H
L E N E N L R I W S B G W M
H D R E H H I S R O B I N T
W N W A Y C I S O M S O C A
W F D D Y A R U S T I C H K
H O L L Y E I N O S R N I I
S L D U P P P F U M E W H E
Y C F A T H P L O U I S A M
U U R C K E L O U M B G O E
G G L O S I E W Y N L Y Y R
O I F R L R M E M E N P C F
U C K N Y L F R E T T U B L
```

THE FINAL "ACT"

It's a FACT that the word list we've provided contains 28 words that end in "ACT". Now it's up to you to EXTRACT them all from the diagram.

ABSTRACT

ATTRACT

BRACT

CATARACT

COMPACT

CONTACT

CONTRACT

COUNTERACT

DETRACT

DIDACT

DISTRACT

ENACT

EPACT

EXACT

EXTRACT

FACT

IMPACT

INTACT

OVERACT

PLAYACT

PROTRACT

REACT

REDACT

REFRACT

RETRACT

RETROACT

SUBTRACT

TRANSACT

```
I M P A C T D T R X B F T E
C M X L C N C F E I F L P T
T O I A A A T A T T R A C T
C C N D R Y C R T C A F C
A E A T C C A E A T R A C A
R R X R A R A C C E E M X R
T E S D T C A R T S I D E E
N F E S T B T N C F I T B V
O R B D R S U R A S R R C O
C A O I L O X S R O A V S C
C C U D C O M P A C T T S S
I T R A N S A C T B O Y T E
M O U C M F T C A R T O R P
T C A T N I I N C F V M O V
```

What do Larry Bird, Michael Jackson, David Letterman, and John Mellencamp have in common? They all hail from the great state of Indiana. You can find 33 of the state's 92 counties below.

ADAMS
BROWN
CLAY
FRANKLIN
FULTON
GRANT

GREENE
HANCOCK
HENRY
HUNTINGTON
JASPER
JOHNSON

KNOX
KOSCIUSKO
LAKE
NOBLE
OHIO
ORANGE
OWEN
PARKE
PERRY
PORTER
POSEY
RUSH
SCOTT
SPENCER
STARKE
ST. JOSEPH
TIPTON
UNION
VANDER-
BURGH
VIGO
WABASH

```
V G K E Y S Y T G L G X O C
B I W R V M J R S R W P L F
O V G A I A O W E N L A K E
K N X O B D H E U C Y R C K
Y O H F R A N K L I N K G R
L I S G N E S H P O S E Y A
O N X C R C O H T T B H P T
G U O B I A N G J K N W E S
O C N R V U N O T P I T R A
K R K O B I S T N O B L E C
H U A W T E B K Y R R E P V
O S B N P L S C O T T Y S J
T D U H G R U B R E D N A V
H H Y R N E H F N R B X J X
```

STREETS OF PORTLAND

The largest city in the state of OREGON, Portland is situated on the Willamette River. As the principal port of the state, it exports lumber, paper, wood pulp, and wool. There's lots to see and do in this northwestern city. Here are some of its streets.

ALDER
ANKENY
BENTON
CLAY
COUCH
DAVIS
FLANDERS
FLINT
FRONT
GLISAN
GRAND
HALL
HOYT
IRVING
KEARNEY
KERBY
LOVEJOY
MAIN
MILL
OREGON
OVERTON
PARK
PINE
RODNEY

ROSS
SALMON
SAVIER
SCHUYLER
STARK
UNION

UPSHUR
VAUGHN
VICTORIA
VISTA
WILSON
YAMHILL

```
N O T N E B G U W I L S O N
R V S C V Y U L P O L U A K
E E I I G Y D N V S A W D S
D R S C V U N E I R H O Y T
L T E I T A J E V O B U S A
A O I L W O D C K D N T R R
V N B B Y R R Y E N R A E K
C O U C H U M I O E A I D F
D G A L L I H M A Y V V N P
L E E D L A L C B A A A A F
H R N L N A Y R S U S R L I
T O I V S A E D G I P I F L
D S P A R K R H L T N I A M
U S I R V I N G K T N O R F
```

200 | BAKLAVA

For a SWEET alternative to candy, have you tried baklava? A popular PASTRY in GREECE, it contains spices and chopped ALMONDS, PECANS, or WALNUTS that are nestled between BUTTERY layers of FLAKY DOUGH, all of which is coated with a spicy HONEY-LEMON SYRUP.

ALMONDS

BAKED

BUTTERY

CHOCOLATE

CINNAMON

COCONUT

CRISP

DELICIOUS

DESSERT

DOUGH

DRIZZLE

FILLING

FLAKY

FLAVOR

FRUIT

GREECE

HOLIDAYS

HONEY

INGREDIENTS

LAYERED

LEMON (juice)

PASTRY

PECANS

SUGAR

SWEET

SYRUP

TREAT

WALNUTS

```
Y B M S D T S N P E C A N S
H D R H E T I U R F N O O Y
G R E E C E K A G K M H M R
U P W L H O L I D A Y S E U
O S C R I S P Y N L R T L P
D U H M R C S N C M S N W Z
E Y O W T T I O H O N E Y S
K R C D U C C O B N D I V T
A T O N E O W U U D I D C H
B S L V N R T R E S S E D C
T A A U A T E L Z Z I R D P
W P T H E L H Y B V E G L B
T A E R T K F L A K Y N R P
K V Y K C R A F I L L I N G
```

MICHIGAN COUNTIES

The state of Michigan is unique in that it consists of two peninsulas completely separated by water. It also borders four of the five Great Lakes. Michigan's key economic sector is the automobile industry. Take a trip through the Wolverine State as you find some of its county names hidden below.

ALCONA

ALLEGAN

ALPENA

ANTRIM

ARENAC

BARAGA

BARRY

BERRIEN

BRANCH

CALHOUN

CHIPPEWA

CLINTON

CRAWFORD

EATON

GENESEE

GLADWIN

GOGEBIC

GRATIOT

HILLSDALE

INGHAM

IONIA

IOSCO

IRON

ISABELLA

JACKSON

KALAMAZOO

MASON

MECOSTA

MONROE

OCEANA

OSCODA

WAYNE

```
B E R R I E N O T N I L C A
B U A W A Y N E U N S R E G
R Z N C H I P P E W A K O A
A D O C S O N E B W B G R R
N O C E A N A O F N E E N A
C A L H O U N O I B L E O B
H L A T N O R I I H L S M A
M L A N S D Z C U A A E I R
S E G K E G L A D W I N R R
M G C D Y P O S M B N E T Y
Z A J O S C L N M A H G N I
J N S T S L L A U O L W A F
B W T O I T A R G G B A N I
D L I H N C A N E R A T K S
```

GREAT PROFILE!

This puzzle showcases words about SILHOUETTE art. A refreshing alternative to painted portraits, this black-and-white SHADOW TECHNIQUE presents a SIMPLE IMAGE while still capturing the many intimate details of a person's FEATURES.

ABSTRACT

ANCIENT

ARTIST

CHIN

COLLAGE

CUTOUT

DETAIL

FACE

FEATURES

FRAME

GALLERY

GENRE

HAIR

HEAD

IMAGE

LIFE-SIZE

LINES

MODERN

MURAL

NOSE

OUTLINE

PAINT

PAPER

PORTRAIT

PROFILE

SHADOW

SILHOUETTE

SIMPLE

TECHNIQUE

```
E U L Y W O I S H A D O W N
S G H F P N E Z I S E F I L
T I A R T R O P I M T M U D
W M H L U E L L T N P M D W
P A G T L D H R E L D L A O
R G A Y I O I I C P A P E R
O E B R U M C S H S T R H W
F U S E T N A L N N N I U C
I F T L A I U O I B I A R M
L T R L F M S A Q A E H E E
E B A A I E P T U O T U C M
E E C G M N M G E R N E G N
E E T W Q E E Q Y N F D D Y
A U D Q C O G S F E I L C W
```

BAKE DATE

RISE to the occasion and circle the following terms associated with baking, a popular KITCHEN activity.

BAKE

BATTER

BERRIES

BLEND

BOWL

BUTTER

COOK

DESSERT

EGGS

FLOUR

FOOD

FRUIT

GLAZE

ICING

INGREDIENTS

KITCHEN

MARGARINE

MEASURE

MILK

MIXER

OVEN

PANS

RECIPE

RISE

SPATULA

SPOON

STIR

SUGAR

TIMER

TOPPING

VANILLA

WATER

WHIP

```
I K E S B V P R K M E B D N
U C N N T E G G S E D Z I V
A F O O D N B F N A R S B L
N E E O I C E I R S E B O Z
E X F P K M R I B U M L W T
H S P S I A R I D R I A L R
C O I X G C I N R E T T A B
T V E R B D E S S E R T D A
I R A P O L S R R A T G C K
K M A N B Z V U N H G T N E
G N I C I F O Z G W M G U I
S M E Z A L G X H A X L Z B
M F B V F K L I M W R I T S
N A B Z O S P A T U L A S H
```

WALL STREET

In the 1987 movie *Wall Street*, Gordon Gekko (Michael Douglas) says, "Lunch is for wimps." We don't know about those words, but we *do* know the Wall Street words below are hidden in the diagram.

ASSET	DEAL	GAIN
BANK	DIVIDENDS	INDEX
BOND	EXCHANGE	INVESTMENT
BROKER	FLOOR	LIST
CASH	FUND	LOSS
		MARGIN

```
R H L D F P D R R I C L C B
Y Y V G Y P U F L I S T A O
L E L C A S H E V K P N M B
Y L I L D I D B R O K E R O
F A O O A P N N V A M M P N
M S Y X O R P I E B H T R D
S S R I U Y I G E D I S I E
S E N T M L N R U O I E N F
P T E K R A M A N O D V C U
M R O S H O N M X E D N I N
R O I C C U O G A P A I P D
N P X C K N L L M T E P A T
Y E O C E T Y N F G L Y L E
N R M Y F M B U O N D V V Y
```

MARKET

MEMBER

MONEY

OPTION

POINT

PRICE

PRINCIPAL

PROXY

RALLY

REPORT

RETURN

SALE

SHARE

STOCK

TAPE

SHUTTLE DIPLOMACY

In weaving, the shuttle is the instrument that carries the horizontal WEFT thread back and forth between the lengthwise WARP threads. We've woven 38 terms associated with this craft into the diagram below. As you WEAVE your way through it, see if you can ROPE all of them.

BALL
BIND
BOWLINE
BRAIDING
BUTTING
CHAIN
CLOVE
CORD
EDGE
FRINGE
HITCH
HOOK
KNOT
LACE
LATCH
LOOM
MACRAMÉ
MARL
MESH
NEEDLE
NETTING
PICK
PICOT
RADDLE
REEF
RING

ROPE
SHAFT
SHED
SINNET
SPIRAL
SPLICE

TASSEL
WARP
WEAVE
WEFT
WHIP
WIND

```
M A G I S B K F W A R P U D
I O N T N H W T F E G W T R
R B M W W E A V E N C T F U
O S M C G S G F I M F P O S
P G H P S N N D T E O H N P
E L D E E N I L W O B O W M
D E L D D A R T K U I O L A
M V R W R A O V T O N K E C
M O U B M C B T C E D G E R
C L F M I N I A H C N C U A
D C P P P N W C L I A N W M
N N W I G K T D R L T I I E
K R I H T A V F N P I C K S
K F D W L A R I P S R G H H
```

COLONIAL GARDEN PLANTS

Many plants and herbs used nowadays for seasoning were appreciated for their medicinal values in colonial America. For example, our forefathers prescribed ANISE to soothe sore throats and used ROSEMARY to cure colds.

AGRIMONY

ANGELICA

ANISE

ARACH

BALM

BASIL

BEDSTRAW

BETONY

BUGLOSS

BURNET

CLARY

CLOTBUR

COWSLIP

CUDWEED

DITTANY

FENNEL

FLAX

HOPS

LOVAGE

MADDER

MAYWEED

MUGWORT

NETTLE

ROCKET

ROSEMARY

SAVORY

SKIRRET

SORREL

TEASEL

WORM-
WOOD

YARROW

```
X N H L R B A R A C H O P S
A M S L E N N E F B A S I L
L D S T W B U R N E T T L E
F D O O W M R O W C E V P S
X N L V D O Y A G D T L L A
Y C G M T E R R I K S E A E
A C U Y G T E T A A M R G T
R L B D S P T W V M E R R E
R O O D W A I O Y D E O I K
O T E V N E R L D A W S M C
W B D Y A Y E A S G M L O O
O U S K P G M D U W A P N R
Y R A L C Y E M B B O E Y K
B E S I N A N G E L I C A P
```

HOCUS-POCUS

No need to consult the STARS, look into a CRYSTAL ball, or even be Harry Potter to solve this puzzle that deals with MAGIC and the supernatural. A little puzzler's WISDOM should be enough.

ADEPT

ALCHEMY

ASTROLOGY

AURA

BABEL
(Tower of)

CARD

CHIRO-
MANCY

CONJURY

CRYSTAL

DELPHI

ELEUSIS

GHOST

ISIS

LUSTRATION

MAGIC

MAGUS

MOLE

MYSTIC

NAILS

NUMBERS

OCCULT

OMEN

ORACLE

PALM

PHILOSOPHER'S
(stone)

RITE

SEER

SOOTHSAYER

SPHINX

STARS

TAROT

WAND

WISDOM

WITCH

```
C R A L C H E M Y C I G A M
L B A B E L O M R H S H T X
Y A T P E D A Y E I I C S N
T A E U N U M B E R S T O S
A A S R E H P O S O L I H P
T I R U W I S D O M T W G H
S Y G O L O R T S A Y I Y I
U E R D T A H M R N R O R N
G E I W E S T T B C U U L X
A L H D A L S S I Y J W A D
M C N Y U U P T Y E N P R B
A A E C L X S H A R O A A O
W R C L D Y E T I R C L J M
H O C O M E N A I L S M U N
```

208

WAYS TO PAY

In this puzzle we **PROVIDE** you with 28 ways to **SPEND** your money! Finding them all will bring a satisfying return on your solving investment.

ALLOCATE

ANTE UP

AWARD

BEQUEATH

CHIP IN

COMPENSATE

CONTRIBUTE

DEFRAY

DISBURSE

DONATE

ENDOW

EXPEND

FINANCE

GIVE

GRANT

INVEST

KICK IN

PONY UP

PROVIDE

PUT UP

REMIT

REMUNERATE

RENDER

REWARD

SPEND

SUBSCRIBE

SUBSIDIZE

SUPPORT

```
R A F E W E X P E N D U D C
R E D N E R A X C H H P O B
E R W K C E T W N T U N N Y
M E T A C O L L A Y T G A Y
I M E V R S L E N R Y T T A
T U S T X D U O I I D N E R
N N R U A Q P B F H P K W F
A E U Y E S U B S I D I Z E
R R B B I T N S U C L C H D
G A S A E X Q E P B R K E C
U T I A N T E U P E V I G P
X E D I V O R P O M N N B K
A R P P U T U P R W O D N E
R W A I N V E S T R Q C M Z
```

SORRY, NO HAMMERS

It's easy to find lots of interesting things in hardware stores. We were able to TRACK down 29 items and hide them in the diagram below. There was a CATCH, though — each item we've listed is spelled with just five letters.

APRON

AUGER

BRACE

CABLE

CATCH

CHAIN

CLAMP

DRILL

ELBOW

GAUGE

GLIDE

HINGE

LATCH

LEVEL

MITER

PAINT

RAZOR

RISER

RIVET

SHANK

SNAKE (plumbing tool)

STRAP

SWEEP

TIMER

TONGS

TRACK (for door)

TWINE

VALVE

WEDGE

```
A C I Z D M G K H Z V P P C
Z I H R E S I R E T P A E U
C O R A D H O T R A C K V S
B T U E I K O S E P C M L T
L E V E L N N C I R O Z A R
I V H L G B L P E O P T V A
N I I S S N A M G N K E N P
H R H D H G I C D Z N I C B
D L N L A T C H E I Z B A P
E W M U N E N L W O B L E A
E C G I K H C T A C A E T K
I E A A D P H E C M W Z O K
R P N R V K H V S S P B C O
V S M A B G T A T D U V K V
```

STREETS OF SAN DIEGO

A trip to San Diego offers such attractions as 17 miles of ocean beaches, Balboa Park, Old Town, the San Diego Zoo, and a quick side trip to Mexico. Take your map and walk along these streets of San Diego.

ALOMA	DATE	HARNEY
ARISTA	DOVE	HAWK
ARROYO	EAGLE	IMPERIAL
BEECH	EUCLID	INDIA
BIRCH	GAINES	ISLAND
CEDAR	GRAPE	JUAN
		JUNIPER
		KALMIA
		LAUREL
		LINWOOD
		MAPLE
		MASON
		MYRTLE
		NUTMEG
		PALM
		REDWOOD
		ROSECRANS
		STATE
		SUNSET
		THORN
		TRIAS
		TWIGGS
		UNION

```
G A E S Y E P A R G R L R L
I O J C A A L S W S D C D V
S N U V I I K G N R O H T Y
L U A T S I R A A R O G J H
A T N H M Y R T L E W U C W
N M V S A C G D D M N R S M
D E O L E R U A L I I U L H
S G O S A T N T P B L A A L
T M O G A I N E S E P C B A
A R P G A R R O Y O V N U B
T M W I K A R E D W O O D E
E L D W N D G C P S H I D E
I N A T E E L P A M M N L C
I H D G Y C L M K O I U K H
```

DOUBLE "T" WORDS

We will ATTEST to the fact that there are 36 hidden words, all containing the letters "TT," FITTING nicely in the diagram below. You'll hit the puzzle LOTTERY by finding them all.

ATTEST

ATTIC

ATTORNEY

BLOTTER

BOTTLE

BUTTE

BUTTON

CATTLE

CLUTTER

COTTON

DITTO

DITTY

FITTING

FLUTTER

GUTTER

KETTLE

KITTEN

LETTUCE

LITTER

LOTTERY

LOTTO

MATTE

MITT

MOTTO

MUTTON

PETTY

PLATTER

POTTERY

PRETTY

RATTLE

SETTEE

STUTTER

TATTLE

TATTOO

WETTER

WITTY

B	B	O	F	G	M	B	M	E	I	W	S	O	Y
C	U	O	O	Y	O	O	P	L	A	T	T	E	R
F	T	F	T	T	R	E	T	T	U	B	N	E	E
N	T	G	U	T	T	E	R	T	K	R	T	T	T
C	O	D	P	T	L	A	T	A	O	T	B	T	T
D	N	T	Y	R	E	T	T	U	L	F	E	O
P	Y	T	T	E	R	P	T	L	O	R	W	S	L
L	T	A	T	U	N	A	C	T	E	P	K	W	B
A	R	C	I	S	M	E	A	T	U	E	R	U	T
M	U	O	D	A	R	N	T	D	T	C	O	S	R
W	I	T	T	Y	R	E	T	T	I	L	E	G	S
U	S	T	A	E	W	Y	L	C	I	T	T	A	S
F	E	O	T	F	I	E	E	K	T	K	T	T	F
M	G	N	I	T	T	I	F	A	P	T	Y	O	S

CONTRACTIONS

YOU'LL like this puzzle that WE'VE created for you because it's full of contractions, the comfortable shortcuts of everyday speech. DON'T wait another second to solve this gem!

AREN'T

CAN'T

COULDN'T

DIDN'T

DOESN'T

DON'T

HADN'T

HASN'T

HAVEN'T

HERE'S

ISN'T

IT'LL

LET'S

MUSTN'T

NEEDN'T

SHE'D

SHE'S

SHOULDN'T

THAT'S

THEY'D

THEY'LL

THEY'RE

THEY'VE

WASN'T

WE'LL

WEREN'T

WE'VE

WHO'LL

WON'T

WOULDN'T

YOU'D

YOU'LL

YOU'RE

YOU'VE

```
Y R D L I T N O D Y E H T C
I V U C A N T A D O T N S I
W H O L L H Y N M U E C Y H
O A Y T A S U R S R V O S L
M U S T N T A S A E U U L D
U R S N N E W L W L O L I M
V M H D T D V D L O Y D S W
U L A L H T E A Y E N N I N
L H S U H H R E H T W T V D
W E N O S E U T N D L U O W
V H T H E Y R E A L A Y S H
W L E S V V R E R A M W A L
W S M E E E S D S D C I S W
I T H T W T T L T N L N M C
```

FINISHING TOUCHES

Some things need just one final touch to make them perfect. Here's a list of things that can be added to make something "just right."

BEADS

BELL

BORDER

BOUQUET

EDGING

EMBROIDERY

FEATHER

FILET

FRET

FRINGE

GARLAND

GLITTER

ICING

LACE

LINING

NOSEGAY

ORNAMENT

PARSLEY

PLUME

POLISH

RIBBON

ROSETTE

STAR

TASSEL

TINSEL

TRIM

VARNISH

WHIPPED CREAM

WREATH

```
E  B  Y  R  I  B  B  O  N  B  V  Q  Q  U
Y  M  U  E  A  N  E  H  T  A  E  R  W  G
L  T  B  D  L  T  F  R  I  N  G  E  W  I
C  B  E  R  B  S  S  O  Q  B  G  H  B  C
N  R  L  O  O  W  R  Y  E  N  I  T  H  I
T  Y  L  B  U  I  P  A  I  P  T  A  T  N
H  M  I  W  Q  V  D  G  P  I  A  E  Q  G
R  S  N  M  U  S  D  E  N  M  L  F  H  L
B  R  I  H  E  E  D  S  R  I  H  S  L  I
Q  R  N  N  T  C  E  O  F  Y  I  E  W  T
T  H  G  A  R  L  A  N  D  L  S  D  Q  T
B  T  N  E  M  A  N  R  O  S  E  T  T  E
S  N  A  L  R  C  V  P  A  B  S  S  V  R
E  M  U  L  P  E  Q  T  P  Y  S  E  Q  F
```

"STU" WORDS

You'll do a STUPENDOUS job if you STUDY the diagram below and circle the 31 words that start with "STU."

STUBBED

STUBBLE

STUBBORN

STUBBY

STUCCO

STUCK

STUDDED

STUDENT

STUDIED

STUDIOUS

STUDY

STUFFER

STUFFING

STUFFY

STULL

STULTIFY

STUMBLE

STUMMING

STUMP

STUNG

STUNK

STUNNER

STUNNING

STUNT

STUPEFY

STUPENDOUS

STUPES

STUPID

STUPOR

STURGEON

STUTTER

```
S S Y I G P R O P U T S U Y
Y D T B M N R O B B U T S D
F G E U B E I R E E Y U E U
E R T B N U B F E S S D P T
P S P N B K T U F T D I U S
U R U G N U T S U U T O T O
T T L F G S T L T R T U S R
S E L B M U T S O G P S T M
T N U T S I I U O E E T U S
U S T U F F E R N O N U P T
B E S Y S T U D E N T C I U
B S T U C C O P S E I K D F
L D E I D U T S B N M N D F
E O G T S T U M M I N G G Y
```

WHEN IN ROME...

The Roman Empire was one of the most powerful dynasties of all time. AUGUSTUS became the first emperor of Rome in 27 B.C. Successive emperors included CLAUDIUS, NERO, and TIBERIUS. Find them, along with 25 other notable Romans, hidden in the grid.

ANTONY

AUGUSTUS

AURELIUS

BRUTUS

CAESAR
(Julius)

CALIGULA

CATO

CICERO

CLAUDIUS

COMMODUS

DOMITIAN

GRACCHUS

HADRIAN

LEPIDUS

MARIUS

NERO

NERVA

OVID

PLINY

PLUTARCH

POMPEY

ROMULUS

SCIPIO

SPARTACUS

SULLA

TIBERIUS

TRAJAN

VIRGIL

VITELLIUS

```
A L A U R E L I U S V H T P
Y J O I P I C S U D I P E L
N S V H L N A I T I M O D I
O A U I U O D I L C P R I N
T M J C T U B G E O O E V Y
N L G A A E O L V M M C O S
A S C L R T L I U M P I E M
L U C I C T R L N O E C C A
L T U G H G U A I D Y A I R
U S U U I S I Y P U E B R I
S U O L B R U T U S S S O U
E G H A D J G R A C C H U S
M U B A V A V R E N E R O B
I A H R S C B G N O E E E J
```

LET'S...

Let us **BEGIN** by saying this list is filled with familiar words and phrases that often follow "Let's." If you **DECIDE** you want to **GO OUT** and **HAVE LUNCH** before completing this puzzle, feel free — there's no solving deadline to **MEET**.

BEGIN

BUY IT

CELEBRATE

DANCE

DECIDE

DO IT

DROP IT

EAT OUT

FACE IT

FIND OUT

FORGET IT

GO OUT

HAVE LUNCH

HURRY

MAKE BELIEVE

MAKE UP

MEET

NOT WORRY

PARTY

PLAY

PRACTICE

PRETEND

RECONSIDER

RELAX

SLEEP ON IT

SPLURGE

START OVER

STOP

TALK

TEAM UP

TRY IT

WAIT

```
Y A L P S P L U R G E O P D
R T U O D N I F N T I I R W
R C L M P M W O A N M O A R
U P U M A E T R I A P I C E
H P X P U W B G K I T E T V
I A I A O E E E T V G D I O
K R V R L B B T C D V I C T
F T R E R E D I S N O C E R
L Y C T L P R T E E A E G A
S R A I U U U F I T M D T T
S L E E P O N I T E I C R S
K V K D O I T C W R C Y E H
E A E G T L X A H P I A U V
M S E H S D K C E T X K F B
```

LONDON is the capital of Great Britain and a city steeped in historical and cultural heritage. Sitting at the head of the Thames River, London is home to many museums, theaters, and markets. Take a trip through Merry Ol' England as you find the names of 30 London streets below.

ALBION

APPOLD

BROAD

BURY

CANNON

CARLISLE

CHRISTOPHER

CULLUM

DOMINION

DUKES

DUNSTER

DYSART

EARL

ELDON

EXCHANGE

FORT

KEATS

LLOYD'S

LONDON

MITRE

MOORGATE

NICHOLAS

PINDAR

PRIMROSE

PRINCESS

SNOWDEN

SPIRAL

ST. MARY

VICTORIA

WILSON

```
F  E  B  R  O  A  D  Y  D  W  V  K  D  B
O  X  S  S  E  C  N  I  R  P  L  Y  D  K
R  C  I  O  O  H  L  M  G  A  S  B  U  V
T  H  L  A  R  I  P  S  N  A  M  S  K  N
B  A  M  K  A  M  O  O  R  G  A  T  E  L
U  N  L  B  D  L  I  T  T  L  T  D  S  M
R  G  B  B  N  N  O  R  O  S  W  C  E  U
Y  E  R  T  I  M  O  H  P  O  I  A  C  L
W  T  T  M  P  O  C  D  N  D  R  R  Y  L
N  I  O  S  S  I  N  S  N  L  K  L  H  U
D  D  L  T  N  V  I  C  T  O  R  I  A  C
S  X  A  S  W  U  N  N  T  P  L  S  X  N
A  E  L  L  O  Y  D  S  P  P  L  L  S  G
K  E  L  D  O  N  O  N  N  A  C  E  E  T
```

Any evening can be a night at the movies if you hit the VIDEO store to RENT one of the latest releases or an old favorite. There's a wide SELECTION to choose from, including films from these categories: ACTION, ADVENTURE, COMEDY, SUSPENSE, and ANIMATION, to name a few. The following entries are related to renting videos and DVDs.

ACTION

ADVENTURE

ANIMATION

BIOGRAPHY

CARTOON

COMEDY

CONCERT

DRAMA

EPIC

FANTASY

FICTION

FOREIGN

MOVIE

MUSICAL

NEW RELEASE

OPERA

PLAY

REMAKE

RENT

RETURN

ROMANCE

SELECTION

SEQUEL

SPORTS

SUSPENSE

TAPE

THRILLER

TITLE

VIDEO

VIEW

WESTERN

```
R U R L A C I S U M E T A K
C M S V I D E O T S H R C Q
Y C U W E I V P A R U E T K
A H S M O V I E I M C C I N
L O P E R A L L N C K N O S
P C E A S E L E C T I O N P
Y Y N N R E T S E W U C G O
N Q S W R G U R K N S R I R
E O E A T O O T O P E Y E T
K N O I T A M I N A Q T R S
A U T T M N T A B T U A O P
M L N A R C A F N R E P F B
E E R S I A V F N C L E D N
R D G F M E C C O M E D Y G
```

GOING FOR A RIDE

Hop in and take a spin through the diagram below as you find the 32 items that are all things you can ride.

AIRPLANE

BARGE

BICYCLE

BOAT

BUGGY

CANOE

CARRIAGE

CHARIOT

ELEVATOR

FERRY

GLIDER

GONDOLA

HANSOM
  CAB

HORSE

MOTORCYCLE

PLOW

PONY

RAFT

SCOOTER

SHIP

SKATEBOARD

SLED

SUBWAY

SURFBOARD

TOBAGGAN

TRACTOR

TRAIN

TRICYCLE

TROLLEY

TRUCK

WAGON

YACHT

```
R R E O N A C H A R I O T L
G E Y S Y T A I S A M I N M
K U D G Y L R U C F K Y U O
K S G I O P R R O T C A R T
L U K D L F I O O H U W B O
B A N A B G A S T C R B I R
Y O N O T Y G W E A T U C C
G E A Y D E E A R Y V S Y Y
N R G T G L B G R R R E C C
D I G R B L W O Y N S R L L
F B A C M O S N A H L E E E
I B B R L R T W I R E L V F
Y N O P T T D P W D D O N S
P H T R I C Y C L E S R O H
```

UNUSUAL MOVIE TITLES

The 31 movie titles that make up the word list below are unique, because by themselves they would probably never work their way into an everyday conversation. Do any of these flicks sound familiar to you?

AKU AKU

ALAMBRISTA!

CABOBLANCO

EEGAH

GIZMO

GORP

GYMKATA

KIPPERBANG

KRONOS

KRULL

LANDRU

NABONGA

NOSFERATU

OBLOMOV

PHFFFT!

POWAQQATSI

RIFIFI

SHALAKO

SKIDOO

SNAFU

SOLARIS

TOBRUK

TOPKAPI

TROG

TRON

TWONKY (The)

XTRO

ZARAK

ZARDOZ

ZAZA

ZOTZ!

```
E P O G A V G U A B V B V G
E Z O A K P S Y U O S O V H
G C D W U H R O M Z I G Z L
A S W Z A R D O Z K R U L L
H L O L K Q L U G G A P S Z
G Y A N U B Q T N U L T N Q
T K T M O C N A L B O B A C
O N F G B R B R T X S S F C
P O F K M R K E U S P K U U
K W F X E R I F I F I I R Z
A T H P T D Z S E N G D T H
P O P K U R B O T B N O A B
I I C N A B O N G A Z O R W
K A R A Z A Z N L F N F X T
```

THE "WRITE" STUFF

Have you ever heard someone say "I could write a book about it!"? Perhaps you may have even said it yourself after an unusual series of experiences or after having acquired a great deal of information about a particular subject or activity. The word list consists of 31 categories or subjects of books.

ALGEBRA	PUZZLES	THRILLER
BIOLOGY	ROMANCE	TYPING
BOTANY	SATIRE	WILDLIFE
CATS	SEWING	YOGA
CHEMISTRY	SHIPS	ZOOLOGY
CHESS		
COMEDY		
DOGS		
DRAMA		
FANTASY		
FICTION		
GAMES		
GEOLOGY		
HEALTH		
HISTORY		
INSECTS		
MUSIC		
MYSTERY		
PHYSICS		
POETRY		
POLITICS		

```
N T O W O F L F A N T A S Y
E O Y I Y M Y H O T A A P N
B P G L C G Z I S E R D I A
I G O D O E T S F G B A H T
O A L L O C I T C H E S S O
L M O I I N E O F O G E D B
O E O F S T H R I L L E R R
G S Z E Y C I Y I Z A H A O
Y N C P C R R C Z T E C M M
M T I I Y I E U S A A D A A
S N S W S G P T L T P S B N
G E U T E Y R T S I M E H C
O W M Y H S H O A Y O G A E
D O Y R T E O P C O M E D Y
```

The sport of FIELD hockey dates back well before the Ancient Olympic Games. Originally considered too dangerous for women, in 1887 the first women's field hockey club appeared in England. Today, the sport is enjoyed by women and men alike, with nearly 14,000 players, coaches, officials, and fans members of the U.S. Field Hockey Association.

BALL

BULLY

CAPTAIN

CENTER

CIRCLE

CORNER

DEFENSE

DODGE

DRILL

DRIVE

FIELD

FLAG

FLICK

FOOTWORK

FORWARD

FOUL

FREE HIT

FULLBACK

GOALKEEPER

HALFBACK

INNER

PUSH

REVERSE

ROLL IN

SCOOP

SHIN GUARDS

SQUAD

STICK

STROKE

WING

```
L T U N G T H D B A U S U A
V L R N R T D R A W R O F A
R A I S D E P I R E D S C G
A W W R N O V V P E T E U L
E O G R D H D E F E N S E F
W T D A Y E E G R T D R K L
N K U K L K Q A E S L I O I
H Q C C L F T R E W E N R C
S D R A U G N I H S I N T K
K I O B B I P F I A F E S T
C G L L L F O O T W O R K H
I Y Q L O L L P O Q N L R K
T O O U D G A A R C H G W F
S R L F C C A B H H S U P Y
```

ADD A "W"

By adding the letter "W" to the terms found in this puzzle, you'll form a different word. See if you can complete the "HOLE" puzzle without a "RINKLE," and remember that you are looking for the words as they appear here.

ADDLE
ALLOW
AVER
EASEL
EAVE
EBBING
EDGE
EIGHT
HALE
HEAT
HEEL
HELM
HELP
HENCE
HERE
HITHER
HOLE
HOLLY
HOPPER
HOSE
INCH
INNING
OMEN
RACK
RANGLE
RAPPER
RATH
REAK

REATH
RECK
RENCH
REST
RIGGLE
RING

RINKLE
RIST
RITE
RONG
ROTE
RUNG

```
N D G W H V T Y B R H E S R
E T I B O S T A H A R O T E
E V M P I L N E E T I R L T
L L S M T Y L L O H E K W E
G D G B K P D A G G N I R S
G E D N C D R H D I C N W O
I R V R A P P E R E P P O H
R I U A R R H L B R N H C V
M N U H E E L M K B I N A H
G N R A N A C H S T I S N L
T I K C C T S K H C N N T O
U N E B H H R E S T E T G O
Y G M A V E R M L M I T G R
P B G D I E G N O R I C S H
```

STREETS OF SAN FRANCISCO

The original name for San Francisco was *Yerba Buena*, which means "good herb" or "good grass." Volunteering is more popular in this city than in any other U.S. city, with approximately 82% of adults getting involved in some way or another. We've listed 37 streets of this fabulous city in the puzzle below.

BEALE	CLAY	FRANKLIN
BLUXOME	DRUMM	FRONT
BROADWAY	EDDY	GEARY
BUSH	ELLIS	GRANT
CEDAR	FERN	GREEN
CLARA	FILBERT	HYDE
		JESSIE
		JONES
		KING
		LAGUNA
		LARKIN
		LOMBARD
		MAIN
		MASON
		MINNA
		NATOMA
		OLIVE
		PINE
		POLK
		POST
		POWELL
		SPEAR
		TEHAMA
		TURK
		UNION

```
P A Y D A M O T A N E E R G
T N F R A E P S F R X V N G
H N E U P H N R Z X A I M J
F I R M T S O P T T K L O P
C M N M O N I O M N B O C V
N E K G T X N W S A K S V P
N T D Y M R U E E R I E I H
I D R A B M O L A G U N A P
L A S W R E L L B C E O G B
K O M D X I H V L Y L J E H
N T Q A S S V Y F D G A S J
A J U O H S J M D D L U Y C
R R Y R A E G T R E B L I F
F Q Q B K J T R N I K R A L
```

WORDS FOLLOWED BY "SHIP"

All hands on deck as you sail through the diagram below and find the 30 hidden terms that can be followed by "ship" to form new words.

AUTHOR

COMRADE

COURT

CRAFTSMAN

DEALER

DIRECTOR

FELLOW

FRIEND

GOVERNOR

GUARDIAN

HARD

HORSEMAN

INTERN

JUDGE

KING

LEADER

LORD

MARKSMAN

MEMBER

OWNER

PARTNER

PENMAN

QUEEN

SALESMAN

SCHOLAR

SHOWMAN

SPONSOR

STEWARD

TOWN

WORKMAN

```
S D E N A M W O H S D G A C
C I I N T E R N A M K R O W
H E T R F E L L O W L M A Q
O W R O N L E A D E R S F H
L G U W W S M N D A P S K N
A O O N M N A I D R A U G F
R V C A R M R E B M E M H K
P E N M E E K N D R M R M D
A R N S C R S P O N S O R N
U N R T F E M N A E E A K R
T O O F R L A M E G W I C A
H R V A O A N A D E N A R G
O I P R A E P U T C U I K F
R C D C P D J S I G B Q K Q
```

226

HIGH FLYIN'

This is your **CAPTAIN** speaking. Grab a pencil, put your seat in an upright position, and prepare for **TAKEOFF!** Can you prove you're a **FIRST CLASS** solver and find these 35 words that all relate to a plane **TRIP**?

ALTITUDE
ARRIVAL
ATTENDANT
BAGGAGE
BLANKET
CABIN
CAPTAIN
CART
CLEARANCE
COACH
DEPLANE
FARE
FIRST CLASS
FLIGHT
FUEL
GALLEY
GATE
MAGAZINE
MEAL
MOVIE
PASSENGERS
PEANUTS
PILOT
RAMP
RUNWAY
SEATBELT
TAKEOFF
TAXI
TERMINAL
TICKET
TRAVEL
TRAY
TRIP
WINDOW
WING

```
T T R I P R E N A L P E D R
C E X D Z M T N I B A C I S
L A K S P E A N U T S E V H
T T P C F D G R Y S S G M O
E T L T I U L T A K E O F F
B R O E A T E L W I N D O W
M A A C B I C L A F G N I W
O V G F D T N A D N E T T A
V E F G S L A N I M R E T R
I L L R A A R E B T S K U R
E N I Z A G A M S X R N Y I
V F G A L L E Y D V W A F V
B A H H P I L O T A R L C A
T H T C O A C H Y T V B Y L
```

Are you EAGER to get started on this puzzle? We bet you'll feel ELAT-ED when every last term that can describe someone in a good mood has been circled in the diagram.

AIRY

BLITHE

BREEZY

BRIGHT

BUBBLY

BUOYANT

CAREFREE

CHEERY

DELIGHTED

EAGER

EBULLIENT

EFFERVES-CENT

ELATED

FREE

GENIAL

GLAD

GLEEFUL

HAPPY

JOLLY

JOVIAL

JOYFUL

KEEN

LIGHT

MELLOW

MERRY

MIRTHFUL

NICE

OPEN

OPTIMISTIC

SERENE

SUNNY

WARM

```
T D V E B U L L I E N T A C
A I E K J U U U U G V D H E
G E P T I F O F S F L E F T
B C H K H S O Y K E E A N N
W F L T U G E O A R R E D A
A T R N I A I J Y N C E L D
R I N E G L J L M S T R N G
M Y Z E E R B A E A N F E E
D P R K P B B V L D K E Y N
C P K R U O R E L L N R L I
J A R B E E I J O V I A L A
C H M M F M G R W A C C O L
O C K F V T H G I L E M J P
F Z E A C I T S I M I T P O
```

Located on Long Island Sound, New Haven, Connecticut, is the home of many historical sites and Yale University, alma mater of the last three U.S. Presidents (George H. W. Bush, Bill Clinton, and George W. Bush). The city's famous residents have included Samuel F. B. Morse, Noah Webster, and Eli WHITNEY. Listed below are 37 streets of New Haven.

ARCH
AVON
CARMEL
CHAPEL
CHURCH
COLLEGE
COTTAGE
COURT
CROWN
DIXWELL
EDGEWOOD
ELLIOT
FOSTER
GRAND
GROVE
HOWARD
HUDSON
JAMES
LEGION
LIBERTY
LINCOLN
LINDEN
MUNSON
NASH
OLIVE
ORANGE
ORCHARD
PARK
PLATT
SPRING
SYLVAN
TEMPLE
TRUMBULL
WATER
WHITNEY
WILLOW
YORK

```
R L E M R A C O T T A G E O
L E G I O N W O R C T H N R
Y T T A L P H H U D S O N C
T J N A V L Y S M R S W H H
R C A C W K W A B N T A C A
E L P M E T H N U B C R R R
B Y T V E R I M L O A D U D
I G O K W S T R L E P A H C
L R I R N F N L E X A S C O
G A L A K E E J W T P V Q R
K N L P D G Y V X R S P O A
D D E N E Q L L I N C O L N
Z W I L L O W N D L Y D F G
G L B T E D G E W O O D X E
```

MIND OVER MATTER

START to REVISE the look of the diagram below by circling 33 ways in which the mind can work.

ADAPT

ADDLE

AGITATE

ALTER

AROUSE

CARE

CLEAN

CONVERT

DIFFER

EDIT

FIRE

HESITATE

IDEA

PROD

REDEEM

REFRESH

RENEW

REVAMP

REVERSE

REVISE

SHIFT

SHUFFLE

START

STIR

SWAY

TEMPER

TRADE

UNDO

VARY

VEER

WANE

WAVER

WIDEN

S	D	A	L	T	E	R	A	R	O	U	S	E	G
I	V	O	N	N	L	S	G	L	I	H	V	H	E
G	E	N	A	W	O	R	I	N	P	Y	G	U	T
Y	N	E	S	D	I	M	T	V	A	R	Y	L	I
G	L	G	N	T	P	M	A	V	E	R	O	O	D
C	Y	R	S	F	H	W	T	V	T	R	A	D	E
E	O	V	W	I	S	L	E	Y	S	F	I	N	A
O	I	N	N	H	I	R	M	L	I	F	M	U	W
P	P	T	V	S	S	N	P	R	F	I	A	L	N
V	W	P	T	E	M	E	E	E	F	E	V	U	
N	C	A	L	R	R	D	R	D	W	N	U	A	U
U	R	D	V	F	E	T	A	T	I	S	E	H	A
T	D	A	L	E	Y	E	C	Y	A	W	S	W	S
A	N	H	M	R	R	I	V	N	C	O	T	W	L

LOGO MANIA

Hey, sports fans! Proudly declare your team spirit and support by finding all of the items listed here that can be adorned with team logos.

BACKPACK

BATHROBE

BEDSHEETS

BLANKET

CLOCK

COMFORTER

CURTAINS

DECAL

DINNERWARE

JACKET

JERSEY

KEY CHAIN

KNIT CAP

MAGNET

MOUSE PAD

POSTER

SCARF

SOCKS

STICKER

SWEAT PANTS

SWEAT SHIRT

THERMOS

TOWEL

TUMBLER

UMBRELLA

WALLET

WATCH

```
J C A Y Y W F P O S T E R S
S T E E H S D E B M E N T O
W E B O R H T A B L K I M C
E E L S W A T C H I C D F K
A Y A C U C W R E K A E O S
T N N A O S U R E P J C H O
S K K R U M B R E L L A G M
H C E F L K F S T N B L L R
I A T Y C E U O M A N M W E
R P E O C O W A R M I I U H
T K L J M H G O S T T N D T
O C L S T N A P T A E W S N
A A A M E D G I Y E S R E J
A B W T Y Y A K N I T C A P
```

A KNIGHT'S ARMOR

We're throwing down the GAUNTLET and challenging you to find all the words associated with armor hidden in this puzzle. May luck be with you, good solver.

AILETTE

BEAVER

BRIGANDINE

CHAIN MAIL

CUIRASS

CUISSE

ELBOW (piece)

FAULD

FOOTPIECE

GAUNTLET

GORGET

GREAVE

HAUBERK

HEAUME

HELMET

KNEEPIECE

PALLETTE

PAULDRON

PLACATE

PLASTRON

PLATE

POLEYN

SHOULDER (piece)

SOLLERET

SURCOAT

TASSE

TUILLE

VAMBRACE

VISOR

```
R W F O O T P I E C E C V G
W O V P B T K A H P N A L R
T B S F U R I A L O U I P E
E L L I E I I H I L G L L A
M E L B V N E G O E E E A V
L L U V M A W S A Y L T S E
E A P A U L D R O N E T T C
H C I M E S H O U L D E R E
C L E B F T D R T R R I O I
U H W R C A A N E E E G N P
I S S A R I U C L V T T D E
S U R C O A T L A Y A P I E
S I T E G R O G D L L E H N
E N V E S S A T A H P I B K
```

232

IN THE RED!

Curious as to what these 40 words have in common? They're all things that can be red in color. You can CHALK up another solving win if you're successful in finding them all.

AUTOMOBILE
BARN
BASKET
BELT
BICYCLE
BIRD
BLENDER

BOOK COVER
CHAIRS
CHALK
COAT
CRAYON
CURTAINS
DESK

FOLDERS
GLOVES
HAIR
HOUSE
JACKET
JEANS
KEY CHAIN
LAMP
LUGGAGE
PAINT
PANTS
PENCIL
PURSE
RADIO
SCARF
SHIRT
SHOES
SOCKS
STAPLER
SWEATER
TELEPHONE
VEST
WAGON
WALL
WALLET
WATCH

```
J B C O A T E L E P H O N E
H S R E D L O F A P U R S E
Y C J E C I S C U B A R N A
D H T Y D R P H T E K C A J
R A C A H N A S O C K S E D
I I R O W F E Y M E V T J R
B R U W R V P L O F S N B E
B S Y A O E R J B N W A T V
E T C L N W T E I A S P A O
L S G C N T A A L K L A H C
T R I H S O T L E P I I A K
Y L R N B R G T L W A N I O
P M A L U G G A G E S T R O
K E Y C H A I N W U T R S B
```

234

WHOLLY HOLY

If you're a fan of the "Batman" TV series, you know that one of the show's most memorable features was Robin's expressive catchphrases. The excitable Boy Wonder kept viewers chuckling with exclamations such as "Holy FLYPAPER" and "Holy MUSH." Use your batpencils and search for 32 of Robin's "holy" phrases.

AGILITY

ALTER EGO

AUDUBON

BANKS

BAT-TRAP

BIJOU

CARUSO

COSMOS

D'ARTAGNAN

EDISON

FLYPAPER

GEMINI

GREED

HOUDINI

JET SET

KOUFAX

MATADOR

MOLARS

MUSH

NAIVETÉ

OLEO

OXYGEN

RAVIOLI

RELIEF

SMOKE

STEREO

TEN TOES

TOME

TUXEDO

UNLIKELIHOOD

WIGS

ZORRO

```
K  B  I  J  O  U  T  C  O  S  M  O  S  O
I  A  A  O  S  U  R  A  C  D  O  M  R  T
L  N  M  F  X  N  E  G  Y  X  O  R  A  F
O  K  A  E  B  L  A  J  Y  K  O  E  L  O
I  S  D  I  R  I  Y  N  E  Z  H  Y  O  P
V  O  Z  L  V  K  G  T  G  T  P  I  M  W
A  L  T  E  R  E  G  O  A  A  S  I  M  P
R  U  F  R  M  L  T  M  P  T  T  E  A  Y
W  I  D  I  S  I  C  E  E  C  D  R  T  X
U  J  N  U  S  H  R  R  N  I  T  I  A  P
L  I  V  G  B  O  E  P  S  T  L  V  D  D
I  N  I  D  U  O  H  O  A  I  O  M  O  P
E  W  Y  P  G  D  N  B  G  D  E  E  R  G
N  J  T  K  O  U  F  A  X  M  M  U  S  H
```

When preparing to step out for the day, knowing the weather conditions and temperature can be very important. This way, if your local forecaster is calling for RAINY or SNOWY weather, you'll be prepared. Search for the 35 terms below which you are likely to hear from a meteorologist.

BALMY	CHILLY	CRISP
BITTER	CLEAR	DISMAL
BREEZY	CLOUDY	DREARY
BRIGHT	COLD	FAIR
CALM	COOL	FOGGY
		FRIGID
		GLOOMY
		GRAY
		GUSTY
		HAZY
		HUMID
		MILD
		MISTY
		MUGGY
		NIPPY
		RAINY
		SNOWY
		STICKY
		STILL
		STORMY
		SULTRY
		SUNNY
		WARM
		WINDY
		WINTRY

```
Y Y H F K K P L B O T P C U
T B A L M Y Y C Y M R O T S
S C M R D Z Z R A E L C H T
U O Z U G E A E T D H A O I
G O O F Y E H T Y L L I H C
M L T W R R D T G R U T D K
C H O D C B R I G H T S I Y
R N B O Y R P B U N E N G D
S W A R M N I M M M I G I H
K U I G I Y I S L P O S R W
I K N L S D A A P F M T F F
A K I N T N C Y R A M I E A
R P N Y Y I N M L I W L L B
T O Y F L W Z R D R Y L K D
```

We'll have to call you on the carpet if you don't have fun finding the 30 items that can be found on top of wall-to-wall carpeting!

AREA RUG

BUREAU

CHAIR

CHEST

CONSOLE

COUCH

CREDENZA

CRIB

DAYBED

DESK

DRESSER

ÉTAGÈRE (set of open shelves)

FUTON

HIGHBOY

HUTCH

LAMP

LOVE SEAT

OTTOMAN

PIANO

PLAYPEN

RECLINER

ROCKER

SCREEN

SETTEE

SIDEBOARD

STOOL

TABLE

TORCHIER (floor lamp)

TRUNK

VANITY

```
K U V I D U H P P G D M D A
C T Y S R E N I L C E R Y F
B H K C C D L E U A E R U B
C U E E E R A O P S M T C S
U T O S I A E C S Y O P F L
H C K A T O C E O N A I P N
Y H H H B B R P N L O L Z R
G C H Y B E E H O K I C P N
L U D I T D D V I K N U R T
T O R C H I E R E G A T E H
D C O A C S N B A Z H L K P
S E T T E E Z A Y B B B C H
R B D A S R A R V A A I O O
E O T T O M A N T Z D P R Y
```

IF I KNEW YOU WERE COMING

APPROACH this puzzle in your usual style and find the 35 ways to **REACH** a destination. If you're planning on doing any traveling soon, don't forget to bring some puzzles along to help pass the time.

ALIGHT

ANCHOR

APPEAR

APPROACH

ARISE

ARRIVE

CHECK IN

CLOCK IN

CROP UP

DEBARK

DEPLANE

DESCEND

DETRAIN

DISMOUNT

DOCK

EMERGE

ENTER

FLY IN

GET IN

GET THERE

HIT TOWN

LAND

MAKE PORT

PARK

PERCH

POP UP

PUNCH IN

REACH

ROLL IN

SHOW UP

STEP IN

SURFACE

TOUCH DOWN

TURN UP

WALK IN

```
F K K A P P E A R R C S C O
A C C N H P R O L L I N H S
L R T O U C H D O W N I E E
I O R N D C H C R E P P C R
G P R I N H K R Y H C E K E
H U U A V I C N W O T T I H
T P V C N E C A F R U S N T
Y O M B S T N U O M S I D T
P P K I L I H P A R K E E E
N U R R H I E C F L P M T G
H A W C A K D N A L C P R R
Y V N O A B A W A E Y B A E
A U U M H C E N T E R I I M
P D N E C S E D G E T I N E
```

"S" BOYS NAMES

A baby's name should have positive connotations, as names make strong first impressions. Try to imagine the child using the name not only on the playground but also as an adult. Here are some examples of names for boys that begin with the letter "S."

SANFORD

SCHUYLER

SCOTT

SEBOLD

SEDGWICK

SELWYN

SETH

SEYMOUR

SHAWN

SHELBY

SHELLEY

SHERIDAN

SHERLOCK

SHERWIN

SIDNEY

SIGMUND

SILAS

SIMON

SINCLAIR

SOLOMON

SPENCER

STACEY

STAFFORD

STANLEY

STANTON

STEFAN

STEPHEN

STERLING

STEWART

SYLVESTER

```
P E D N S N A D I R E H S E
T S L Y A H I D K U T W T R
W I O W N R E C N E P S E U
U D B L F I O L S U L M F O
G N E E O L W K B I M N A M
N E S S R M C R S Y I G N Y
I Y N E D I O T E R R Y I E
L N H O W Y A N E H P E T S
R S O G M F E L C A S L W T
E I D T F I Y C C L A L H E
T E L O N U S T A N L E Y W
S T R S H A W N N T I H W A
D D S C O T T L H F S S F R
M V S Y L V E S T E R N L T
```

YOU GOTTA HAVE HEARTH

When the weather outside is frightful, the best place to be solving puzzles is surrounded by the WARMTH of a roaring FIRE. So get COZY, and find these items that may be found on or near your HEARTH.

ANDIRON

ASHES

BELLOWS

BRICKS

BROOM

CHIMNEY

COZY

DAMPER

DRAFT

EMBERS

FIRE

FLAME

FLUE

FUEL

GLOW

HEARTH

HEAT

KINDLING

LOGS

MANTLE

MATCH

PAPER

POKER

SCREEN

SHOVEL

SMOKE

TONGS

WARMTH

WOOD

```
R D P G T P O Y M K U B H P
L T L S R E B M E I Z L I A
T O N G S C R E E N Z D N H
W H F E L E Y M L D M O A E
S N B D U K A E A L R I S S
T T L L O L V M S I O P H K
Y T F T F O P A D N S W E C
S Z M A H E W N H G V A S I
D M O S R M A T C H W D G R
G G O C W D R L G B R F O B
M D R K P A M E N A M K L O
Y B B H E A T U K Z K W V B
G T K H U H H F Y O A S H A
Y K W V F I R E P A P N B S
```

PLENTY OF PRONOUNS

We have gathered 32 pronouns for you to uncover in the grid below.

ANOTHER

ANYBODY

ANYONE

ANYTHING

EACH

EVERYBODY

EVERYONE

HERSELF

ITSELF

MANY

MINE

MYSELF

NOBODY

NONE

OTHERS

OURSELVES

SOME

SUCH

THAT

THEIR

THEM

THEMSELVES

THESE

THEY

THIS

THOSE

WHAT

WHERE

WHICH

WHOM

WHOSE

YOUR

```
O S O W G T A H W H E H M H
M M S U C H T H I S F R S F
Y S S D R O O N T N V L I L
D B E R N S T F N H A A S E
O L U V E E L L F V M H S
B O M F L S Y L L E O A S R
Y R N W H E R E V H S N S E
R D A A S H S E W E Y Y V H
E M O S N T R M E A S B M T
V H H B I Y H N E C W O B O
E M H C O H O E T H T D T N
D G L N G N G N I H T Y N A
W U E N I M E C E R A T I U
E D N Y S D H M Y E H T E L
```

241

I ACCEPT!

All of the terms in this puzzle are things that can be accepted. Of course we can't AWARD you any MONEY for completing it, but we can REWARD you with PRAISE and an INVITATION to remain a respected solver. Now that's an OFFER you can't refuse.

ADVICE

APOLOGY

AWARD

BLESSING

BONUS

CHECK

CONTRACT

CRITICISM

DONATION

EXCUSE

FAVOR

GRATUITY

INVITATION

MEDAL

MONEY

OFFER

PAYMENT

PLAQUE

POSITION

PRAISE

PRESENT

PRIZE

PROMOTION

PROPOSAL

RESIGNATION

REWARD

SITUATION

TROPHY

```
C H E C K T N R I F A V O R
R P I N V I T A T I O N E O
I E R N E S U C X E O W T P
T U S O F F E R A I A N W R
I Q U I P S K N T R E Y N A
C A N T G O K I D M T E Y I
I L O O R N S H Y I P N L S
S P B M I O A A U G R O O E
M F O O P T P T L G E M I C
A W A R D O A H I H S H M I
X X I P L R K U Y O E A E V
Y Z X O G N O I T A N O D D
E W G Q T S Z K E I T H A A
C Y H T H F G N I S S E L B
```

A BEVY OF B'S

241

You may **BUBBLE** over with enthusiasm as you tackle this puzzle. There are 35 words hidden in the diagram that contain the letter "B" at least two times. You deserve a blue **RIBBON** if you find them all!

ABSORB

BABBLE

BABY

BARBECUE

BARBELL

BARBER

BASEBALL

BILLBOARD

BLUEBELL

BLUEBERRY

BOBBER

BOBBIN

BOBCAT

BRAMBLE

BUBBLE

BULB

BUMBLEBEE

CABBAGE

CRIBBAGE

DABBLE

EBBED

HOBBLE

HOBBY

KNOBBY

LOBBY

PEBBLE

RABBIT

RHUBARB

RIBBON

RUBBER

RUBBLE

SCRIBBLE

SUBSCRIBE

TABBY

WOBBLE

```
S B C H U K T S Y Y Y P N B
H U A Y N D A B B L E E C R
B O B O B N M A R M G B H O
D R B S T B O B I E A U Y S
Y B A B C B O B A R B E R B
Y A G M L R I L B A B B Y A
B S E U B E I E R I I R U T
B E B B I L L B O A R D Y R
A B U M B L E B E E C A B A
T A B T A C B O B B E R B B
E L B B U R Y E N I B B O B
T L L E B E U L B C R E H I
C P E B B L E S O E R C D T
W K E L B B O W M B C G S M
```

243

HUNTING, OF A SORT

Hidden away in the diagram below are 29 ways to describe the act of pursuit. So DIG DEEP in the diagram, and see how quickly you can TRACK these tricky terms!

BURROW

CAST ABOUT

CHASE

COMB

DELVE

DIG DEEP

DOWSE

EXPLORE

FERRET

FOLLOW

FORAGE

HUNT

INVESTIGATE

LOOK FOR

PROBE

PROSPECT

PURSUE

QUEST

ROOT

RUMMAGE

SCAN

SCOUR

SCOUT

SEARCH

SEEK

SLEUTH

TRACE

TRACK

TRAIL

```
L U C F S U O E A L I A R T
Q P R K P D M T I N H E X P
T R A C E E V I V K G M H E
O O V L E E B E H A F T F S
S B V U D U S U R E O S I A
P E M S G T S O R O L H H H
R C S W I B F R R R L A W C
O F O G D K E V U U O P X R
S Q A M O T V G K P W W X A
P T U O B A T S A C X N L E
E S L E U T H V A M A Q A S
C K W Q S R A E B C M R N W
T N U H M T V R S C O U T O
M A Q E B B Q A S C O U R D
```

TOUR OF INDIA

At over 28,000 feet, the Indian peak Kanchenjunga is the world's third highest mountain. Due to its steep altitudes, not many of the more than 1 billion Indian people reside there. Instead, they're scattered among such cities as **CALCUTTA**, **MADRAS**, and others listed below.

AGRA

AHMADABAD

AJMER

BANGALORE

BARODA

BHOPAL

BOMBAY

CALCUTTA

CALICUT

DHULE

HYDERABAD

INDORE

JABALPUR

JAIPUR

JHANSI

KANPUR

KOTA

MADRAS

MADURAI

MEERUT

MYSORE

NAGPUR

NEW DELHI

PATNA

PUNE

RAIPUR

RAMPUR

SAGAR

SALEM

SURAT

UJJAIN

VARANASI

```
C A C R A G A S U R A T O K
T U A N B E M D I S N A H J
D R T L R M E E R U T A Y I
B A B H H N O L L T B I D N
P H B O I J M H U A J M E R
I U O A M A I C N H S W R V
B I J P D B L G R R D Y A P
T J P U A A A C E N R B I
U S R N C L M Y L B A A A J
C A I E O P Y H A N G P D J
I R G R U U I R A I P U R W
L D E R E R O S Y M U B B U
A A O B A D I N D O R E P P
C M L K A N P U R U P I A J
```

STREETS OF FORT WORTH

Will Rogers once referred to Fort Worth as "where the West begins." Established as a military post in 1849, this Texas city is now home to two international airports, eight universities and colleges, and a population of more than half a million people. You won't need a map to find the streets of Fort Worth we've hidden in the grid below.

ADAMS
BLUFF
BURNETT
CALHOUN
CEDAR
CHERRY

COLLIER
CROCKETT
CRUMP
DARCY
DELGA
DEXTER

EVANS
GRANT
GREER
HARLEY
HAYS
JONES
LAKE
LAMAR
LINDEN
LIVE OAK
LOCKE
LOCUST
MACON
MAIN
MAPLE
MORTON
NICHOLS
NOWLIN
PEACH
PECAN
PHARR
STARK
SWIFT
TERRY
WALL
WINDMILL

```
S R X M A C O N U O H L A C
E T E R R Y I H X W D S C R
N K P W Y C R A D E C N U O
O H C E H M O R T O N A K C
J S V O A B F L E V F V P K
U P L P L C P E L H M E A E
R S L U H C H Y W I C O N T
K E F L G R A N T A E I K T
D F E E I U R D N V L R R E
D A K R S M R E I W N L E N
E A R M G P D L O C U S T R
L L A K E N T N G F Y F X U
G D T F I W S N I A M R E B
A I S L A M A R H W J N D M
```

GHOST TOWNS

During the mining boom in the Old West, many small towns sprang up virtually overnight, but were vacated as soon as the mines were exhausted. They're now known as ghost towns, and the names of 28 located in Montana and Idaho make up the word list here.

BAY HORSE*

BEAR-
   MOUTH**

BONANZA*

BURKE*

CABLE**

CUSTER*

DE LAMAR*

ELKHORN**

GARNET**

GILMORE*

GILTEDGE**

GOLD
   CREEK**

GRANITE**

KENDALL**

KEYSTONE**

LAURIN**

LEESBURG*

MAIDEN**

MAMMOTH**

MURRAY*

PARDEE**

PIONEER**

PONY**

RIMINI**

SHOUP*

SILVER CITY*

WARREN*

ZORTMAN**

*Idaho
**Montana

```
H R P S I L V E R P L V L W
W V L O M N N V T R P E Y K
A Z N A N O B R Z I E Z H G
D W C I T Y O C O D N T G W
E C U S T E R N R H O A A U
B L Y A K A E A T M K R R M
T E B K M E P U M N R L N G
K G A A R C E A A E Y A E V
E D L R C I M R N D A Z T E
N E R O M L I G C I R Z K P
D T C P U O H S T A R R W A
A L E E S B U R G M U U G H
L I N I M I R T E B M R A Y
L G O L D B A Y H O R S E L
```

May 22 to June 21 marks the third sign of the zodiac, Gemini. Gemini is the sign of duality, hence its symbol of the twins. Geminis are ADAPTABLE, CHATTY, NERVOUS, and VERSATILE. They are also very RESTLESS as they need change and excitement in their lives. Johnny Depp, Nicole Kidman, and Patti LaBelle are just a few famous folks who were born under this sign. Reel in 28 traits that describe Geminis.

ADAPTABLE

ASTUTE

CAREFUL

CHATTY

COMPLEX

COURTEOUS

CULTURED

CUNNING

CURIOUS

ELOQUENT

ELUSIVE

FICKLE

FLIGHTY

GENEROUS

IMPATIENT

KIND

LIVELY

LOVING

NERVOUS

PLAYFUL

QUICK

REFINED

RESTLESS

SMART

TALKATIVE

VERSATILE

WITTY

YOUTHFUL

```
F E E L B A T P A D A C G V
N L T M P S L L D C E U E Y
E T I U E L U S I V E R P P
R N F G T F Y O I N S I K L
V E F I H S U T R A D O C A
O U S T C T A O T E O U I Y
U Q U T U K Y I N A N S U F
S O O C L E L I E N H E Q U
Y L E A T E F E I Y T C G L
L E T R U E S N T R T V I Q
E Q R E R K G S A C Q T K B
V Y U F E C O M P L E X I V
I Y O U D E S P M Q N F N W
L W C L D G G N I V O L D T
```

WASHINGTON'S TOWNS

AMBER, GEORGE, and JOYCE can all be found in the state of Washington. The names of these three towns, plus 27 others are hidden in the diagram below.

ALOHA	OTHELLO	SAPPHO
AMBER	PASCO	TIGER
BUENA	PE ELL	TWISP
FARMER	PLAIN	YELM
FIFE	QUEETS	ZILLAH
FORKS		
GEORGE		
HOQUIAM		
INDEX		
IONE		
JOYCE		
KELSO		
KENT		
KLICKITAT		
LA PUSH		
LEBAM		
LIND		
MEAD		
NEAH BAY		
OMAK		

```
S L W K D O S L E K N J H N
D T S A P P H O L C Y S N P
Y C E L F S I L O K Y S J X
N M A E U Z I L L A H O L A
S I F P U K R E B M A T J R
R M A I U Q O H N O M W E S
I L N L F T A T I K C I L K
C E E I P E P O E F P S A R
K Y U B N B G K D A O P U O
D P B O A D Q R S R A P T F
E Z I K N M E C O M E R D C
R K G I C G O X G E G G O O
P O L C I H Z M L R G G Q S
K E N T D L Y L S F N Z Y B
```

You might call this a handyman's special. All of the terms hidden in the grid below are items that can be found in a workshop.

APRON

BRUSH

CHISEL

CLAMP

COMPRESSOR

DRILL

FILE

FUSE

GLUE

GREASE

GRINDER

HAMMER

LEVEL

MALLET

MILLER

NAIL

OILER

PAINT

PLIERS

PULLER

RASP

REAMER

ROUTER

SANDER

SANDPAPER

SCREW

SHAPER

SOLDER

SQUARE

TAPE

TORCH

TROWEL

VARNISH

WASHER

WHETSTONE

WIRE

```
S Q U A R E H S A W N S N V
H A F U S E T E C R V W A B
S P N F M N D D P E V R I E
U H M D I T U L I A N E S H
R D A A P R O N O I T A A L
B W P P L A W W S S E M N R
H R I L E C P H R R M E D W
V G L R V R Q E G E F R E L
G D F F E E I T R H T R R E
D R I L L L E S I H C U H W
S E L P P L I T N S O R O O
P U E S L I R O D O W I O R
P L N A P M G N E P H L P T
U G M R O S S E R P M O C U
```

ORDERS TO THE CHEF

If the Style Network is part of your cable TV package, perhaps you've watched British culinary personality Nigella Lawson's show "Forever Summer with Nigella." In each half-hour episode you might see Lawson **BASTE, BEAT, CHOP, DICE, GARNISH, GRIND, SHRED,** or **STUFF** some ingredients as she prepares the featured meal. At the **CORE** of this puzzle is a collection of 38 cooking verbs.

BAKE
BARBECUE
BASTE
BEAT
BLEND
BRAISE
BROIL
BROWN
CHOP
CODDLE
CORE
CRUSH
CUBE
DICE
DRAIN
DREDGE
DRESS
FILLET
FREEZE
GARNISH
GRATE
GRILL
GRIND
MARINATE
MASH
MELT
MINCE
PARBOIL

POACH
SAUTÉ
SHRED
SIMMER
SLICE

STEAM
STEW
STIR
STUFF
WHIP

```
L N D R E C I D C E A A T W
E N W M G B B O N A K L M N
I D E O A G R W H I P A C G
C L R D R E M M I S R W B G
T E B A N B T D I I L G W S
T Z T A I T K S N N P T W E
D E R H S N S A D E C A S H
D E S L H T T F I L L E T P
E R S H I E E C I L S B U M
C F E R L O W E I I A P F K
M T R D F K B R A O U H F M
L M D M G U G R W R T F T A
U O E U C E B R A B E H R S
C R U S H N C H O P O A C H
```

250

Did you know that major credit for the discovery and charting of the FIJI Islands goes to Captain William Bligh of the HMS *Bounty*? After being cast adrift by the ship's mutinous crew in 1789, he passed through this southwestern Pacific island group in his open longboat and returned to explore it in 1792. An archipelago consisting of several hundred islands, Fiji won its independence from Great Britain in 1970 after being a crown colony for 96 years.

BALI

BORNEO

CHRISTMAS

FIJI

GUADALCANAL

GUAM

HAWAII

HONSHU

IWO JIMA

JAVA

KAUAI

KING

LOYALTY

LUZON

MANUA

MAUI

MIDWAY

NEW GUINEA

NEW ZEALAND

NORTH

OAHU

PITCAIRN

SADDLE

SAIPAN

SOLOMON

SUMATRA

TAHITI

TASMANIA

TRUK

WAKE

```
L T L Y V L O L U Z O N C L
F J R U C T W A K E L W P L
T C V M H U A I N A M S A T
S A S W R A I R O F U N E U
A O H G I W O J I M A A N H
I K L I S B V N I C U E I S
P F O O T R R F L F W L U N
A L Y B M I U A M Z A M G O
N E A Y A O D H E B A P W H
H A L C S A N A T T W M E J
O O T D U Y L W R R A H N C
C I Y G D A V A J U O N L J
P R A U N A M I G K I N G U
Y A W D I M S I M Y U A D N
```

MAKE A CHANGE

It's been said that the more things CHANGE, the more they remain the same. ALTER the look of the diagram below by circling 29 terms that describe ways to make changes.

ADAPT

ADJUST

ALTER

AMEND

CHANGE

CONVERT

DEVIATE

DIVERSIFY

EDIT

EMEND

FLUCTUATE

INNOVATE

MODIFY

MODULATE

REDO

REFORM

RESHAPE

REVAMP

REVERSE

REVISE

REVOLUTIONIZE

ROTATE

SHIFT

SWITCH

TRANSFER

TRANSFORM

TRANSMUTE

VARIEGATE

VARY

```
M N H Y F I S R E V I D E Y
Z R E V O L U T I O N I Z E
T R O C P M A V E R E D O F
P E L F W G R M W C T U F S
A F T R E V N O C S U M W M
D S L I D R L D F O M P I O
A N R U H C T I W S S N E D
M A E I C E P F T H N P V U
V R T M G T J Y I O A A M L
F T L N A A U F V H R D R A
O F A E D I T A S Y T J M T
J H F I W V T E T W N U I E
C E S I V E R E V E R S E G
V E M E N D S R O T A T E G
```

It's time for a shopping spree! As you browse the word list below, see if you can find these women's clothing items in the diagram. We know you bargain hunters won't be able to resist this!

APRON

BIKINI

BLAZER

BLOUSE

CAFTAN

CAPE

CARDIGAN

COAT

DRESS

GLOVES

GOWN

HOSE

JACKET

JEANS

LEOTARD

PONCHO

SARI

SCARF

SERAPE

SHEATH

SHOES

SHORTS

SKIRT

SLACKS

SMOCK

SUIT

SWEATER

VEST

WESKIT (a vest or waist-coat)

```
K K L C S F M W J P L D K W
K S B G O H O I T F R C E N
H F N E Z A O V L E O S M B
M C W O Z J T E S M K M L G
A V O U R R F S S I M C G L
J F G T I P C T T U P Z A N
P K B K N R A L M R O Z D J
O B S U I T F S E V O L G E
N A V E K C T T P O U H B M
C A R D I G A N A F T T S H
H W B I B E N P R E Z A L B
O H F V W S N A E J R E R H
S F T S L A C K S I W H D D
E Z N G G S O P W O I S Z V
```

SPELLING STUMPERS

The 32 words listed here have a reputation for being difficult to spell correctly, but you can rest assured that we've got 'em right!

ANOINT

BEIGE

CALENDAR

CEDE

COURIER

CURRENT

DYEING

ECSTASY

EXCITE

HARASS

INNOVATE

INOCULATE

KHAKI

KIMONO

LAVENDER

LIAISON

LIQUEFY

MAUVE

NAPHTHA

OCARINA

OCCASION

OCCURRENCE

PARALLEL

QUEUE

RAREFY

RAZE

RHYME

SEIZE

SHRIEK

SIEGE

WEIRD

WIELD

```
S X R G S I E G E U E U Q S
D Y E I N G E C S T A S Y E
L K I M O N O T W E I R D R
E H R E D N E V A L I C Y A
I A U N C E O N E V N Z X R
W K O D V N I L C G O M E E
C I C U R R E N T L I N N F
M L A A A L A R T I S E N Y
T M I C L P K A R Q A B B I
Q T O A H E T A L U C O N I
D R R T I S N E D E C X Z R
X A H R K S I D N F O C D A
P A H T N I O N A Y O P O Z
V S S A R A H N E R H Y M E
```

Chastity, courage, HONOR, loyalty, piety, and VALOR are the chief virtues of CHIVALRY, the system of ethical ideals that began in medieval days. Travel back and find 35 terms associated with the days of KING ARTHUR.

ARCHER
ARMOR
ARTHUR
BARON
CAMELOT
CASTLE

CHAIN MAIL
CHIVALRY
CRUSADE
DRAWBRIDGE
DUKE
EARL

ENGLAND
HELMET
HERALD
HERO
HONOR
KING
KNIGHTS
LADIES
LANCE
LEGEND
LORDS
MOAT
NOBLES
PAGE
PEASANTS
QUEEN
SERF
SHIELD
SQUIRE
STEED
SWORD
TITLE
VALOR

```
R Q S S U G Q W T M B V Y D
O K H T Y N L I S Q U I R E
V L I M O A T Q K P L A L G
Y L E B C L S V S I W R A A
F D L G E Y E D A B D Q V P
H E D A E K C M R L C Q I Y
S E C E D N N I A O O P H R
E T L D N I D R A C L R C R
F S A M A G E B A R O N O H
N S N H E H L S K U C M O L
L W C S E T T A I S R H R B
L O E K M S S T N A S A E P
K R U H T R A K G D E O H R
F D P M D D C Q U E E N E Y
```

STRAIGHT TALK

With the right STRATEGY, you should be able to take this puzzle in STRIDE. Search for all 31 words, each beginning with the letters "STR."

STRAGGLE

STRAIGHT

STRAIN

STRAIT

STRAND

STRANGE

STRAP

STRATEGY

STRAW

STRAY

STREAK

STREAM

STREET

STRENGTH

STRESS

STRETCH

STREW

STRICT

STRIDE

STRIKE

STRING

STRIPE

STRIVE

STROBE

STROKE

STROLL

STRONG

STRUDEL

STRUGGLE

STRUM

STRUT

```
G W W E R T S U S T R O L L
Y E K B D H U T T A V Y W E
A I K H N M S T R A I N A K
R U R O A T O N I I Y T R I
T G L E R H U O D G P E T R
S H R I T T C S E S Y E S T
I T N S S O S T T I A R T S
S G R S T K A R E R K T R T
T N S U E R U A V R A S O R
R E S S T D U I A S T N N I
A R G S E L G G A R T S G V
P T M L L R H H G C U R V E
K S T R I C T T L L L U U B
O P E B O R T S T R E A K M
```

Statistics show that the reading of ponderous, factual works of non-fiction falls off sharply as the temperature rises. That explains why you see more people reading ROMANCE and MYSTERY novels on the beach instead of BUSINESS and SCIENCE books.

ADVENTURE

BIOGRAPHY

BUSINESS

COMEDY

DRAMA

EPIC

FAIRY TALE

FASHION

FOOD

GARDENING

HEALTH

HISTORY

HOW-TO

INTRIGUE

JUVENILE

LOVE

MEMOIRS

MYSTERY

MYTH

OCCULT

POLITICS

RELIGION

ROMANCE

SAGA

SCIENCE

SCI-FI

SPACE

SPORTS

SUSPENSE

TRAVEL

WESTERN

```
N C T I H I S T O R Y S E H
R O M A N C E U G H P Y S T
E M E J R E H A S W H A N Y
T E D P U G U P M P G G O M
S D I S I V A G A A E A I Y
E Y N R T C E R I O R N H S
W L I H E R G N D R U D S T
O S A F T O O H I E T E A E
S C I T I L O P F L N N F R
I I H B Y C A W S I E I I Y
M E M O I R S E S G V V N F
O N W B W T I U H I D U O G
O C C U L T B A W O A O I L
L E V A R T O B F N D A L Y
```

STREETS OF ATLANTIC CITY

The streets of ATLANTIC City have been made famous by the popular board game Monopoly®. In fact, the names have become so well-known that, in 1972, when the Atlantic City public works commissioner wanted to change the name of BALTIC Avenue, there was a public outcry! Stroll down the boardwalk while you solve this puzzle featuring Atlantic City street names.

ARCTIC

ATLANTIC

BALTIC

BEACH

BELMONT

CASPIAN

CONGRESS

DEWEY

FLORIDA

ILLINOIS

INDIANA

KENTUCKY

LOGAN

MAINE

MARYLAND

MELROSE

MICHIGAN

MORRIS

NEW YORK

OHIO

PACIFIC

PARK

SEASIDE

STATE

ST. JAMES

SUNSET

TENNESSEE

TEXAS

VERMONT

VIRGINIA

```
T K R O Y W E N S R P U U C
B O E E Y K A M Y A L Y O I
T J W O O G C V O S X N U T
E E M I O P I U E R G E N L
D I H L H R U M T R R O T A
C O M L G C C V E N M I E B
I N D I A N A S K L E O S Y
T E N N E S S E E R R K N U
N I A O A D P B B M A O U T
A U L I R C I F I C A P S X
L X Y S C K A S X V F J S E
T I R B T E N I A M F N T G
A B A D I R O L F E T A T S
R X M I C H I G A N S K A K
```

DEEP-SEA LIFE

The SEA ROBIN is a reddish fish with winglike pectoral fins. This water-loving creature also has a broad head shielded with plates of bone. It lives in the benthos, the deepest part of the ocean. See if you can find the sea robin, along with 27 other deep-sea creatures.

ANEMONE

ANGLER

BLUEFISH

CLAM

CORAL

CRAB

EELPOUT

FLOUNDER

GULPER (eel)

HAGFISH

HALIBUT

LOBSTER

MACKEREL

MYSID (shrimp-like animal)

OARFISH

POLLOCK

PRAWN

SCULPIN

SEA ROBIN

SEA URCHIN

SEA WHIP

SKATE

SOLE

SPINY (dogfish)

SPONGE

STARFISH

VIPERFISH

WORM

```
O O K E T H S I F R E P I V
C I L H Y U N W A R P A A H
S O O E F S O I H T N F N R
S H B U K S B P B G L D E O
K T S A K C O L L O P G M A
I S T I N L K E U E R L O R
T E E H F E R N W E E A N F
R U R Y G R D U O Y F N E I
T R B N S E A U R C H I N S
M E O I R K N T M M T P S H
Y P B P L C B U S A I L S H
S L U S E A W H I P L U H G
I U W T R M H L A R O C K V
D G K C L U H A G F I S H P
```

ALL ABOARD!

Before you ARRIVE at the winner's STATION, you must travel LINE by line and TRACK down the following terms dealing with trains. Have a nice RIDE!

ABOARD

ARRIVE

BAGGAGE

BRIDGE

CABOOSE

CARGO

CARS

CITIES

COACH

COMMUTER

CONDUCTOR

DEPOT

ENGINE

EXPRESS

FREIGHT

LINE

LOCAL

PULLMAN

RAILS

RIDE

ROUTE

SCHEDULE

STATION

STEAM

STOP

SWITCH

TICKET

TOWNS

TRACK

TRANSIT

WHISTLE

```
B B L W A U N C E B D W T E
N R L F W T A B A V M I T L
S W I T C H A S C B W U O K
N M N D T G E H C A O C N D
W B E N G I N E D R A O B A
O S V A T E S B R L I N S D
T S G I I R V N I T O D R E
D E C A C F E I A G U U A P
X R H H K L T T R R H C C O
L P M A E T S A U R T T L T
G X A D T D C T A M A O A R
E E I B P F U I O I M R D A
R R B N A M L L U P K O W C
R O W H I S T L E B W I C K
```

AT THE CASINO

Why not try your LUCK at solving this puzzle that relates to casino ACTION? The ODDS are in your favor, and there's no RISK involved. Once you've circled all 30 terms, you'll be a WINNER!

ACTION

BACCARAT

BANK

BLACKJACK

BLUFF

CARDS

CROUPIER

DEALER

DICE

HOTEL

JACKPOT

KENO

LOUNGE

LUCK

MAXIMUM

MINIMUM

MONEY

ODDS

PAYOFF

POKER

RISK

ROULETTE

SEVEN

SLOTS

SPIN

STAKES

TABLE

WAGER

WHEEL

WINNER

```
S M P B B S R O U L E T T E
L E I A N N H P L E B V A F
O M F N W A O I N E T R B W
T W L J I U N I S H T L L J
S E V E N M P S T W A O E Y
H C A S N S U I I C R U H J
F I D Y E N O M K E A N S R
W D D F R K U J I N C G D O
O A F F O Y A P L X C E R G
R B G A L C U T B J A N A J
M X R E K O P N S L B M C C
G C Y P R N H Y E M U R I R
H B O C Y E A R I S K F D O
F T L U C K J B E S I X F J
```

"A" WORDS

Each of the words below starts and ends with the letter "A."

ABACA

ABRA-
  CADABRA

ACACIA

AFRICA

AGENDA

AGORA

ALFALFA

ALGEBRA

ALOHA

ALPACA

ALPHA

ALUMNA

AMBROSIA

AMERICANA

AMMONIA

AMNESIA

AMOEBA

AMPHIBIA

ANESTHESIA

ANGORA

ANNA

ANTENNA

AORTA

AQUA

ARCADIA

AREA

ARECA

ARENA

ARIA

ARISTA

ARMADA

AROMA

ASEA

ASIA

ATLANTA

AURA

AURORA

AUSTRALIA

AZALEA

```
A A L U M N A A G E N D A A
L R N A N E T I F A A U A R
O C Q N G N L C N E R I B O
H C A D A M R A L O S U R M
A H P L A U Z C R E M A A A
R I T A N A S A H H M M C C
B A S B L O A T B B E P A A
E N Q E A P S C R R M H D B
G G A O N E A O I A S I A A
L O A M N M S C I R L B B R
A R C A D I A A A B F I R I
T A E R A N N E T N A A A S
A O R T A F L A F L A B Z T
B P A G O R A U Q A N E R A
```

HI-FI SYSTEM

If you're under the age of 25, chances are good you've only listened to music on a CD player as opposed to a STEREO SYSTEM with a TURNTABLE. Many people still own hi-fis, though, so they can still listen to their albums on vinyl.

AM/FM

AMPLIFIER

BALANCE

CABINET

CIRCUIT

DECK

DIAL

FILTER

JACK

MICROPHONE

MIXER

PLUG

RADIO

RANGE

RECEIVER

RECORD

RESPONSE

SPEAKERS

STATION

STEREO

STYLUS

SYSTEM

TAPE

TERMINAL

TONE

TREBLE

TURNTABLE

VOLUME

WATTS

```
R F E R M E T S Y S T T A W
E S N O P S E R M E U O R O
T O O X R A N G E R L E N D
L A H B A T I K N B I L T E
I I P V D B B T C F L P R C
F S O E I L A N I M R E T K
L T R I O B C L O J C L A D
M A C E L Y P V A E I C R N
G T I E K M E C I N R O A K
I I M D A A K V S R C E D O
V O L U M E E C U E U E T G
B N N F L R A P R X I X U S
W G M S T Y L U S I T L T L
U K D D P B T N V M P P K L
```

GREEK LIFE

Fraternities and sororities can be academic, SOCIAL, or professional, and are usually based on a commitment of SERVICE to the CAMPUS and the community. STUDENTS interested in becoming a part of these organizations must PLEDGE during the beginning or end of a semester. Circle these terms that pertain to GREEK life in the diagram below.

ACTIVITIES

ADVISOR

CAMPUS

CHARTER

COLLEGE

DUES

FRESHMAN

FRIENDS

GREEK

HONORS

HOUSE

JOIN

JUNIOR

LETTERS

OFFICERS

PARTIES

PLEDGE

PROJECTS

RUSH

SCHOOL

SENIOR

SERVICE

SOCIAL

SOCIETY

SOPHOMORE

STUDENTS

SYMBOL

TRADITION

VOLUNTEER

VOTE

```
V S Y M B O L M E K N L K G
E E E F O E A S R E T T E L
B R T S C U G R O S I V D A
Y V O L U N T E E R H A N S
A I V M C O I C L U O D O N
I C V F O L H I D L N S I E
R E T R A H C F C P O F T R
J U N I O R P F R C R C I B
P R C E V L K O I E S Y D S
J O I N E I J E S U P M A C
S I V D C E T H E E C T R H
T N G S C Y M I S R U N T O
S E I T R A P J E U G D U O
C S S T N E D U T S R M F L
```

AFTER "ALL"

This puzzle shouldn't keep you up all NIGHT, because it's really quite straightforward. While it may appear to be full of all KINDS of words, the terms are really all ALIKE, as each one becomes a common phrase when preceded by the word "all." So all IN ALL, we think you'll be all SMILES before long!

ABOARD

AGES

AGOG

ALIKE

ALONE

ALONG

ASEA

ASHORE

CLEAR

COSTS

COUNTS

EARS

EVEN

EYES

FOURS

HEART

HOURS

IN ALL

IN A ROW

KINDS

LENGTHS

MINE

NATURAL

NIGHT

RISE

SECURE

SIDES

SMILES

STOPS

TALK

THERE

THE TIME

THUMBS

WORK

YOU CAN EAT

```
A T E E R G G N I S Y B F M
H W Y K S N W O R K D C E N
U S E T I Y P U H E L N M G
C P S G A L O N G W Y A I S
H O H C A F A U D O P I T K
C T H U M B S L C R N I E B
Y S R U O H U E O A A A H C
M S N A T U R A L N N G T O
T I R G S U T L B I E E R U
A D N F C H T L R D M S A N
P E R E H T O I F G T S E T
L S S L V B S R A E L C H S
G O G A R E M L E M C V H R
C R M U O O V S M R D N W P
```

"CHINESE" FLORA

Don't put away your gardening tools yet! Wander through this botanical puzzle and fill your wheelbarrow with clippings from these plants whose names all begin with the word "Chinese."

AIR PLANT

ANISE

ARTICHOKE

AZALEA

CHESTNUT

CORK TREE

DATE

ELM

EVERGREEN

FAN PALM

FIR

HAT PLANT

HIBISCUS

HOLLY

JUJUBE

LEMON

LILAC

MILLET

OLIVE

ORANGE

PEAR

QUINCE

RHUBARB

ROSE

SUMAC

WISTARIA

YAM

```
Q E G N A R O M C W H F P L
U E J R I I H O Y I H H G A
I A U V G J R U B S A R H U
N Z J E M K I I B T W A D H
C I U V T R S E P A I E B N
E H B R A C O L V R R P M E
L B E O U C A Y P I T B K E
J E E S I N A L F A L O P R
A U F E T S A L Z W H O C G
L E M O N N U L I C O G V R
J A L E T F U M I L L E T E
Y H E A V L E T A D L G Z V
V R R O Z Y R M Y C Y R F E
J V P M L A P N A F C E A T
```

VOWEL POWER

The 29 6-letter words below all have the unusual property of containing four vowels. See if you can uncover all of the words in this UNIQUE list.

ADAGIO

AERATE

AERIAL

AMOEBA

APIECE

AROUSE

AVENUE

AZALEA

BEANIE

BOOGIE

BOOHOO

BOOTEE

BUREAU

COOKIE

EQUATE

EUREKA

GOALIE

GOATEE

GUINEA

HOAGIE

IGUANA

MILIEU

MUUMUU

ODIOUS

OPAQUE

ORIOLE

ROOKIE

SOIREE

UNIQUE

```
B O G C A T O H K U P E A G
A E S U O I D O T K L T O A
E I V O G O B B U R E A U P
R A R A M K K R A E T U D H
A N D O D H O I B E U Q G N
T A E O P O Z H E U N E V A
E U R E K A N U A E R I A L
K G A I R G Q E N B T G U A
E I E Q Z I C U I H E O R G
N K L U N E O H E L K O O B
K M A U I K C S O I U B M B
H Q Z P H O V I A S L S T A
G O A L I E R G E T H I E E
R O O H O O B U U M U U M S
```

LEAGUE OF NATIONS MEMBERS

The purpose of the League of Nations, an organization established in 1920 after the first World War, was to promote international peace and security. Although the League was dissolved in 1946 (after failing to prevent World War II), it served as a model for the United Nations, which was formed in 1945. The 29 countries listed below were among the members of the League of Nations.

AUSTRALIA

AUSTRIA

BELGIUM

BOLIVIA

BRAZIL

BULGARIA

CANADA

CHILE

CHINA

CUBA

ECUADOR

FRANCE

GREECE

GUATEMALA

HAITI

HEJAZ

HONDURAS

HUNGARY

INDIA

ITALY

JAPAN

LIBERIA

PANAMA

PERU

POLAND

PORTUGAL

ROMANIA

SIAM

URUGUAY

```
J R B E Y O V P B T M L E J
N S I U C C M E A N I H C R
U A C B L N L R D Z D N E O
T R L H V G A N A C G O E M
L U O A I L A R T S U A R A
H D Y U M L B R F C I O G N
J N M N O E E I I N D I A I
F O A P O R T U G A L S U A
H H Y P P I A A U S T R I A
Z S A D A N A C U R U R A T
A L I H N J E U T G E D U E
J C U A A M N B U B I P B H
E S D E M N I A I V I L O B
H U N G A R Y L A T I N C R
```

When summer arrives, our thoughts turn happily to the garden. Lots of hard work will bring the **FLOWERS**, **PLANTS**, and shrubs that are a gardener's delight. Here are 33 necessities to make your garden grow.

BORDER

BULBS

COMPOST

DIRT

FENCING

FERTILIZER

FLATS

FLOWERS

GLOVES

HERBICIDE

HOSE

KNEEPADS

MULCH

PEAT MOSS

PLANTS

POSTS

POTS

RAKE

SEEDS

SHEARS

SHOVEL

SOIL

SPHAGNUM

SPRAYER

SPRINKLER

STAKES

STICKS

STRAW

STRING

TROWEL

TWINE

WATER

WIRE

```
P H U W S Z W B W O M L V C
E G B K B P E A T M O S S B
P L A N T S Y O T F R D R S
U O E D I C I B R E H A S D
R V T W I N E S W N R P H E
R E D R O B M O T C R E O E
R S Z G V R L U G I D E V S
W T G I B F T M N N C N E C
V S B S L U L K I G M K L O
Z O M K H I L A R S A H S M
E P D C O E T B T T O H I P
U R L S R V A R S S T O P O
S U Y I E K A R E Y A R P S
M I W C A W C O S F D I R T
```

"E" NAMES: GIRLS

Are you expecting? In this assortment of "E" appellations, prospective parents may find the perfect choice for their progeny. Choose from **EDNA** (rejuvenation), **ELAINE** (light), **EMILY** (industrious), or any of these others.

EARTHA	ERIN	ETTA
EDEN	ERMA	EUDORA
EDIE	ESTELLE	EUGENIA
EDITH	ESTHER	EUNICE
EDNA	ETHEL	EVELYN
EDWINA		
EILEEN		
ELAINE		
ELEANOR		
ELECTRA		
ELENA		
ELISA		
ELIZABETH		
ELKE		
ELLA		
ELLEN		
ELLIE		
ELOISE		
ELSA		
ELVIRA		
EMILY		
EMMA		
ENID		
ERIKA		

```
G G A T L B O N T C R S E M
G G W A V W Y O D O T U Z G
D Y R E I L E E N Y A T O E
N Y Y B E N S A O R R H G N
O T C V H T E B A Z I L E I
N W E D H L N G Z S V L I D
B A A E E C I N U E L I S A
H K R C A H A L L E E E E K
U I T O M N L E T D D L O I
N R H T D O E S M W L I E V
A E A E A U E L O I S E T O
B W K A M Y E D E N L Y H H
E I H L R M G C I A Z Y E E
O A T T E C A C C E S W L H
```

SHIP SHAPE

Since the "ship" we're looking for in this particular puzzle is used merely as a descriptive word and not a seagoing vessel — you don't have to worry about getting seasick! All the words listed below can be followed by the word "ship."

AUTHOR

BRINKMAN

CHAMPION

CITIZEN

COURT

CRAFTSMAN

FELLOW

FRIEND

GUARDIAN

HEAD

HORSEMAN

KING

LADY

LEADER

LORD

MARKSMAN

MEMBER

PARTNER

PENMAN

QUEEN

READER

RELATION

SALESMAN

SCHOLAR

SEAMAN

SPORTSMAN

TOWN

WORKMAN

```
R N F Q S B C E N E E U Q O
D S R C U E R N W A R B N H
B R I N K M A N Z D M U O A
Y P E M A M F M N P N N F U
O R N N S M T Q A O S E E D
Z E D K T M S K I N G Z L P
N D R O L R M T D B O I L N
S A L E S M A N R I C T O A
M E M E B L N P A O A I W M
H L S K E M E K U H P C S E
Y E E R R Z E R G M U S T S
C D A N W O T M A U T H O R
R E A D E R W H O L T A N O
C R A L O H C S H Q N M R H
```

SURNAMES FROM NATURE

Surnames can be as unique as first names and come from a variety of sources. We've collected 33 surnames that are also the names of animals, minerals, or plants and hidden them in the diagram below.

BIRCH

BURR

BUSH

CARDINAL

COLT

CRANE

CROW

DIAMOND

DOVE

ELDER

FINCH

FISH

GOLD

GRASS

HAWTHORN

LAMB

LEAF

MARTIN

MOSS

PEARL

PIKE

PINE

ROOT

ROSE

RUBY

SILVER

SPARROW

STONE

SWAN

SWIFT

TROUT

WOLF

WREN

```
Y S T O N E S B Y N B F C B
L Y P S T F L W I M Y M R H
H H B I B K D D I R D L A F
V S W U G K P I E F C W N L
B W I C R O W V E R T H E O
F U I F A E L E N H M S F W
Y B M I S I L D O A B U R R
P C B O S P A R R O W B F E
A G R R O F N T A R Y S N F
E D N O M A I D E E K I P G
G T L O C N D N H H P V O E
V O K T U O R T C A W V H L
N U R H V B A P K H H Y O O
W B R E A I C G T D W G S V
```

PLACES IN WISCONSIN

Welcome to Wisconsin, a cheese-lover's paradise! A tour through the state's many cities and towns will reveal lush green fields dotted with cows, as well as urban areas such as Milwaukee.

ADAMS	ARPIN	COBB
ADELL	BIRON	DALLAS
AFTON	BOYD	EAGLE
ALMA	BRUCE	ELCHO
AMERY	CASCO	ELEVA
ANIWA	CECIL	FENCE
ARGYLE	CHILI	GENOA
		GOTHAM
		IOLA
		JUDA
		KOHLER
		KRAKOW
		LENA
		LUCK
		ODANAH
		OGEMA
		OKEE
		PENCE
		PEPIN
		PHLOX
		POTOSI
		REWEY
		ROME
		SENECA
		SIREN
		STRUM
		TOMAH
		TREGO
		WALDO

```
G P J W X D W D K P E N C E
R A L M A C A S C O H C L E
D F N A D E L L B K H E A X
I N F E T Y D U L R V L C D
V A I O L M O E C A U I E N
U D M P U G M B M K S C N R
C A Y R E M A H T O G E E F
H M T N C P C E T W R C S A
I S O A N Y X O L H P N A M
L A L G E O P T D Y R I N I
I A M W F U R H V A G P I U
O K E E F E S I R E N R W K
L R D G G X C B B O C A A A
A V U O N O T F A D U J H F
```

WEARABLE WOOL

Search the diagram below for CASHMERE, FLANNEL, TWEED, and 29 other types of wool. Wool is a natural fiber that breathes, to help keep you cool in summer and warm in winter.

ALPACA
ANGORA
BAIZE
BATISTE
BOILED
BOUCLÉ
CASHMERE
CHALLIS
CHEVIOT
CREPE
FELT
FLANNEL
FLEECE
FRIEZE
GABARDINE
GRENADINE
HOPSACK
JERSEY
LODEN
MACKINAW
MELTON
MERINO

RAGG
SERGE
SHALLOON
SHODDY
STAMMEL

TARTAN
TWEED
TWILL
VICUÑA
WORSTED

```
M A C K I N A W T L T K I Y
O T A R O B T S U Z C Z A E
K W S F I O A C H A L L I S
E E H L I N N I S O P S T R
P E M V A K G P Z A D A R E
E D E T S R O W C E M D R J
R H R N A H R A A M Y J Y E
C A E N I D A N E R G H L T
T N T Z E D U L O S P C N T
A E S L E C R S L N U A O W
O D I D I I E A H O I S T I
U O T V D R R E B K O R L L
B L A G G A R F L A N N E L
B H B E Z O T L E F G K M M
```

275

274

TAKING STOCK

By TAKING stock of the list below, you'll discover that each term forms a new word or phrase when followed or preceded by the word "stock."

AUCTION

BOOK

BREEDER

BROKER

CERTIFICATE

CLERK

COMPANY

CRIB

DIVIDEND

DOVE

EXCHANGE

FARMER

FISH

GUARD

HOLDER

HORN

HORSE

IN TRADE

JOBBER

LEDGER

MARKET

OPTION

PILE

POWER

RACK

RAISER

ROUTE

SADDLE

SHOT

SOLUTION

TAKING

TICKER

TRADING

YARD

```
X O H L B R K G N J C Y H Y
B R O K E R O U T E D R A J
Y R L G X T O A P N A R I O
C M D I E H B R E E D E R B
F E E K O E L D D A S K R B
L G R R G N I D A R T C X E
X A N T O V J Y R E S I A R
M B X I I N H Y T M S T K P
T O T D K F O S N R F R R I
P P O F R A I I I A T X O V
O K C F E E T C T F P O T H
W Y H V L Y D R A C K M H D
E S O I C R N O I T U L O S
R D P E X C H A N G E A W C
```

276

GEM OF A PUZZLE

Whether you're a March baby in the market for your birthstone, AQUA-MARINE, or a St. Patrick's Day reveler in need of an EMERALD, feel free to launch your very own treasure hunt in the diagram below. There are 29 gems ranging from AGATE to ZIRCON, so whatever you're looking for — it's in there!

AGATE

ALEXANDRITE

AMBER

AMETHYST

ANDALUSITE

AQUAMA-RINE

BERYL

CARNELIAN

CITRINE

CORAL

DIAMOND

EMERALD

GARNET

IOLITE

JADE

JASPER

LAPIS LAZULI

MOON-STONE

ONYX

OPAL

PEARL

PERIDOT

QUARTZ

RUBY

SAPPHIRE

TOPAZ

TOURMALINE

TURQUOISE

ZIRCON

```
Z T R A U Q L D E J N I M N
A J E G L N M D S I L A G T
P X B A P E A R L U H Q Q S
O Y M T G J X I Z T R U B Y
T N A E M E R A L D N A Y H
T O U R M A L I N E G M G T
O C E T I S U L A D N A U E
D R U D I A M O N D R R N M
I I J P Y P J X I N Q I A A
R Z A P L P G O E U R N T C
E L S O Q H L T O T H E Z E
P H P D J I O I I J Q E M C
U A E G T R S C O R A L G G
L Y R E B E N O T S N O O M
```

277

PAYING OVER TIME

In the '50s, Diners Club and American Express launched their charge cards in the United States, making certain purchases easier for consumers. Here are some items that, because of their cost, may take some time to pay for. Get comfy in your favorite CHAIR as you uncover them in the diagram.

APPLIANCE

ARTWORK

AUTOMOBILE

BICYCLE

CABIN

CAMCORDER

CD PLAYER

CHAIR

CLOTHES

COMPUTER

DRYER

FURNITURE

GASOLINE

HOUSE

JEWELRY

ORGAN

PIANO

SHOES

STEREO

TABLE

TELEPHONE

TICKETS

TOASTER

TRAILER

TRUCK

VACATION

VACUUM

YACHT

```
R E T S A O T H C A Y M V E
T U W E U U V N S A T E Y T
R Y L K P B T A S I B B K E
U R E T U P M O C H A I R L
C L O T H E S K M A O U N E
K E B E S T E R E O T E D P
R W I Y N T G E E I B I S H
O E C N S I L D N L M I O O
W J Y N W B L R R U I N L N
T O C A A Y U O U Y A A L E
R E L T L F K C S I E G R U
A H E F S P A M P A P R R T
O M G E K V D A M B G O D Y
A P P L I A N C E S U O H W
```

WINDSURFING

Windsurfing basically combines sailing and surfing with the use of a one-person craft called a sailboard. A SAIL, which is often made of DACRON, is attached to a MAST on the sailboard, and by LUFFING the sail, the windsurfer can control his speed. The boards have no rudder but instead have a SKEG which is a rear bottom fin. A sea of terms related to this thrilling hobby can be found in the diagram below.

BACK
BEAM
BEAR OFF
BEAT
BLANKET
CENTER-
  BOARD
CURRENTS
DACRON
DAGGER-
  BOARD
DIPS
GYBING
HARNESS
HEADER
HEAD UP
INHAUL
KEEL
KNOT
LAUNCHING
LEEWARD
LIFT
LUFFING
MARKS
MAST
OUTHAUL
OVERLAP
PEARL

REACH
SAIL
SHIMS
SINKER
SKEG

TACKING
UGLY
VEER
WAVES
WINDWARD

```
L R T O N K K G R R F H C L
P E A R L T I G H I O E P N
D K C A B G N I H C N U A L
R P K S M I H S N T A E B S
A L I O B E T N E H F E P S
W U N Y W N Y R O P A I R U
D A G G E R B O A R D U L M
N H V R N O R L O R C H L A
I T R E A I R F A B E A M R
W U E R S E F W G N H R D K
C O D M V L E F R E K N I S
C N A O H E A D U P K E C A
F S E O L E E U G L Y S T I
T V H N P K G R G P P S E L
```

"A" ADJECTIVES

Here's an ADORABLE puzzle for your solving pleasure. Find 32 AUTHENTIC "A" adjectives that we've strategically placed in the grid. If you find them all, you'll be an ALL-STAR solver!

ABLAZE	ABSORBENT	ACIDIC
ABRASIVE	ABSTRACT	ACTIVE
ABRUPT	ABSURD	ADHESIVE
ABSENT	ACADEMIC	ADORABLE
ABSOLUTE	ACCURATE	AGILE

```
Y C L Y P E C P N R U B U A
A I I E E D E I A G I L E B
R T A M A V V C L Q N H I L
D A C B E C I T N E H T U A
E U T B S D S S Y R G N A Z
N Q I S I O A A E E S N O E
T A V C L B R C L H C I A T
A C E Y S L B B A I D N C E
Y I I U L O A M E U V A C Y
B T R M V R P N A N R E U T
B D U Y O L T I U T T R R R
C M S D E T N E S B A E A A
C I A H C R A B S O L U T E
I T P U R B A M I A B L E Y
```

AIRY

ALERT

ALIVE

ALL-STAR

AMIABLE

AMPLE

ANCIENT

ANGELIC

ANGRY

AQUATIC

ARCHAIC

ARDENT

ARTY

ATOMIC

AUBURN

AUDIO

AUTHENTIC

CHIEF REEFS

If you become a scuba-diving enthusiast, you may find yourself traveling to Australia's Great Barrier Reef. Located in the Coral Sea, it's composed of over 2,100 individual reefs, stretching 1,200 miles long. It's a big tourist attraction because of its islets, coral gardens, and unusual marine life. Hidden below are 31 of the larger reefs that make up this diver's paradise.

BOWDEN
BRIGGS
BURKE
CELEBRATION
DART
DAVIES
DINGO
ENDEAVOUR
FITZROY
FLINDERS
FLORA
FREDERICK
HARDY
HASTINGS
HEDGE
HERON
HOLMES
HOOK
HOSKYN
LLEWELLYN
MAGPIE
MCINTYRE
NODDY

NOMAD
NORTHWEST
OTTER
PRINCE

RIBBON
SAUMAREZ
VIPER
YONGE

```
Y Y E D M F Z E K E F A L M
T D K K C I R E D E R F N D
N D R D G T N N O O S B A L
Z O U A A Z O P L A O M D S
L N B R H R I F U T O R G M
P L N B E O T M T N U G C A
N F E H I Y A E Z O I I K G
E A L W K R R K V R N O I P
D A V I E S B A B T O A E I
W Y F Z N L E V Y H E D G E
O O G N I D L R N W G S N G
B P R I N C E Y S E M L O H
V I P E R L C R N S Y A Y T
S N Y K S O H A S T I N G S
```

GOVERNMENTAL GUIDE

The **MONARCHY** was established during periods of external threat and internal crisis because it provided a more efficient focus of **POWER** than **ARISTOCRACY** or **DEMOCRACY**. Have fun finding the terms in our governmental guide.

AMBASSADOR

ARISTOCRACY

AUTHORITY

BUREAUCRAT

CZAR

DEMOCRACY

DICTATOR

DIPLOMAT

EMPEROR

EMPRESS

ENVOY

GUIDANCE

HIERARCHY

KING

LAWS

MINISTER

MONARCHY

OFFICIAL

POLITICS

POWER

PREMIER

PRESIDENT

QUEEN

REGIME

REGULATIONS

REPUBLIC

RULE

```
A U T H O R I T Y N R K A D
P R E S I D E N T A E M R G
E R E I M E R P Z S B E A O
C D Y G T A R C U A E R U B
N S G C U Q F A S B Q T R Q
A S E M A L S S R U L E D D
D E M O C R A C Y C T I I W
I R P N F D C T I S H P C L
U P E A O F Y O I T L Y T R
G M R R Y B I N T O I Z A E
N E O C N O I C M S N L T W
I R R H C M V A I W I S O O
K D Z Y K C T N Y A R R R P
C F N R E G I M E L L Y A N
```

CAMPAIGNING TERMS

The first Tuesday of November has long marked the end of the RACE for every CANDIDATE in the NATION who has been running for some kind of OFFICE. For months they have expended both effort and energy in hopes of achieving victory; now it all comes down to one day of voting. There's no pressure for you, however; circle these campaign-related terms in the grid, and you're a shoo-in! Oh, and as Al Capone said, "Vote early and vote often."

ADVISOR
BUDGET
CANDIDATE
CITY
CONGRESS
DEBATES
DELEGATE
ELECTION
FLIERS
FUNDS
GOALS
IDEAS
ISSUES
LETTERS
MEDIA
NATION
NEWS
OFFICE
PARTY
PICTURES
PINS
PLATFORM
POLLS
POSITION
POSTERS

RACE
SENATE
STICKERS
STRATEGY

TERM
TICKET
TOWN
VOTERS

```
B  R  Y  K  N  O  I  T  I  S  O  P  Y  O
P  A  T  P  L  E  T  T  E  R  S  E  F  G
O  I  I  O  W  E  T  A  N  E  S  F  R  O
L  D  C  S  W  S  R  A  S  K  I  F  M  F
L  E  K  T  R  N  D  S  D  C  K  R  U  F
S  M  E  E  U  V  E  U  E  I  E  N  Y  I
L  W  T  R  I  R  S  L  B  T  D  U  T  I
O  O  E  S  G  R  E  B  A  S  E  N  R  R
V  N  O  N  E  C  R  S  T  B  L  Y  A  A
M  R  O  F  T  A  L  P  E  C  E  A  P  C
O  C  N  I  S  S  U  E  S  L  G  K  O  E
Y  G  O  N  T  E  G  D  U  B  A  S  T  G
F  N  I  D  E  A  S  T  R  A  T  E  G  Y
B  P  U  G  W  Y  N  F  L  I  E  R  S  B
```

282 CARL SANDBURG POEMS

Carl Sandburg (1878-1967) is the quintessential American poet. His verse, using strong, simple language, celebrates the people and places of America. Our list contains 32 of his poems, including "CHICAGO," which is considered his most famous piece.

ALIX

ANSWER (The)

BONES

BUTTONS

CHICAGO

CHILD

DOCKS

DUNES

FIGHT

FLUX

FOLLIES

GONE

HAPPINESS

HARBOR (The)

IRON

I SANG

IT IS MUCH

JUNE

LOST

MASK

MIST (The)

MONOTONE

PALS

POPPIES

RED SON (The)

SHIRT

SKETCH

STYLE

SUBWAY

WAITING

WARS

WHO AM I?

```
S T Y L E C K M A S K C O D
K F S A X B H O K T H U X U
D U Y I W R N O H I H W M N
L L E G M B E C L I A G C E
X O E N U J U D M R P R I S
W T S I O M R S S F P S N F
F A K T S T F N F O I I M Y
A S E I P P O P G O N E J R
H E T A L T G N R N E O E O
H I C W T J A S O U S W R A
F L H U R S C E B M S M A I
F L B W I R I N R N N L X X
G O U X H W H O A M I G A C
H F T X S J C B H X N W H P
```

284

THOSE WONDERFUL MAMMALS

Tree-dwelling marsupials, koalas live on the east coast of Australia. Contrary to popular belief, the KOALA is not a BEAR; it is related to the KANGAROO and the wombat. There are about 8,000 koalas left in the wild, but they're becoming extinct due to agricultural and urban developments in their natural habitats.

AARDVARK	KANGAROO	MULE
ANTEATER	KOALA	OCELOT
ANTELOPE	LEOPARD	TIGER
BADGER	MONGOOSE	WALRUS
BEAR (black)	MOOSE	ZEBRA
BEAVER		
BISON		
BOAR		
BOBCAT		
BUFFALO		
CAMEL		
CARIBOU		
CHEETAH		
COUGAR		
COYOTE		
DEER		
DONKEY		
GIRAFFE		
GORILLA		
HYENA		
JAGUAR		

```
B H G I F M J K C S R K F S
C Y B J L S A R O T R E W B
K E L E U S G O L A F F U B
V N M R Z K U O V C L F R G
K A L M E D A D D B E A O E
C A U O B I R A C O E R L K
W O N N R A R A O B I I W C
F Z Y G A E R L P L T G H I
B N E O A N T E L O P E L T
E O K O T R B A D G E R O R
A S N S E E O H E T N L M Y
V I O E B G Z O A T E C U W
E B D O P I O H Y C N T U M
R G S D M T O C O U G A R Y
```

Here's a puzzle that proves the *shoe* must go on! All of the terms in this list are related to that fashionable FOOTWEAR favorite, a pair of sandals.

ANKLE
ARCH
BACKLESS
BEACH
BUCKLE
CASUAL

CLOG
COMFORTABLE
CONTOURED
DESIGNER
FASTEN
FEET

FLAT
FLIP-FLOPS
FOOTWEAR
HAND-CRAFTED
HEEL
LEATHER
MATERIAL
NYLON
OPEN
PLASTIC
RUBBER
SIZE
SLIP-ON
SOLE
STRAP
STROLL
STYLE
SUPPORT
TOES
TREAD
VACATION
WALK
WIDTH

```
B Y S F O M Y M Y C C L O G
A R U B B E R R F N O L Y N
C E B E L K N A S H N L K L
K H E L Y T S E P P T C G D
L T A E T T O W O L O D A S
E A G N E T R T L M U E I I
S E I N D R N O F B R Z B W
S L L R Y C R O P T E Y L H
L K E O E T R F I P D A C K
I C E K S T S A L T U R C O
P U H S A T A L F S A S K H
O B Z B R G Z M A T W C L E
N P L A S T I C F E E T A C
N E P O R E N G I S E D W V
```

TOWNS OF SICILY

Italian opera composer Giuseppe Verdi once said, "You may have the universe if I may have Italy." After a trip to the island of Sicily you might share his sentiment. The results of 2,500 years of changing rule are still to be seen — Greek theaters and temples, Roman bridges and aqueducts, Saracen mosques and towers, and Norman churches and castles. Plan your itinerary with these Sicilian towns in mind. Note that each line is a separate entry.

ACIREALE	PATERNO	RIBERA
AGIRA	PIAZZA ARMERINA	SIRACUSA
AGRIGENTO	PRIZZI	TRAPANI
ALCAMO	RAGUSA	VITTORIA
BARCELLONA		
CALTAGIRONE		
CANICATTÌ		
CATANIA		
COMISO		
ENNA		
ERICE		
GELA		
LICATA		
MARSALA		
MAZZARINO		
MENFI		
MESSINA		
MODICA		
NOTO		
PALERMO		

```
M E N F I B G P R I Z Z I S
A C P O P V B V A R E B I R
R N A C A N I C A T T I V U
S O O L O T L O M R E L A P
A P S L T T A S U C A R I S
L E E O L A O O G G R I N R
A U R S R E G N R P M G A O
G I A I V L C I T F E R T S
A R G M C A G R R L R L A I
Z A U O L E Z A A O I N C C
Z D S C N R L Z P B N P I E
T M A T O I R Z A E A E L F
M M O D I C A A N I S S E M
O L A D D A I M I T P Z C N
```

Born in 1475 near Florence, Italy, Michelangelo Buonarroti was a true Renaissance man. A sculptor, painter, poet, and architect, his work has left a lasting impression that continues to influence artists even today. Below are the names of 39 subjects of Michelangelo's work.

ABEL
ABRAHAM
ADAM
ANDREW (St.)
BATHSHEBA
BERNARD (St.)
BOAZ

CAIN
CASTOR
CUPID
DANIEL
DAVID
ESTHER
GABRIEL (Archangel)

GOLIATH
ISAAC
ISAIAH
JACOB
JEHOSHAPHAT
JEREMIAH
JESUS
JOHN (the Baptist)
JONAH
JOSEPH (St.)
MADONNA
MARK (St.)
MARTHA (St.)
MARY (Magdalene)
MICHAEL (Archangel)
MOSES
NOAH
PAUL (St.)
PETER (St.)
PHILIP (St.)
PLATO
POLLUX
RACHEL
RUTH
SARAH

```
M B S Y R A M K H E O P C G
A O U H E A M A H A R B A C
B A S L H D R A N R E B A U
O Z E E T A I D D N R J S D
C B J M S M R M A I O G I K
A A O A E E L C E N P D X R
J B S R W V G L A P I U A A
G P E T E R O H I I L E C M
J J P H O V L L I L N I L T
H W H A S R I E O D S H P D
J E H O S H A P H A T A I I
O T A L P L T B I C U V O D
H S O M I C H A E L A X B V
N J N R U T H G B D Z R C X
```

PILOT LINGO PAST AND PRESENT

Pilots must often communicate with each other under circumstances in which radio transmissions aren't the clearest. To aid in clarity, they have developed a set of code words representing the letters of the alphabet. Listed below is the pilot's alphabet of today, along with that which existed during World War II. Starred entries in the first group were also used in WWII. Please be aware that the headings aren't hidden in the diagram.

CURRENT
ALFA
BRAVO
CHARLIE*
DELTA
ECHO
FOXTROT
GOLF
HOTEL
INDIA
JULIET
KILO
LIMA
MIKE*
NOVEMBER
OSCAR
PAPA
QUEBEC
ROMEO
SIERRA
TANGO
UNIFORM
VICTOR*
WHISKEY*
X-RAY*
YANKEE
ZULU

WORLD WAR II
ABLE
BAKER
DOG
EASY
FOX
GEORGE
HOW
ITEM
JIG

KING
LOVE
NAN
OBOE
PETER
QUEEN

ROGER
SUGAR
TEAR
UNCLE
YOKE
ZEBRA

```
A D C W Y O K E T W E K I M
R E K A B S S E H D I R I S
B L P Z R U A I D N I A O H
E T R U G R S E G A C C I Z
Z A Y A N K E E M N H S T M
G B R T E C M I Y X A O E Z
R L G Y O R L Q S J R V M K
B E G R O E G E U T L A W B
E V G F T B M L X E I R Y Q
U C I O B M I O Q U E B E C
L N H C R E F P R T A N G O
U M G O T V H A E F W Y O L
Z I E O B O Q P L O V E L I
J N S P D N R A H X I J F K
```

TROILUS AND CRESSIDA

First published in 1609, William Shakespeare's play *TROILUS and CRESSIDA* is set during the TROJAN War, which was fought between ancient Greece and the city of Troy. Take a literary tour through this puzzle to find several of the characters found throughout the play.

ACHILLES

AENEAS

AGAMEMNON

AJAX

ALEXANDER

ANDROMACHE

ANTENOR

ATTENDANTS

CALCHAS

CASSANDRA

CRESSIDA

DEIPHOBUS

DIOMEDES

GREEK (soldiers)

HECTOR

HELEN

MARGARELON

MENELAUS

NESTOR

PANDARUS

PARIS

PATROCLUS

PRIAM

THERSITES

TROILUS

TROJAN (soldiers)

ULYSSES

```
A N T E N O R T R O I L U S
R K B R E D N A X E L A H U
D E I P H O B U S A J A X R
N S U L C O R T A P T C U A
A O H T A M I D Y T A H D D
S K L H M G E U E U K I I N
S C Y E O S A N N E S L O A
A A S R R P D M E S T L M P
C L R S D A A R E L L E E R
A C O I N L G R O M A S D I
S H T T A I C R I T N U E A
D A S E A E N E A S C O S M
N S E S S Y L U J M A E N T
M O N A J O R T N E L E H Y
```

ON STAGE

Here is a list of various stage presentations, including BURLETTA (comic opera), EXODE (Roman satirical afterpiece), MASQUE (English mythological drama), and MUMMERY (pantomime).

BALLET

BURLESQUE

BURLETTA

CHARADE

CHORAL

COMEDY

CONCERT

DRAMA

EXODE

FARCE

LECTURE

MAGIC SHOW

MASQUE

MIME

MONO-LOGUE

MUMMERY

MUSICAL

MYSTERY

OPERA

PAGEANT

PARODY

PLAY

POETRY

PUPPETRY

REVUE

SATIRE

SKETCH

SKIT

TRAGEDY

```
C X W X R E V U E B F I C P
M O N O L O G U E U U K U A
R Y N F H F Q S S R S P V G
U R S C Y S U A K L P G K E
D E B T E K C T I E G D U A
Q M R L E R V I T T Q E N
L M R U H R T R G T S C U T
E U U Q T Y Y E D A R A H C
B M I S N C D W M S M S H Q
P E I K I P E O P A N O U N
Y D E M O C G L R B R S F D
O O U F R C A D B A L L E T
B X C A W Y R L L G P U L G
V E F S Y R T E O P E R A C
```

It's quite appropriate that much of Shakespeare's work was first performed at the Globe Theatre because his plays were set all over the world. Since some of the 32 locations camouflaged below haven't been known by these names for hundreds of years, you'll probably have a much easier time finding them in the puzzle than you would if you had to pinpoint them on a map!

ACTIUM

ARDEN

ATHENS

BARNET

BOHEMIA

BRITAIN

CYPRUS

DOVER

DUNSINANE

ELSINORE

EPHESUS

FIFE

FLORENCE

FRANCE

ILLYRIA

LONDON

MANTUA

MESSINA

NAVARRE

PADUA

ROME

ROUEN

SICILY

THEBES

TROY

TUSCANY

TYRE

VENICE

VERONA

VIENNA

WINDSOR

YORK

```
A R E V O D C B Y E T Y R E
U V F R K R O Y D P A M C V
T E I B O H S C P I Y N P E
N R F E E N H E R R A V A N
A O O M N B I Y B R U E T I
M N I Y A N L S F E N S H C
M A I R N L A W L O H U E E
U L N S I P K I D E S T N O
I E T U S C A N Y C O I S A
T T I S N E O D C L A W R S
C N M E U L M S U T I D A H
A E U H D W V O I A E C A F
V O H P F L O R E N C E I I
R O M E O H B T L A P H K S
```

A "FUL" PLATE

Look closely at this list and you WILL see that each entry is a word that can be followed by "ful." If you take CARE as you locate the 39 entries in the diagram below, we have FAITH that yours will be a solving SUCCESS story!

BASKET
BLISS
BOAST
BUCKET
CARE
CHEER
COLOR
DOUBT
EVENT
FAITH
FLAVOR
FORCE
FRET
FRUIT
GLEE
GRACE
HAND
HARM
HELP
HOUSE
MIND
MOUTH
NEED
POCKET
PURPOSE
RESPECT
SCORN

SUCCESS
TACT
TASTE
THANK
THOUGHT
TRUTH

WASTE
WATCH
WILL
WISH
WONDER
YOUTH

```
D  V  E  V  E  N  T  H  E  V  W  E  W  N
N  O  M  H  T  G  R  F  I  U  U  I  A  R
I  O  U  H  S  D  O  E  E  L  G  T  S  I
M  A  E  B  A  B  V  C  R  F  A  I  T  H
D  L  T  K  T  S  A  O  B  L  Y  W  E  W
P  N  H  H  F  R  L  S  L  C  T  A  K  M
E  U  A  O  G  O  F  I  K  H  A  T  C  W
I  N  R  H  C  U  W  S  S  E  C  C  U  S
K  C  M  P  T  P  O  C  K  E  T  H  B  Y
E  H  T  U  O  M  N  H  P  R  O  Y  M  N
H  B  L  I  S  S  D  S  T  U  O  K  G  K
B  Y  N  O  U  E  E  S  U  U  B  D  Y
L  C  A  R  E  R  R  E  T  N  R  O  C  S
L  N  A  N  V  F  F  H  H  Y  N  T  D  Y
```

Good **MUSIC** is just a postage stamp away when you **JOIN** a music **CLUB**. But before you place that **ORDER**, pick up your pen or pencil and draw a loop around these terms associated with getting your music through the **MAIL**.

ACCOUNT

AGREEMENT

ALBUM

ARTIST

BAND

CATALOG

CHARGES

CLUB

COMPACT DISC

COUNTRY

DEAL

DELIVERY

DISCOUNT

GOSPEL

JAZZ

JOIN

MAIL

MEMBER

MUSIC

OFFER

ORDER

PAYMENT

PRICE

REGGAE

ROCK

SALE

SAVINGS

SELECTION

SERVICE

SHIPMENT

SINGER

SOUL

SOUNDTRACK

```
A  T  S  I  T  R  A  C  S  C  Z  U  T  E
C  N  L  Z  I  L  M  H  H  I  E  Z  C  I
C  U  G  A  B  L  M  A  I  L  N  I  A  S
O  O  D  U  E  C  I  R  P  S  V  G  E  J
U  C  M  N  A  D  V  G  M  R  H  L  E  Z
N  S  K  P  A  G  R  E  E  M  E  N  T  R
T  I  C  A  A  B  Y  S  N  C  L  B  J  G
R  D  O  Y  K  C  A  R  T  D  N  U  O  S
Y  L  R  M  U  V  T  I  E  I  Z  L  O  P
P  D  E  E  I  D  O  D  O  V  A  C  O  S
Z  J  G  N  B  N  B  J  I  T  I  E  F  C
S  M  G  T  U  M  A  F  A  S  A  L  F  C
O  S  A  L  E  R  E  C  U  K  C  P  E  B
B  L  E  P  S  O  G  M  O  R  D  E  R  D
```

"UN"BELIEVABLE FUN!

Here's your UNIQUE opportunity to UNCOVER 32 words that start with "UN." Don't stop UNTIL you've looped them all!

UNANIMOUS

UNCANNY

UNCOVER

UNCUT

UNDO

UNEARTH

UNEASY

UNFOLD

UNICORN

UNIFORM

UNIQUE

UNISON

UNIT

UNIVERSE

UNLESS

UNLIKE

UNLOAD

UNLOCK

UNMASK

UNPACK

UNRAVEL

UNROLL

UNSEEN

UNTIE

UNTIL

UNTO

UNTOLD

UNTRUE

UNUSUAL

UNVEIL

UNWISE

UNWRAP

```
I L U N F O L D K O H K I L
W U N T O L D W E U D C Q P
O E R O I R A Y U U P O L A
Y S A E N U O D N U F L A R
U V V U S U O M I N A N U W
O N E N N C A U F I A U S N
U O L T T S Q N O S W C U U
N N R O K I E N R O C I N U
L U I V A K E E M N L E U U
E T V V I D V U N P A C K N
S F W L E O U H Q R A T H R
S A N E C R U N T I L U C O
T U C N U F S H I P N C E L
I R U N W I S E I T N U A L
```

"E"ASY DOES IT

The letter "E" is the most commonly used vowel in the English language. In fact, you will notice that the entries that are concealed in the grid all have at least two "E's" and no other vowel.

BEETLE

DEED

DEFEND

DELETE

ELEMENT

EMERGE

ESSENCE

ESTEEM

EVENT

FEEBLE

FEED

FENCE

GREEN

GREET

HEED

JESTER

KETTLE

LEGEND

LEVEL

MEDDLE

NEEDLE

PEWTER

RECEDE

REDEEM

REFEREE

RENEW

REVERSE

SECEDE

SELECT

SETTLE

SEVERE

SKEWER

TEEN

VENEER

WEED

WESTERN

```
D R N S B P B R D S L E L J
E E E R E F E R E K D N F L
E T E W N L K N E E R G N E
W S T D B M R E F W N T V E
F E N E T E L E D E C E R K
R J E M T D N K L R N D V C
L F M S V D L T B T J E S G
H J E K R L T S M N T C S E
M W L D E E S S E N C E N R
W E E V K G V E M L V S S K
M E E T S E C E E E J L R
H L N D E N F F R F L C K F
N W N E E D L E G R E E T L
W F G F R R B E E T L E B C
```

NAUTICAL FASHIONS

You'll look like you just stepped off a SHIP when you OUTFIT yourself in the NAVY BLUE or WHITE APPAREL synonymous with the nautical look.

ANCHOR

APPAREL

BEACH

BLOUSE

COTTON

DRESS

DUSTER

EMBROIDERY

FABRIC

FISH

JACKET

JERSEY

LIGHTHOUSE

NAVY BLUE

OUTFIT

POCKETS

POLYESTER

PRINT

ROBE

ROWBOAT

SAILOR

SHIP

SHORTS

SKIRT

STRIPES

SUMMER

SWEATER

TANK TOP

TERRY (cloth)

TRIM

T-SHIRT

WAVES

WHITE

```
I P S E M B R O I D E R Y C
P R C G W B S S U W B O V G
A I D H E Y T E A P C W Y A
M N I A E R Y V P H S B R B
S T C S O E E S A I L O R R
E H R H S S U M M E R A E R
O E S U O H T H G I L T T T
J U O W S R A E O M S S S U
E L T I E T N B K E M H U P
B B F F E A K B Y C I I D C
O Y S K I R T L Y R O P R W
R V C U L T O E T R M P E T
T A W L A P P A R E L V S L
J N O T T O C I R B A F S U
```

We've all heard the old saying "Be careful what you wish for because you might just get it." That's something to ponder as you circle these 32 terms that describe ways to GAIN and RETAIN things.

ACCEPT
ACCRUE
ACCUMULATE
ACQUIRE
AMASS

ANNEX
APPROPRIATE
BARTER
BORROW
COMMANDEER

EARN
GAIN
GARNER
GATHER
GLEAN
GRAB
HARVEST
HAVE
HOLD
INHERIT
KEEP
MAKE
OBTAIN
POSSESS
PROFIT
PURCHASE
REAP
RECEIVE
RETAIN
SECURE
TAKE
TRADE FOR

```
A L H G T I F O R P B Q S X
C E H D N I A T B O H N U S
C G V E B W R D A C A P G S
R S A I C A L E G L E A N E
U E E X E O R Q H E R O T S
E T H C H C M T K N V A G S
M A Q T U M E M E S I A A O
T L H B A R G R A R I N H P
P U A K I G E B P N N R A N
E M E U F T R O F E D A R T
C U Q G A I R R X S T E V F
C C O I K P U R C H A S E W
A C N A P O N O S P W D S R
M A M A S S G W G E K A T D
```

Our image of a medieval knight is that of a chivalrous, ARMOR-clad warrior, armed and mounted on his trusty steed, always ready to help the weak and protect women. Actually "CHIVALRY," which came to mean a knightly CODE of HONOR, derives from the Old French *chevalerie*, meaning "horse soldiery."

ARMOR
BATTLE-AX
CASTLE
CEREMONY
CHIVALRY
CLOTHING
COAT OF
    ARMS
CODE
DAGGER
FIGHT
HERO
HONOR
HORSEBACK
JOUSTING
KING
LADY
LANCE
LEGEND
LOYALTY
MACE
MERIT
PAGE
QUEEN
RANK
SERVICE

SHIELD
SPURS
SQUIRE
SWORD
TILTING

TRAINING
VALET
VASSALS
WARS
WEAPONS

```
G P P N Q F D H M B G M G R
N S Q U I R E G G A D X O C
I U E G O L C N B W A M F O
K E H W T Y N O M E R E C D
N T S S B S Y T L A Y O L E
A K A M J S L T S P U R S C
R C C R R O T A R O N O H I
T E G A P A U Y S N O I I V
E I W F B L T S D S V Q E R
H C L O M E R I T A A G L E
H E N T L G S X L I L V D S
Y C R A I E T R A I N I N G
I A V O L N Y X O X A G P B
O M K C L D G N I H T O L C
```

Did you know that in ancient Rome a kiss was used as the legal bond to seal contracts? That is how it became customary for a BRIDE and GROOM to kiss at the end of their wedding ceremony, as a way to "seal" their marriage VOWS. Here's a word list that can double as a checklist for those couples planning a wedding.

ALTAR

BAND

BEST MAN

BIBLE

BOUQUETS

BRIDE

BRIDESMAID

CAKE

CLERGY

COCKTAILS

DANCING

DRINKS

FLOWERS

FOOD

GOWN

GROOM

GUESTS

LACE

LIMOS

NUPTIALS

PARENTS

PHOTOGRA-
PHER

PROMISES

RICE

RINGS

SPOUSE

TEARS

TUXEDO

USHER

VEIL

VIDEO MAN

VOWS

```
S C L E R G Y M K G S H P L
R V S V U S E D I R B R A B
G H V E I L N G R A B C R R
F Q S P S A N V N I E I E I
N T S O M I L D B T N H N D
S U D T C T M L G G P K T E
F X S N E P E O S A B L S S
U E A H V U W V R O A N W M
B D C A E N Q G E P L G O A
A O W W L R O U W S F R V I
I S L I A T K C O C U O L D
V I D E O M A N L B B O O U
M O F H H K U R F E D M P D
E O P R E C I R O T E A R S
```

SCOOT ALONG

Scooters first appeared near the end of the 19th century, and in the 21st century they've made a comeback — only now they're motorized! They still have the same look as their foot-powered ancestors, but now they can also pack a small gasoline or electric engine!

ACCELERATION

ACCESSORIES

BALANCE

BATTERY

BRAKE

CONTROL

DECK

FOLD

FRAME

FUEL

HANDLE

HORN

IGNITION

KIDS

LIGHTS

MANEUVER

MIRROR

MODEL

MOTOR

PORTABLE

POWERED

RIDER

SAFETY

SCOOTER

SPEED

STABILITY

START

STEEL

STOP

TIRES

TRACTION

TRANSPORTATION

WHEELS

```
P O R T A B L E U F R Y F F
P D E R E W O P L E K A R B
N O C A E F O L D E B M K A
Y S T N O I T I N G I C C L
S T R S E I R O S S E C C A
H H H P E M U T V D E Y B N
O G O O S T A B I L I T Y C
M I R R O R B N E C V K L E
S L N T T A V R E T O O C S
A E V A T C A I L U R V P L
F M R T L T L E D T V E E E
E A E I I I D K N Y E E O E
T R M O T O R O A D T K R H
Y F N N M N C Y H S G D A W
```

Taking a trip to Europe? When you get to Germany, here are some places to visit. *Auf Wiedersehen!*

ALTONA

AUSBURG

BONN

BREISGAU

BREMEN

BRÜHL

DORTMUND

DÜLMEN

DÜREN

EMDEN

FULDA

FÜRTH

HAMBURG

HEIDELBERG

KIEL

KREFELD

LANDAU

LEER

LÜBECK

MAINZ

MANNHEIM

MOSBACH

MOSEL

MÜNSTER

NEUSS

ORTENAU

RHINE

SAAR

SIEGEN

SOEST

STUTTGART

USLAR

WEIDEN

WIESBADEN

WORMS

```
U R G U S L A R U S S U E N
N N E D A B S E I W E H E N
E U A N E T R O E T L D T T
M C D U R E N E B E I L H H
L A L M S A A S I E G E N F
U B U T L B M K W S I E U H
D N F R S K U I I D G R C A
E M E O N R L R E O T A O M
L N O D E E U L G H B A U B
W H I S M F B D T S N N O U
O N U H E E E F O O S N R R
R G A R R L C M T T N T A G
M I L G B D K L E Z N I A M
S T U T T G A R T S E O S L
```

BATIK WORDS

The ancient art of batik is a method of dyeing designs on cloth by coating the parts that are not to be dyed with removable wax. Results are unexpected and exciting, as no two pieces are ever the same. We've made our own DESIGN of words in the diagram below. It's up to you to complete the PROJECT by finding these 35 terms that pertain to the batik PROCESS.

ABSORB
BEESWAX
BRUSH
BUCKET
CLOTHES
COLORS
CRAFT
DARK
DESIGN
DRAWING
DYES
FABRIC
FRAME
HOBBY
IRON
LIGHT
LINEN
LIQUID
MATERIAL
MELT
PARAFFIN
PATTERN
PROCESS
PROJECT
RINSE
SCARF

SHEET
SILK
SOAK
STREAKS
SWIRLS

TJANTING
(drip method)
WASH
WATER
WOOL

```
S  C  A  R  F  M  S  H  N  Y  X  P  Y  G
R  B  T  A  S  Y  S  N  B  D  H  S  K  X
O  N  U  E  P  S  D  B  L  G  K  L  J  Q
L  M  Y  C  E  S  O  Y  O  A  I  P  P  M
O  D  A  C  K  H  B  R  O  S  B  A  M  H
C  L  O  T  H  E  S  S  W  I  R  L  S  W
P  R  O  J  E  C  T  M  K  A  C  U  I  T
P  E  W  S  D  R  R  N  F  D  R  C  R  L
T  T  W  W  E  L  I  F  R  B  A  T  O  E
S  A  P  A  S  Y  I  A  G  E  F  R  N  M
X  W  K  S  I  N  W  Q  L  S  T  E  K  A
R  S  T  H  G  I  L  S  U  N  N  T  X  R
G  N  I  T  N  A  J  T  C  I  R  B  A  F
O  T  M  G  H  H  U  F  L  R  D  T  A  P
```

NORTH AMERICAN VOLCANOES

The REDOUBT volcano began erupting on December 14, 1989, southwest of Anchorage, Alaska. Volcanic ash caused about 23 explosions between December 1989 and April 1990. The explosions produced hot, fast-moving clouds of ash, rock debris, and gas.

AKUTAN

ANIAKCHAK

CLEVELAND

COLIMA

DOUGLAS

GARELOI

GRIGGS

ILIAMNA

KANAGA

KATMAI

KISKA

KOROVIN

KUKAK

MAGEIK

MAKUSHIN

MARTIN

OKMOK

PARICUTIN

PAVLOF

POGROMNI

REDOUBT

SEGUAM

SHISHALDIN

SPURR

TANAGA

TORBERT

TRIDENT

WRANGELL

```
K G D U M U N I T R A M P M
M M O A D A N I A K C H A K
A A U U N I R R U P S K R N
U C G V H M F T G O U E I M
G L L E G N A R W S G D C K
E T A E I N U I H C L O U O
S N S N V K C I L A P K T H
G T R I D E N T H I A M I R
G R C V E M L S B K V O N U
I E H O O B I A S U L K S C
R B G R L H R I N E O D L A
G R G O S I K A R D F D N O
V O B K A T M A I W T D E R
P T K A N A G A N A T S N R
```

IDENTIFYING MARKS

CHECK out the grid and if you're successful in uncovering all the entries associated with identifying marks, you'll get our SEAL of approval!

ADDRESS

ARROW

ASTERISK

BADGE

BAR CODE

BRAND

CHECK

CHEVRON

CREST

EARMARK

EMBLEM

ENGRAVING

IMPRINT

INSCRIPTION

INSIGNIA

LABEL

LETTERING

LINE

LOGO

MARKER

MONOGRAM

NUMBER

PATCH

SEAL

SIGN

STAMP

STRIPE

SYMBOL

TABS

TAGS

TITLE

```
Y  E  N  I  L  O  B  M  Y  S  L  M  C  O
T  T  R  O  R  A  C  E  A  A  T  O  G  N
L  G  N  I  R  E  T  T  E  L  N  N  K  T
U  K  L  C  N  V  K  S  K  R  I  O  R  E
H  N  O  B  T  S  E  R  C  V  R  G  A  B
M  D  G  P  A  T  C  H  A  T  P  R  C  P
E  W  O  I  G  D  G  R  C  M  M  A  O  C
L  O  I  N  S  I  G  N  I  A  I  M  R  H
B  R  S  R  S  N  P  E  R  P  S  M  C  E
M  R  B  T  E  L  T  K  M  D  T  C  E  C
E  A  A  L  R  B  A  S  T  E  R  I  S  K
K  M  T  N  D  N  M  B  H  T  I  B  O  S
P  I  H  D  D  N  I  U  E  A  P  U  K  N
T  Y  H  T  A  M  G  W  N  L  E  L  R  B
```

Building blocks provide children with hours of playtime fun, while at the same time encouraging them to use their minds and imagination. They allow little ones to expand their creative horizons and BUILD on their dreams! And unlike other TOYS, these COLORFUL PIECES of SOLID wood are almost indestructible!

ACTIVITY

ALPHABET

BUILD

COLORFUL

COORDINATION

CREATE

CUBE

CYLINDER

EDUCATIONAL

LETTERS

NUMBERS

PERSONAL-IZED

PICTURES

PIECES

PILE

PLASTIC

PLAY

SHAPES

SIDES

SOLID

SQUARE

SYMBOLS

TEACH

TODDLERS

TOPPLE

TOYS

TRIANGLE

WOODEN

```
Y E L P P O T E A C H D T A
Z A N O I T A N I D R O O C
H L L T L C L N R Q S N D T
E P A P E P T S D R B E D I
R H Y N I E Y U E I Z D L V
A A O E O M T T R I L O E I
U B C Y B I T A L E G O R T
Q E Y O P E T A E B S W S Y
S T L E L G N A I R T Y L O
E S I M A O C I C N C D O E
P N N I S D R E I U L D F T
A G D R T T B F S I D E S T
H Z E S I U W N U M B E R S
S P R F C N I B Q L G M Q I
```

If you sleep like a log, even the RUMBLE of THUNDER during a storm can't keep you from your dreamy doze. But if you're a light sleeper, an incessant car ALARM or a barking dog can be a nightmare. Quietly search the diagram below for 30 types of annoying noises.

ALARM

BANG

BAWL

BELLOW

BLAST

BOOM

CLAMOR

CLANG

CLAP

CLATTER

CRASH

DISCORD

GUFFAW

HOWL

OUTCRY

PEAL

POUND

RACKET

RATTLE

RING

RIOT

ROAR

RUMBLE

SCREAM

SCREECH

SHRILL

SLAM

THUNDER

TUMULT

YELL

```
I E T S W T U M U L T U W P
N G W M G H U B N R S D H M
M P G O R U G R L C T P G O
G R P O U N D W O L O A L S
L W A B A D M O L A I R W K
T S A L B E D L U T R R O O
G N C R A R E L T T A R H S
G N I R O Y F E U E C N C S
W G Y C E M E B L R K R C F
B G S A C A A B P T E T Y B
W I L P W B M L U E T C L F
D W A F F U G Y C C A E K S
K L M C R A S H D O K L C R
C R S O L U C U H U C F R E
```

TIME WARP

It's about time that you got to this puzzle! With all of your solving experience, you should be able to discover the hiding places of these "timely" terms in no more than a HALF-HOUR.

ANNUM

CENTURY

CYCLE

DATE

DECADE

EPOCH

FISCAL YEAR

FORTNIGHT

GENERATION

HALF-HOUR

JUNCTURE

LIGHT YEAR

MAN-HOUR

MINUTE

MOMENT

MONTH

SEASON

SECOND

SEMESTER

SPACE

SPAN

SPELL

STAGE

STRETCH

TENURE

TERM

TRIMESTER

WEEK

```
D D L F S E T Y P M J J E G
U N L L E P S C R L U R E W
G F P K A O A U E N U N L L
L E E M S C O C C N E A C I
D E A S O H C T E R T S Y G
W T T T N M U T A A R U C H
D U H A D R E T S E M I R T
E N M G E N I N T Y U F N Y
C I R E I O O S T L N G C E
S M E L N N E C L A N S L A
P H T N O M T D E C A D E R
N S I D E R A R D S P U H F
I E I S G H D H O I S T L H
A O R E A N H A L F H O U R
```

Put on your solving shades as we take off for balmy Bermuda, where the weather is summerlike all year long, and where you might get to view these 30 birds who are nesters of this island paradise.

ALBATROSS

BUNTING

CAHOW

CORMORANT

DOVE

EAGLE

FALCON

FLYCATCHER

GANNET

GOATSUCKER

GREBE

GROUSE

GULL

HAWK

HERON

HUMMING-BIRD

IBIS

OSPREY

PELICAN

PETREL

PLOVER

RAIL

SANDPIPER

SHEARWATER

SNIPE

SPARROW

STORK

SWALLOW

TERN

WOODPECKER

```
Y C Y L R E T A W R A E H S
I E K F L E B E R G V Y A S
E H R N L U K K R O T S W O
L G R P N Y G C D N D W K R
G O A T S U C K E R L A T T
A D I N A O S A I P P L N A
E N L B N V O B T E D L A B
G Y A O D E G K T C P O R L
F R R C P N T R E L H W O A
I E S N I P E S O W W E M W
H Y P M P L U V O K B C R F
H V M L E O E H F A L C O N
K U W O R R A P S I B I C E
H B N G K C U L L G H U E O
```

FIT AS A FIDDLE

You don't have to be at your ATHLETIC best to solve this puzzle filled with a host of adjectives used to describe human physical qualities. But you might improve the MUSCULAR coordination of your hands by circling all 31 terms.

AGILE	CHIPPER	HARDY
ATHLETIC	ENERGETIC	HEALTHY
BEEFY	FRESH	HEARTY
BONNY	FRISKY	HEFTY
BRAWNY	HALE	HUSKY
		MIGHTY
		MUSCULAR
		ROBUST
		RUDDY
		RUGGED
		SOLID
		SOUND
		SPRY
		STOCKY
		STOUT
		STRONG
		STURDY
		TOUGH
		TRIM
		WELL-BUILT
		WIRY

```
U E Y N W A R B F O W Y E B
B G R D K S T H A R D Y W L
E N F W D I K H Y I I G Y F
E O I Y B U R A L U C S U M
F R E S H B R O W E S R K E
Y T T U O T S E F M T C L Y
G S S O O Y L L Y M I I F O
C K D U T L S A D T G R C E
Y W G F B H T H E A H I T Y
K H E U W O U G G H M G R B
C H I P P E R B G A E P I P
O L H O W E D N U O S M L M
T L B O N N Y T R A E H Y F
S P T E G K U W I E K I B A
```

EMBASSIES IN WASHINGTON, D.C.

Many countries from all over the globe maintain diplomatic relations with the United States via their embassies in Washington, D.C. Here are just some of the countries with embassies in our nation's capital.

ANDORRA

BELIZE

BURUNDI

CAMEROON

COMOROS

DJIBOUTI

FIJI

GEORGIA

HONDURAS

INDONESIA

JAMAICA

KYRGYZSTAN

LATVIA

LESOTHO

MALAWI

MOLDOVA

MYANMAR

NAMIBIA

NEPAL

OMAN

PANAMA

PERU

QATAR

RWANDA

SENEGAL

TOGO

TONGA

UKRAINE

VATICAN CITY

YEMEN

ZIMBABWE

```
K N T A A Y E W B A B M I Z
M Y S N E P A L A G E N E S
O C R O O R S A R U D N O H
L A I G R O E G T O N G A Z
D H S O Y O R J N E M E Y B
O A D T B Z M E A M A N A P
V N D E T A S O M M R A N D
A R L N I I H T C A A M J A
E A A V A T I C A N C I T Y
Z T T M O W I I P N B B C N
I A K S N J R E B O N I Y A
L Q E N I A R K U L M A O G
E L V F Z U Y T V E A N M G
B U R U N D I M A L A W I O
```

REFINISHING

Creative refinishing of old furnishings can transform the APPEARANCE of otherwise dull pieces into beautiful heirlooms or unique antiques. Change the SURFACE of the diagram by drawing a circle around the following words associated with refinishing.

ANTIQUE

APPEARANCE

BASE

BRONZE

BRUSH

CLEANER

CLOTH

COAT

FINISH

GILD

GLAZE

LACQUER

MARBLE

MATERIAL

POLISH

PUTTY

SANDPAPER

SATIN

SCUFF

SEALER

SHELLAC

SPONGE

STAIN

STEEL WOOL

STYLE

SURFACE

TACK

TOWEL

TREAT

VARNISH

WASH

WIPE

WOOD

```
S K A U H S I N R A V P W L
N H G T B R U S H P I I R K
P S E L E Y L Y T P P E C Z
O A H L T U S A T E N A C L
L W A T L P Q N I A T S O F
I E U D O A I I E R M T A B
S P Z N O L C L T A E R T I
H T G A W O C Q R N C T O N
I E Y D L G W B U C A I A W
S M Y L E G L C S E F O A M
C A K I E E E Z N O R B B T
U S T G T O W E L P U A N G
F I N I S H P L B V S R S S
F R S A N D P A P E R O O U
```

FOOTBALL FEVER

Hall of Famer Alan Page was a part of the "Purple People Eaters," the Minnesota Vikings' fierce defensive unit of the 1970s. In 1971, he became the first defensive player in NFL history to receive the league's MVP award. While still playing for the Vikings, he obtained his law degree in 1978 and in 1992 was elected to a seat on the Minnesota Supreme Court where he still sits today. The terms below relate to His Honor's previous occupation.

BLITZ
BLOCK
CLIPPING
DEFENSE
DOWN
END ZONE
FLANK
FLARE
FORMATION
FOUL
FREE KICK
FUMBLE
GOAL POST
HOLDING
HUDDLE
OFFENSE
OFFSIDES
OPTION
PASS
POSITION
POSSESSION

PUNT
ROLLOUT
SACK
SAFETY

SCRIMMAGE
SNAP
SWEEP
TACKLE

```
G Y O E G F R E E K I C K T
G T T E I O Z G N R C W R Z
I R A E E R A L F O M O F E
M E P N F M P L F L Z C L P
D I P O M A A F P L S D A B
O Z R I S T S N W O D N N D
R F R S K I Y G G U S Z K E
E C F S D O T N H T A T A N
S W E E P N I I O U C I R G
N C S S N D A P O P K L L K
E G S S L S T P U N T B F E
F L Y O K I E I G M U O I Z
E K H P O C E L B M U F A P
D U W N U T A C K L E Z N K
```

DÉPARTEMENTS DE FRANCE

If Julia Child's creations inspire you to search out some authentic French cuisine, why not take a trip to the source? Metropolitan France, which includes the island of Corsica, is divided into 96 departments, 33 of which are hidden in the grid below.

AISNE	AUDE	GARD
ALLIER	CALVADOS	GERS
ARDÈCHE	CANTAL	GIRONDE
ARIÈGE	CHER	HAUT RHIN
AUBE	CÔTE-D'OR	INDRE
		ISÈRE
		LOIRET
		LOZÈRE
		MANCHE
		MAYENNE
		MEUSE
		NORD
		OISE
		ORNE
		RHÔNE
		SARTHE
		SAVOIE
		SOMME
		TARN
		VENDÉE
		VIENNE
		VOSGES
		YONNE

```
I C C B A I S N E H D V U H
N O A L A T N A C I D C M R
B S M L N Y S T R L O N A M
C O C E V E T R E T R V H M
S M R V B A R D E C H E A E
E M S U R A D D L G O E V S
D E A N L Y O O N H N I H C
U E D N O R I G S I E U S V
A E O N Z R H M A N C H E R
O R N E E D D T N H A G G G
B E U T R V T E S U E M S E
M S H A E Z Y A L I O G O B
U I G E H A U T R H I N V D
E O D I M U H A L L I E R L
```

BUSINESS NOTES

If you have a PLAN, you should have no PROBLEM locating the 33 terms associated with BUSINESS meetings in just a few MINUTES.

AGENDA

ATTENDEES

BOARD

BOOK

BUSINESS

CAUCUS

CHAIRMAN

CHART

COFFEE

CONFERENCE

COPIES

DATA

FORMAT

LEADER

MEMO

MINUTES

MOTION

NEWS

NOTICE

ORDER

PLAN

PRESIDENT

PROBLEM

REPORT

ROOM

SECRETARY

STAND

SUBJECT

TABLE

TAPE

TREASURER

VETO

VOTE

```
T M E M O O R N N U L A P T
A R H T O E F P L A N Y R R
U T E C A U C U S E R E O A
A V U D B R C I E A A M B H
O B D V R D N A T S E D L C
E A N A O O P E U O C M E S
P F T A I T R R N O N I M R
A O W T M C E D I B E U C C
T R O P E R S F M D R A O B
T M S S E N I S U B E F P O
W A A G E N D A T A F M I O
E T B W C T E E H E N J E K
L N S L G O N G E C O O S N
S U B J E C T E L S C U B G
```

These belles all have Texas towns named after them. You don't actually need to go to the Lone Star State to find the locations, just travel through the puzzle below.

ALICE

ALMA

ANNA

DESDEMONA

DIANA

DONNA

EDEN

EDNA

ELSA

FLORENCE

GAIL

GENEVA

HELENA

INEZ

IOLA

IRENE

JEAN

KATY

LEONA

LEORA

LILLIAN

LORAINE

LORENA

LUELLA

LYDIA

MARIETTA

MARION

MAUD

OLIVIA

ROWENA

SELMA

VERA

WHITNEY

WINNIE

```
D F E C A N Z A M F V M O L
C Y L D R J R F Z I A L M A
D E S D E M O N A F O V Z I
A N A I D D W L J R N S D I
A T C T A O E F E E O V R D
W I N Y I M N N C O O E E M
S H D O V N A N C G N R L V
G W L Y I I E R A E D A F C
H A S A L R J E I N N I W S
V K I L O R A I N E N K J M
E C I L A M S M L V T A D L
D L F E A N D E L A O T G V
H T A U E N H I N E Z Y A W
N S D L A O Y Y W S S U H Y
```

WHERE DID YOU READ IT?

This puzzle is ripped from the front page of today's newspapers! Well, that's because its word list consists of 27 newspaper names. See if you can find your hometown BANNER hidden in the diagram below.

ADVERTISER

BANNER

BEACON

BULLETIN

CALL

CITIZEN

COURANT

COURIER

DISPATCH

ENQUIRER

EXAMINER

GAZETTE

HERALD

JOURNAL

LEDGER

MIRROR

NEWS

OBSERVER

POST

PRESS

RECORD

REVIEW

STAR

TIMES

TOPICS

UNION

VOICE

```
N D Z X D B C G R E C O R D
P P E R L V E O E C I O V N
R H B R P X W A U O R L J S
E T A M W N I B C R J C W J
S T S D N D R J I O A E T E
S C T O Z I S M U D N N N X
I Z I E P S T R V P N U T A
O N M P Z P N E Z I T I C M
U L D B O A R V L I P D B I
P S L S L T G R M L L M A N
M Q A A I C R E R I U Q N E
L D R S C H S S C E G B N R
V L E D G E R B W E I V E R
S R H B G N C O U R I E R E
```

Craters are the most numerous features of the moon's surface, ranging in diameter from a few feet to many miles. Astronomers believe craters are caused by the impact of huge meteorites which have bombarded the moon. Fly to the moon and capture the following five-letter crater names.

ARAGO	BILLY	EULER
ATLAS	BLAGG	FAUTH
BAILY	BORDA	GAUSS
BAYER	DAWES	GEBER
BIELA	DELUC	KIRCH
		KLEIN
		LINNE
		MAYER
		METON
		MUTUS
		NEPER
		PARRY
		PEARY
		PLANA
		PLATO
		ROMER
		TYCHO
		UKERT
		VIETA
		VLACQ
		VOLTA
		ZAGUT

```
R H C O M B A Y E R K A B C
B Z C U N Y L I Y L A I B Z
E I T R L L G B R U E H Q E
R U V N I E L K R L E C A N
S K L B B K D E A G A H O N
D V I E T A P Y P L A T O I
L K R T R E K U V B E U S L
C B O P N P U M O M O A S R
L A M Z E L O K L H L F W S
D I E A F H Q G T T C Q K Z
Q L R G Y D Z G A A O Y G S
T Y B U S E W A D R O B T G
V O N T H W R L P L A N A A
C V O C O Y M B B B L H S N
```

Though food was plentiful in Colonial America, for many settlers, small luxuries were often difficult to obtain because of the great distance to the nearest town. The Colonial peddler would fill this need by loading his wagon with goods that helped make the Colonial family's life more comfortable and enjoyable, and then make his rounds, offering the housewife those items. Here are some of the sought-after items the peddler generally carried.

BASKET
BOOK
BROOM
BUCKLE
BUTTON
CALICO
CLOCK
COMB
CUTLERY
DISH
FABRIC
FIDDLE
FLATIRON
GINGER
GINGHAM
KETTLE
KNIFE
NAIL
NEEDLE
NUTMEG
PEPPER
PEWTER
PICK
PLATE
RAZOR
RIBBON
SALT

SCISSORS
SHOESTRING
SHOVEL
SPECTACLES

SPOONS
TEXTILES
THREAD
TOOLS

```
B O O K D D B A V W G K L K
A W C C G I U S B R O O M S
S S H O E S T R I N G A E C
K E F L M H T O O H H L I N
E L G C T B O S C G C R A R
T K E I U K N S N A B I S N
T C C V N O R I T A L F Z R
L U I I O G G C F O I I E A
E B F P P H E S U D O E C Z
U E S E R P S R D T V L D O
C N N W S G T L A S L D S R
P L A T E S E L I T X E T P
N D A E R H T P E P P E R U
O B M R Y H R I B B O N V Y
```

America's first inns were established in the 1600s and offered FOOD, drink, and OVERNIGHT accommodations to road-weary travelers. At that time, Pennsylvania had more than any other state, including the HISTORIC William Penn Inn, which was established in 1714. Located in Gwynedd, Pennsylvania, it is among the nation's oldest continuously operated Colonial inns.

BATH

BUILDING

BUSINESS

CLEAN

DECOR

ESTABLISHMENT

FOOD

GUESTS

HISTORIC

HOSPITALITY

HOUSE

INNKEEPER

LODGING

MEALS

OVERNIGHT

OWNER

PUBLIC

REST

ROOMS

RURAL

SERVICE

SITE

SLEEP

SMALL

STAY

TAVERN

TRAVELER

VACANCY

```
N H R W D G R L I H O T I O
T H O U S E N H A D T T P V
R N C S S E N I S U B A U V
A N E T P T C L D O O F B O
V S D M F I H I O L S I L V
E A E L H S T N R D I B I E
L U C P H S O A G O G U C R
E N P A S W I E L A T I B N
R T N M N K K L M I V S N I
S L A E M C P C B R T G I G
P L R V I E Y K E A M Y W H
L P G U E S T S Y O T A C T
K B H L A R U R O O M S P R
N R S A D I N N K E E P E R
```

TROPICAL FLORA

The Tropical Zone is the area of the Earth's surface between the Tropic of Cancer and the Tropic of Capricorn. It receives the rays of the sun more directly than any other area of the Earth and has a higher annual temperature. The seasonal change of temperature is also smaller than in other regions. These factors create just the right climate for the blossoms below to burst forth in an array of tropical flora.

AIR PLANT
AKEE
BOMBAX
BROWNEA
CASSIA
CEREUS
CHALICE
CONGEA
CORAL
CORDIA
DATURAS
FLAME
GEIGER
HELICONIA
HIBISCUS
IXORA
JACARANDA
JASMINE
LONG JOHN
MIMOSA
ORCHID

PETREA
POINCIANA
POINSETTIA
POUI

RAYO
ROSE BAY
TURK'S CAP
WOOD ROSE

```
S O H W X C E A I D R O C F
C A S S I A T N A L P R I A
H K R A P C B D W X E C O D
T E P U E E L M Y S L H E N
U E L R T C T A O O J I C A
R F E I G A B R N B X D I R
K U O B C E D G E O I T L A
S U Y R S O J D R A T U A C
C A A O O O N A G E X B H A
A S R W H I B I S C U S C J
P O I N C I A N A M H I I Y
F M S E A U I R E G I E G R
Y I L A R O C I A E G N O C
I M O F P P A D F L A M E O
```

COMMON U.S. STREET NAMES

What do ADAMS, JACKSON, JEFFERSON, LINCOLN, MADISON, WASHINGTON, and WILSON have in common? If you guessed that "they're some of this nation's most popular street names," you'd be right. Oh, wait a minute, they were U.S. Presidents, too. Anyway, you can find them and several other traditional thoroughfare tags hidden in the grid below.

ADAMS

CEDAR

CHERRY

CHESTNUT

EASTERN

FIFTH

FIRST

FOURTH

FRANKLIN

HIGHLAND

JACKSON

JEFFERSON

LARK

LINCOLN

LINDEN

MADISON

MAIN

MAPLE

NORTHERN

PARK

PINE

ROSE

SECOND

SUNSET

THIRD

VIRGINIA

WALNUT

WASHINGTON

WILLOW

WILSON

WOODLAND

```
E O V A H I N O W I L S O N
N L O C N I L K N A R F T R
T G P U R N G Y C P L T C J
L A D A M S R H J H K N A A
A I D H M G E E L W M C U H
U E N S N R F Y T A K D P T
C W O D R F M T I S N N F R
G I C Y E F U N O H A D I U
E L E R H N I N P I N E F O
L L S K T G L S U N S E T F
L O T S R I F E H G P O H N
N W E I O A E P S T H A I E
R H V D N A L D O O W R R O
C I J M A D I S O N R M D K
```

PARTY PAVILIONS

Pavilions, which can be large tents or parts of a building, let you ENTER-TAIN outdoors in STYLE as they provide overhead protection from the sun and an open VIEW of the LANDSCAPE. The terms in this puzzle relate to the large tents that were popular among East Coast resort and estate festivities of the early 20th-century.

AWNING

BACKYARD

BREEZE

CANOPY

CHAIRS

COUCH

DINING

ENTERTAIN

FLOWERS

FURNITURE

GATHER

GUESTS

HAMMOCK

LANDSCAPE

LANTERN

LAWN

LOUNGE

MARBLE

MEALS

PLANTS

PORCELAIN

PORCH

RELAX

RUSTIC

SCREEN

SHADE

STYLE

SUNSHINE

TABLE

TENT

UMBRELLA

VIEW

WICKER

```
B W U M B R E L L A V X K Y
R X I M A N C N D K A G C P
E E E C C M H D U L E F O L
E T H L K N A H E N S R M O
Z L Z T Y E I R I K C R M U
E R A Z A T R H B E R U A N
W L V N R G S U L L E S H G
Y W B L D N I A T R E T N E
W P E A U S I G N I N I D D
K E O S T N C T T M N C K A
G N I N W A L A N T E R N H
Y I A V A S O U P N Z A U S
Y L C O U C H S R E W O L F
P O R C H G U E S T S I C S
```

ALL IS "WELL"

It's time to focus on the word "well," and find these 28 words that can follow it to form adjectives. The well-ROUNDED solver should be DONE in no time at all. One might say this is a "deep" puzzle.

ADJUSTED	BUILT	GROOMED
ADVISED	CHOSEN	HANDLED
BALANCED	DEFINED	HEELED
BORN	DONE	INFORMED
BRED	DRESSED	KEPT
		KNOWN
		LIKED
		MADE
		MANNERED
		MEANING
		PAID
		READ
		ROUNDED
		SPENT
		SPOKEN
		USED
		WORN
		WRITTEN

```
I M M S T O C O A V E L L M
A U A P T A H B P A I D M T
G D E D N U O R R K E E G D
F K J S E A S E E M M L R I
C W N U P A E D R E T E O C
K W O O S N N O E U S E O D
N N H R W T F H U S S H M V
N V M A N N E R E D I E E A
N E T T I R W D E E A V D N
H J K K L B A L A N C E D I
N K M O D I D K I I A O R A
P M W C P N U N W F N R O B
I W B E A S G B U E I F J D
S A A H L G H B D D T R P H
```

So as not to be long-WINDED, we'll just tell you that all of the terms in this LIST form new words or phrases when preceded by the word "long."

BEACH

BOAT

CASE CLOCK

DISTANCE

DIVISION

DOZEN

FACE

GREEN

HAIR

HAND

HAUL

HORN

HORSE

HOUSE

ISLAND

JOHNS

JUMP

LEAF PINE

LINER

LIST

MEASURE

SHIP

SHOREMAN

SHOT

SIGHTED

SPLICE

SPUR

SUIT

TERM

UNDERWEAR

VIEW

WAYS

WINDED

WISE

```
N L S I G H T E D N R O H C
N P E V C N C I I E S U O H
R T I A L A V H S I D P P M
J E E H F I A R T L O N W S
W B K W S P O E A M A F I H
K O D I C H I S N E R N I W
L J O H N S H N C A I E D B
L N Z K C O L C E S A C W F
U J E P R U Z W H U H I N H
A G N E L B R O E R S L R B
H T M M R E T S J E K P T Z
W A Y S D G Y O U N G S J L
N O N N S H Y E M I I K R U
U B U D A R Z G P L T L J Z
```

LET'S GET FLUENT

As technology progresses and global communication continues to be ever more accessible, it can be useful to LEARN another language. There are many ways to STUDY a new language including attending a class or using software, audio tapes, and books.

ACCENTS

ADVERBS

ALPHABET

CD-ROM

CONVERSE

DICTIONARY

EXERCISE

FILMS

FLUENT

GRAMMAR

LAB HOURS

LEARN

NOUNS

OBJECT

PRACTICE

PRONOUNCE

PRONOUNS

REPEAT

SENTENCE

SPEAK

STUDY

SUBJECT

TENSES

TEXTS

TRANSLATE

VERBS

WORDS

WRITE

```
E X P S V W K A E P S C U A
A B L R O S O Y T E U C E C
D H L J O V E R I Y B H S C
K D A L S N A S D A J K I E
M W P R O N O U N S E J C N
P O G S S T T U I E C I R T
D A R L L S E C N E T N E S
T S A D V E R B S C T N X W
C T M W C E C R A B E R E T
E X M L T M E R E H R A X N
J E A I I V P T A E P E R E
B T R M N F E F P N O L V U
O W N O U N S R U O H B A L
D I C T I O N A R Y H E W F
```

THAT SMELLS GOOD!

Spice up your home with some HOMEMADE pomanders. These natural air fresheners are made from apples or citrus fruits and then pierced with GROUND cloves. After being rolled in a spice mixture, pomanders are DRIED, and often tucked away in closets.

APPLE

AROMATIC

BOWL

CARNATION

CINNAMON

DECORATION

DISPLAY

DOORKNOB

DRIED

FRAGRANT

FRESH

GINGER

GROUND (cloves)

HANG

HOMEMADE

KUMQUAT

LEMON

LIME

NUTMEG

ORANGE

PERFUME

RAFFIA

RIBBON

ROOMS

SCENT

SPICES

WHOLE (cloves)

YARN

```
L H T M D T E M Y F B G R H
U Y S O N N Y T P L H A N G
L B D E G A S N F L F O G W
D E C O R L W O B F I L E C
L S M N O F Y M I T H M G H
N I S O U R M A A P P L E A
Q D P E N T K N L F H G M L
F P I L D N R N H P I I T Q
D E C O R A T I O N S A U K
D R E H C R M C G B U I N N
U F S W E G O E L Q B T D C
W U E G N A R O M A T I C G
K M D K Q R Q U M O I P R R
D E I R D F K P K S H M E U
```

Well, it's true that all good things have a TENDENCY to end. Oh, don't worry, we're not saying this is the last puzzle; we simply want you to DESCEND upon the grid below and start circling these words that contain the letters "END."

ADDEND	CONTEND	ENDLESS
AMEND	DEFEND	ENDURE
ASCEND	DEPEND	EXTEND
ATTEND	DESCEND	FENDER
BLEND	ENDEAR	FIEND
		FRIEND
		GENDER
		LEGEND
		OFFEND
		PENDING
		PRETEND
		RENDITION
		SLENDER
		STIPEND
		SURRENDER
		SUSPEND
		TENDENCY
		TREND
		VENDOR

```
V O D T E P M A S C E N D L
O P N B G A C V U N I Y E S
D N E L B D T L S R C R Y L
N R G A Y N D R P N U T C X
E R E D N E L S E D C L R G
M Y L D P C E D N E T N O C
A B I E N S N E D F V I D D
V R N N R E N D I T I O N N
A D A D T D R X N F Y E E E
E T N E L E E R G E T I V I
S U R E D N E F U X P S O F
V P S N I N V S E S A I D L
A S E N T R E N D N E T T A
L G N C T O F F E N D F G S
```

LONDON LANES

London has many streets which have gained fame for various reasons. Here are 44 of Central London's famous and not-so-famous streets.

ABBEY
ALBERT
ALDFORD
ANLEY
ARGENT
BAKER
BEAR
CAREY
CONS
CORK
CRAVEN
DOVER
DOWNING
DRUID
DRURY
EARL
EMBA
EXTON
FLEET
FOLEY
FOSS
GRAY
HINDE
KENT
LEAKE
NOEL
ORCHARD
ORME
OXFORD

PEMBROKE
REGENT
SANDELL
SCOTT
SERLE
SHELTON
SOHO
STRAND

TENT
THEED
TILNEY
TUDOR
VYNER
WATERLOO
YORK

```
E V M F M V T N E G R A Y B
S M O R H B E A R T N E K C
R S B C V V F L E E T N N Y
S A T A A Y K L G R Y O A B
N N D R S E O R E V O D C C
O D C E A L A B N A R S O S
C E R Y E N L I T O K H P Y
R L L A S A D O F Y O E E E
E L E A H N F X R S M L X B
N D O T D C O U R B O T I B
Y U N I E M R O R F O O D A
V E U I E D D O W N I N G K
T R L C H U K R O C L R A E
D E W A T E R L O O L C X R
```

TONS OF TOMATOES

When Spanish explorers brought tomato seeds back from South America and introduced them to Europe in the 16th century, the plant was grown mainly for ornament. This is because it was thought to be poisonous as it was recognized by botanists as a relative of the deadly nightshade (the roots and leaves of the tomato plant are in fact poisonous). Hidden in the diagram below are 29 varieties of tomato.

ATOMIC

CALMART

COLDSET

CURRANT

DROPLET

FIREBALL

GENEVA

HY-TOP

JETFIRE

MANITOBA

PATIO

PORTER

PRESTO

RIDEAU

ROCKET

SCOTIA

SIOUX

SMALL FRY

SPRINGSET

STARFIRE

STARSHOT

SUNSET

TANANA

TIGERELLA

TINY TIM

TINY TOM

VALIANT

VIVID

VOGUE

```
M A N I T O B A I T O C S X
O N B A S I O U X P P B M H
T A M T E S G N I R P S U Y
Y N J E O P T E K C O R X T
N A R L I H R N R V T H C O
I T I P B I S E R E T R O P
T C D O F S M R S R L J L A
S C E R V I A D A T E L L T
U L A D T A L M G T O V A I
N T U Y T O L X F H S V B O
S J N O C A F I X Y E I E C
E I M B C U R R A N T V R H
T I E C T E Y F E N R I I C
C B T E M V O G U E T D F A
```

THE WORLD AT YOUR FINGERTIPS

You'll have the world at your fingertips when you pick up a copy of *The World Almanac*. It's filled with information about ARTS, NATIONS, SPORTS, and lots more interesting tidbits. So don't delay; solve this puzzle, then get one of your own!

AGRICULTURE

ARTS

AWARDS

BOOK

CENSUS

CITIES

CONTENTS

DATES

ECONOMICS

EMPLOYMENT

EVENTS

FACTS

FLAGS

GEOGRAPHY

HISTORY

INDEX

LANGUAGE

MAPS

NATIONS

PAGES

PEOPLE

PICTURES

POLITICS

SCIENCE

SPORTS

STATES

STATISTICS

STORIES

TRAVEL

```
E  S  E  G  A  P  C  Y  I  X  E  D  N  I
R  H  E  M  O  G  U  S  D  A  T  E  S  E
U  P  E  O  P  L  E  D  U  W  K  D  C  G
T  H  W  A  I  L  D  K  Y  S  R  O  I  A
L  S  G  N  C  S  O  H  W  A  N  C  E  U
U  O  T  O  T  T  P  Y  W  O  K  E  N  G
C  B  O  O  U  A  H  A  M  S  K  W  C  N
I  S  P  O  R  T  S  I  M  E  B  O  E  A
R  T  R  G  E  I  C  L  S  I  N  I  O  L
G  N  O  S  S  E  T  A  T  S  T  E  B
A  E  C  B  G  T  R  S  E  I  O  V  Y  I
G  V  N  A  T  I  O  N  S  C  A  R  M  I
D  E  L  F  A  C  T  S  T  R  A  N  Y  M
I  F  X  K  A  S  C  I  T  I  L  O  P  R
```

SCHOOL DAZE

Today we're having a pop quiz. No groans, now! I'll need someone to hand out the TESTS for me. All you have to do is find the classroom terms in the diagram below. Ready, set, go for those high GRADES!

BELL	CHAIRS	FILM
BLACKBOARD	CHALK	GRADES
BINDER	COUNSELOR	HIGHLIGHTER
BOOKS	CREDIT	HOMEWORK
BREAK	DESKS	LUNCH

NOTES

PAPERS

PENCILS

PENS

PROJECTS

RECESS

REPORTS

SCIENCE FAIR

SLIDES

SPORTS

STUDENT

SUBJECTS

TEACHER

TESTS

TRIPS

```
H O M E W O R K B E L L S G
L S E S K S E D A R G N S D
C C H A L K T F F S E T O N
L I S W N E H C R P R A T I
C E G R A F G R E O K I K T
W N C C I B I S P J D C R R
R C H L E A L S O E B O M I
S E M D J I H S R D L U N P
R F C U D C G C T E S T S S
E A P E N C I L S U D F P K
P I S U S K H N H E D N H O
A R L C T S U B P S R E I O
P L D R A O B K C A L B N B
F N S T C E J O R P B C F T
```

INDIAN CUISINE

One of the most enjoyable aspects of a visit to India is the opportunity to experience true Indian cuisine. Hidden below are 35 Indian ingredients and dishes to savor, if only in your imagination!

ARBI

BAASI

BOMBIL

CHILIES

CHUTNEY

CINNAMON

DUCK

IMLI

KADHI

KARI

KEBABS

LAMB

MALAI

MATTHI

MINT

MULLI-
  GATAWNY

MURGHI

NAAN

PAAN

PANEER

POMFRET

POORI

PRAWNS

PULLAO

RAISINS

RAITA

RICE

ROTI

SAAG

SHARBAT

SONF

SWEETBREADS

TANDOORI

VARK

YOGURT

```
O N G L N E E G G O D M F A
Y S O A S K E B A B S T P M
A O A M D U C K C M E W U E
F N G T A N D O O R I L L T
K F E U E N T L F T L R L U
F K I B R A N M N I I C A B
A F P O B T O I G C H B O K
R G T R T P M A C I C M S I
A I A Y E N T U H C B A V V
I H C P E A A T R I A L A M
S D A E W O T T L G R D R M
I A Y N S A V M I K H O K Y
N K Y U M A I B A A S I O S
S N W A R P A N E E R L E P
```

COYOTE STATE COUNTIES

South Dakota has 66 counties. Below we've listed 31 of them, including HUGHES, which is home to Pierre, the state capital.

BEADLE

BENNETT

BON HOMME

BROWN

BRULE

BUFFALO

BUTTE

CLARK

CLAY

CORSON

CUSTER

DEUEL

GRANT

HAAKON

HAMLIN

HANSON

HARDING

HUGHES

JACKSON

JERAULD

LAKE

LYMAN

MEADE

MINER

POTTER

SANBORN

SHANNON

TODD

TRIPP

UNION

YANKTON

```
U W O W F U F H A N S O N K
L N R R T A Y T C M H N S P
G N I D R A H O T H A A H J
M O B O N H O M M E N H R T
I S A K N J I P N B N H S S
T R T S Y N E I O R O N E R
K O K O E G L R K L N H E E
N C D R K M N H A Y G T K B
O T E D A E M F A U T A R E
S G U H B L F L H O L O W A
K R E T S U C J P P W D I D
C A L E B R T P P N A M Y L
A N F O L B W T T I K S N E
J T R I P P O T E P S U N S
```

QWERTYUIOP

Are you wondering where you've seen this puzzle's title before? Well, it's not a word but it is familiar, as it represents the letters on the top line of a TYPEWRITER or computer keyboard. This puzzle contains 36 words that are made up of only these letters.

EERIE
EYRIE
OUTER
PERRY
PIETY
PIQUE
POETRY
POPPY
PORTER
PRIORITY
PROTOTYPE
PUPPET
PUPPY
PUREE
PURPORT
PUTTER
PUTTY
QUERY
QUIRE
QUITE
REPORT
RIOTER
RIPER
ROTOR

TERROR
TERRY
TORQUE
TRIPE
TRITE
TROOP

TUTOR
TYPEWRITER
UPPER
WEEPY
WIPER
WORRY

```
P R I I E Q Y I P W O I I Q
W R T R I P E R U U R P R O
E I I P I Q U E Y Y R R O W
O U U O Y T Q R T O T W O U
Q I Q P R Y R R E P E T Q R
Q R P P R I O O I E P Y U I
E U E Y O E T U P O R R I P
P Q O T R R U Y E E U I T R
E R E T R T T U P R T E E
T R I T E O R Q P O U P E Q
U O Y R T Y P E W R I T E R
I U R O T O R R W W W T Q
T Y R O U U I I U T I Q O Q
R P U P P E T W E P R U E I
```

WAY TO GO!

Want something fun to do on a nice spring day? You can go for a BIKE ride or take a TRAIN to a nearby city and go exploring. Find 33 means by which you can travel in the grid below.

AIRBUS	BUGGY	GLIDER
AIRPLANE	CAMEL	HANSOM
AUTO	CANOE	HORSE
BARGE	CART	JITNEY
BIKE	COACH	KAYAK
BOAT	DINGHY	LIMO

```
A C W N I Y H R W Y D W O Y
K A C X S A E G R R R A H M
T R A I N P I N L E W G I G
L T N S K C U R T D N O J H
W D O I O R K O P I W N C E
T M E A U T O T D L J C J S
O U C L N C K C E G A D P B
M H O R S E T A K S B N O A
O O L K C G I R Y E I A E X
R N P K C R I T S A T K P P
S E K I B A P O H M K A S P
Y G G U B B M M I C B U K M
C B S S O I G E P R A M A X
T M K J L T R O L L E Y C L
```

PRAM
ROCKET
SCOOTER
SCOW
SHIP
SKATES
SKIS
SLED
TAXI
TRACTOR
TRAIN
TROLLEY
TRUCK
WAGON
YACHT

CRICKET

Cricket is a popular game in England and other parts of the Commonwealth. Like baseball, cricket is played with one TEAM in the FIELD and the other at bat, but that's about where the similarities end. In cricket, the BATSMAN stands in front of the WICKET and attempts to hit the ball as the BOWLER throws it to him. The fieldsmen each occupy a POSITION, three of which are called SLIP, GULLY, and SILLY MID-ON.

BAILS
BATSMAN
BOWLER
BREAK
CAPTAIN
CATCH
CREASE
FIELD
GROUND
GULLY
HIT BALL
INNING
KEEPER
KNOCK
LEG BYE
MATCH
NO BALL
ONE SHORT
OVER
PITCH
POSITION
RUNNING
RUNS

SIGNAL
SILLY MID-ON
SLIP
SQUARE

STRIKER
STUMP
TEAM
WICKET

```
L S H C T A M L K A E R B R
O Q I U T N A E G M U Y F P
V U T G K L E G K N O C K I
E A B R N P T B S D I O B H
R R A S E A V Y L P N N G B
P E L R D K L E M O A R N I
S I L L Y M I D O N M C I I
P S T W H F T R O H S E N O
Y L K C O K C I T U T I N G
P I T W H B T R K S A O U P
S A N M W I C K E T B L R D
C B Q K S T U M P A L U D R
D N U O R G A A L Y S F Y K
M I P D K F C L P W M E O T
```

During the 13th and 14th centuries, the châteaux of France were built more for defense rather than for dwelling. Later, these magnificent structures became royal residences, and today many are available for vacation getaways, allowing guests the chance to live like aristocrats — or at least like TV's "Joe Millionaire"! We've listed 28 of France's more famous châteaux.

AMBOISE

ANGERS

BEAUREGARD

BLOIS

BRISSAC

CHAMBORD

CHATEAUDUN

CHAUMONT

CHENON-CEAU

CHEVERNY

CHINON

DUNOIS

GIEN

GIZEAUX

LANGEAIS

LAVARDIN

LE LUDE

LOCHES

LUYNES

MEUNG

SAUMER

SERRANT

ST. MALO

TALCY

TROUSSAY

USSÉ

VILLANDRY

VILLESAVIN

```
S  S  T  M  A  L  O  A  T  S  V  S  V  Y
C  E  S  I  A  E  G  N  A  L  I  I  E  Y
H  H  N  D  U  N  O  I  S  O  L  O  C  V
I  C  E  Y  R  M  D  V  M  L  L  L  L  B
N  O  H  N  U  D  U  A  E  T  A  H  C  B
O  L  C  A  O  L  Y  S  U  T  N  O  S  L
N  Z  H  T  E  N  A  G  N  L  D  E  T  Y
E  C  A  G  S  V  C  V  G  T  R  S  A  N
I  A  M  A  I  G  E  E  A  R  Y  S  C  R
G  S  B  N  O  Z  B  D  A  R  S  U  E  E
U  S  O  G  B  R  E  N  U  U  D  M  I  V
C  I  R  E  M  X  T  A  O  L  U  I  V  E
M  R  D  R  A  G  E  R  U  A  E  B  N  H
O  B  V  S  M  E  T  R  S  X  V  L  V  C
```

At 22,834 feet, Argentina's ACONCAGUA is the highest mountain in South America. Conquer the puzzle below by finding it, as well as 28 others, in the diagram.

ACONCAGUA

AMPATO

ANCOHUMA

ANTOFALLA

BONETE

CACHI

CHACHANI

CONDORIRI

EL MUERTO

FAMATINA

GALAN

HUANDOY

HUASCARAN

ILLAMPU

INCAHUASI

JUNCAL

LAUDO

MERCEDARIO

PALERMO

POLLERAS

PULAR

QUELA

SAJAMA

SAN JUAN

SOLO

TORO

TORTOLAS

TUPUNGATO

YERUPAJA

```
D H O U P M A L L I C S G T
O F I C H A C H A N I A A O
T I R I R O D N O C T L L R
A M A J A S F D H A E O A O
G H D J U N C A L H S T N P
N U E I C J E L M U E R T O
U A C O N C A G U A L O O L
P N R T M F A J Y S T T B L
U D E A O R F C A I A I O E
T O M T C Y E N H P N D N R
O Y N G N S J L M I U N E A
R A L U P U A A A A G R T S
Q U E L A C L U L P E L E B
B L N N B A M U H O C N A Y
```

"IN" WORDS

We'd like to INTRODUCE you to a puzzle that's sure to pique your INTEREST! Using your keen INSIGHT, search the puzzle diagram below, where we've hidden 33 "IN" words. Can we INSPIRE you to find them all?

INCENSE	INDOORS	INGOT
INCH	INEPT	INITIAL
INCLINE	INERT	INLAND
INDEED	INFER	INNER
INDICATE	INFINITE	INNING
		INPUT
		INRUSH
		INSERT
		INSET
		INSIGHT
		INSIGNIFI-CANT
		INSPIRE
		INSTANT
		INSTEP
		INTACT
		INTEND
		INTENSE
		INTEREST
		INTO
		INTRODUCE
		INVADE
		INVENT
		INVITE

```
T U A P E T S N I H P D S S
N N I F N L I R E N N I I G
A T N E V N I C O A S V N P
C S R L V C U A L O U E E L
I E R A A D I N T O D I R F
F R D P O I I N S T A N T T
I E A R I N T A C T O T I S
N T T O V T O I O E L E I D
G N D I I H N G N I N N I D
I I T N N G N E R I P S N I
S E C R E I L E L U N E E T
N H G U P S F C T E T S D A
I L N S T N N N I N D E E D
V U D H I I N D I C A T E T
```

ON WHEELS

Some things are just taken for granted, and (as simple as it may seem) one such thing is the wheel. Just think about what an integral part of our society the wheel plays and how essential it is in our lives. And even though we may not know exactly who invented it, one thing is for sure — the wheel is everywhere you look.

AUTO	TRACTOR	TROLLEY
BICYCLE	TRAILER	TRUCK
CARRIAGE	TRAIN	WAGON
CHARIOT	TRICYCLE	ZAMBONI
COMBINE		
DOLLY		
FORKLIFT		
GO-CART		
GOLF CART		
MOPED		
MOTORCYCLE		
MOWER		
ROLLERBLADE		
ROLLER SKATE		
SHOPPING CART		
SKATEBOARD		
SNOW-BLOWER		
SNOWPLOW		
STROLLER		

```
O G S N O W P L O W A G O N
F N T H E T R A C T O R S O
Y D R A O B E T A K S O N R
I M O Z Y P T R A C F L O G
O K L L A A P A E W E L W E
K Y L C O M B I N E L E B L
C O E E T I B N N E C R L C
D T R L C F D O R G Y B O Y
M L R Y L E I S N A C L W C
O T C U P O K L U I R A E I
W L G O C A R T K R O D R R
E Y M P T K O T I R T E F T
R Z R E L I A R T A O C H U
W A A T O I R A H C M F S G
```

Atlanta has come a long way in the 138 years since it was burned during General Sherman's "March to the Sea." The city is the home of CNN, Coca-Cola, Delta Airlines, IBM, and many other international corporations, in addition to having been the host city for the 1996 Summer Olympics. Why not take a stroll down some of its streets?

BAKER
BATTLE
BEDFORD
BRYAN
CAPITOL
DECATUR

DURANT
EAST
ELLIS
FAIR
FORREST
FORSYTH

FORT
FRASER
FULTON
GRANT
HILL
JUNIPER
KELLY
LINDEN
LOGAN
LOVEJOY
LUCKIE
MARTIN
MILLS
MYRTLE
NELSON
NORTH
PARKER
PEACHTREE
PENN
PIEDMONT
PINE
STONEWALL
TAFT
TRINITY
VENABLE
WELLS

```
K U A W N H V M M J P E N N
F O R R E S T I N R I K L C
F P K E I L L Y O J E V O L
K U A L S L L Y S L D K G S
S D L R S A N S L R M E A W
E E L T K W R Y E G O K N B
I T I Y O E L F N P N F B R
K N H T P N R B A T T L E Y
C A P I T O L U N R N L D A
U R N N T T F A T I B I F N
L U F I S S R L T A I N O C
J D O R S G A R N F C D R N
E E R T H C A E P I N E D L
E L T R Y M V H T R O N D J
```

"ALL" INCLUSIVE

Here's a SMALL challenge for your solving skills. It should be a GALLON of fun for you to TALLY up these 32 terms containing the word "ALL."

ALLERGY

ALLEY

ALLOY

APPALL

BALLET

BALLOON

BALLOT

CALLOUS

CALLOW

DALLY

FALLACY

FALLOW

GALLANT

GALLERY

GALLON

GALLOP

GALLOWS

HALL

INSTALL

MALLARD

MALLET

PALLID

PITFALL

RALLY

RECALL

SHALLOW

SMALL

SQUALL

TALLEST

TALLOW

TALLY

WALLET

A	L	B	T	M	S	N	H	Y	A	O	G	Y	P
H	F	Y	P	O	O	H	H	L	C	U	C	A	A
C	A	L	O	L	S	T	A	L	O	A	G	C	M
B	A	L	L	O	T	S	E	L	L	A	T	P	R
D	F	A	L	L	O	W	O	L	L	A	T	C	Y
S	G	R	A	R	E	C	A	L	L	O	U	S	Q
M	Y	U	G	B	I	F	O	C	P	A	W	Q	T
Y	N	B	C	T	N	W	M	I	Y	P	B	H	S
U	G	O	E	N	S	B	T	R	F	P	W	W	W
I	W	R	O	A	T	F	E	E	Y	A	O	A	W
F	F	U	E	L	A	L	N	B	L	L	L	T	F
U	S	M	A	L	L	A	R	D	I	L	L	A	P
Y	O	L	L	A	L	A	A	U	E	E	A	A	D
C	G	N	G	G	Y	A	B	T	I	Y	C	M	D

BOWLED OVER BY BOCCE!

The **ITALIAN GAME** of bocce is a version of **LAWN BOWLING**. Played along a narrow **COURT** of dirt or **SAND**, **POINTS** are given for each ball that's tossed closest to the object ball.

ACCURACY

ALTERNATE

BALLS

BOWLING

CLAY

CLOSE

COMPETITION

COURT

DISTANCE

GAME

ITALIAN

KNOCK

LAWN

MEASURE

NEAR

OPPONENT

PLAYERS

POINTS

POSITION

RANGE

REBOUND

RELEASE

ROLL

RULES

SAND

SCORE

SKILL

SURFACE

TEAM

THROW

TOSS

TOUCH

TURNS

```
G W S S D I S T A N C E T I
C L O S E O A S P O I N T S
W G O R K R D G O I T A N L
P R O E H C U B N T L R M L
O C R C S T L S R I U L K A
S A U M S K Y A A T L P O B
I O L S E K N N Y E O W W R
T M E T I G I C U P M E O E
I A S R E Y A L P M L C M B
O I A U L R W O L O E A N O
N E N O U W N T M C G F W U
N S D C G E S A E L E R M N
L K C O N K E N T D F U G D
M A E T F F U O C E P S O N
```

VISITING INDIA

Every January 26th, a grand Republic Day parade is held in New Delhi, India's capital city, to observe the anniversary of the Indian Republic, established in 1950. It is marked by several days of military parades and festivals. Many visitors schedule their vacations to see the pageantry, and to explore other parts of this vast country. In the puzzle below find some of the places, things, and events a tourist might encounter.

AGRA
BAZAAR
BIHAR
BOMBAY
BRASS
CAMEL
CAVES
COBRA
COWS
CRICKET
DEEG
DELHI
ELEPHANT
FORTS
GANGES
GEMS
HIMALAYAS
HINDI
LION
MARKETS
PALMS
PARKS
POLO
PUNE
REPUBLIC DAY
RUINS
RUPEES
SARI

SARONG
SHRINES
SITAR
TAJ MAHAL
TEAK

TEMPLES
TIGER
TOMBS
TURBAN
YOGA

```
F O R T S O C O I A W R J S
H S R V E S A R O N G E W M
T E N E E R E G I T V O E Z
Z N C I P N T V E C C I Y S
L I O N U U S E A E K S M L
Z R B P R R B M A C D E E N
R H R B O A E L H K G L T H
W S A Y A L A M I H L E D T
U N T Y G H O Z P C M P C Y
K A I R A S K R A P D H R I
F R S M N B U S L B F A D Z
D G J Z G J M E M H H N Y Y
M A R K E T S O S I I T E R
T O M B S S A R B H N O S A
```

SOLUTIONS

WORD SEEK 1

WORD SEEK 2

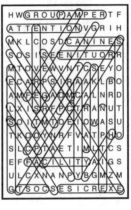

WORD SEEK 3

WORD SEEK 4

WORD SEEK 5

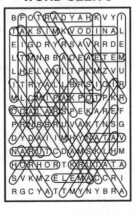

WORD SEEK 6

WORD SEEK 7

WORD SEEK 8

WORD SEEK 9

WORD SEEK 10

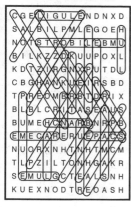

WORD SEEK 11

WORD SEEK 12

WORD SEEK 13

WORD SEEK 14

WORD SEEK 15

WORD SEEK 16

WORD SEEK 17

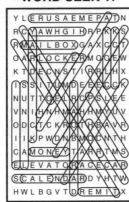

WORD SEEK 18

WORD SEEK 19

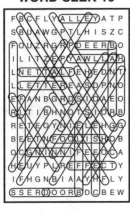

WORD SEEK 20

WORD SEEK 21

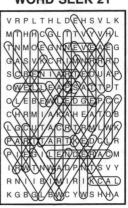

WORD SEEK 22

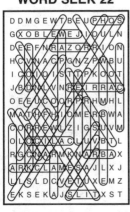

WORD SEEK 23

WORD SEEK 24

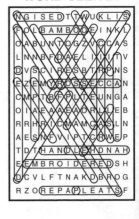

WORD SEEK 25

WORD SEEK 26

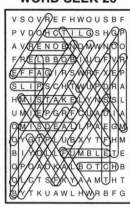

WORD SEEK 27

WORD SEEK 28

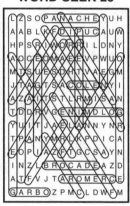

WORD SEEK 29

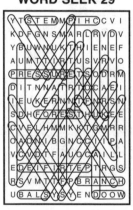

WORD SEEK 30

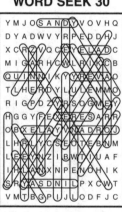

WORD SEEK 31

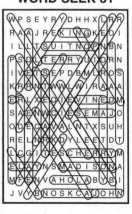

WORD SEEK 32

WORD SEEK 33

349

WORD SEEK 34

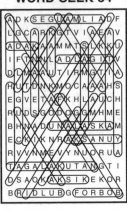

WORD SEEK 35

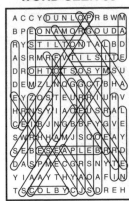

WORD SEEK 36

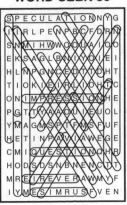

WORD SEEK 37

WORD SEEK 38

WORD SEEK 39

WORD SEEK 40

WORD SEEK 41

WORD SEEK 42

350

WORD SEEK 43

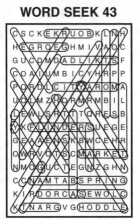

WORD SEEK 44

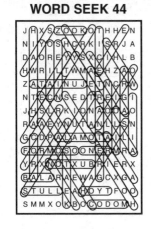

WORD SEEK 45

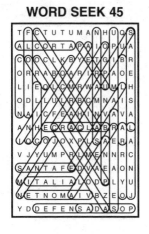

WORD SEEK 46

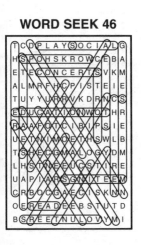

WORD SEEK 47

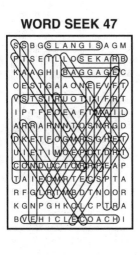

WORD SEEK 48

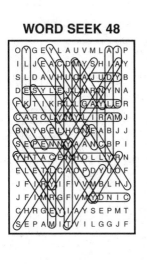

WORD SEEK 49

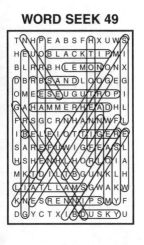

WORD SEEK 50

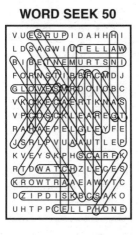

WORD SEEK 51

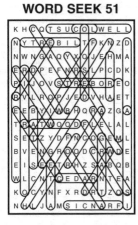

351

WORD SEEK 52

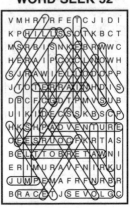

WORD SEEK 53

WORD SEEK 54

WORD SEEK 55

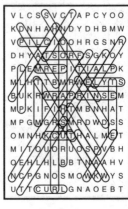

WORD SEEK 56

WORD SEEK 57

WORD SEEK 58

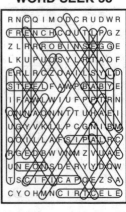

WORD SEEK 59

WORD SEEK 60

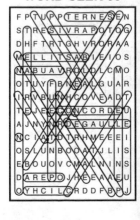

WORD SEEK 61

WORD SEEK 62

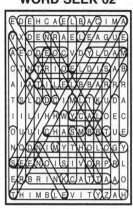

WORD SEEK 63

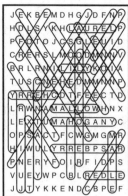

WORD SEEK 64

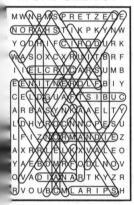

WORD SEEK 65

WORD SEEK 66

WORD SEEK 67

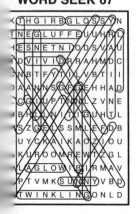

WORD SEEK 68

WORD SEEK 69

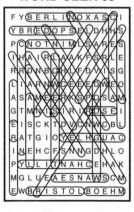

WORD SEEK 70

WORD SEEK 71

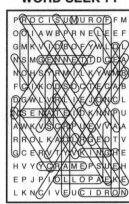

WORD SEEK 72

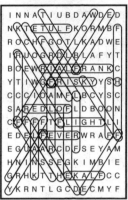

WORD SEEK 73

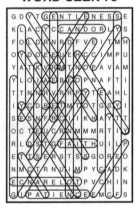

WORD SEEK 74

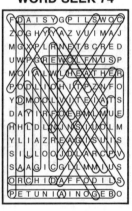

WORD SEEK 75

WORD SEEK 76

WORD SEEK 77

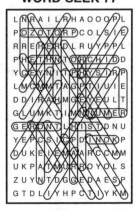

WORD SEEK 78

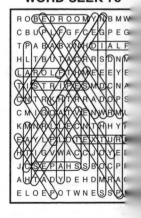

354

WORD SEEK 79

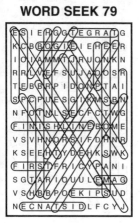

WORD SEEK 80

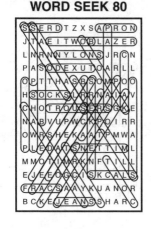

WORD SEEK 81

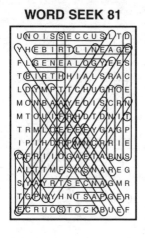

WORD SEEK 82

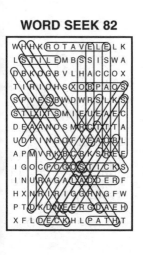

WORD SEEK 83

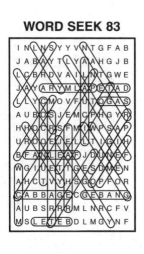

WORD SEEK 84

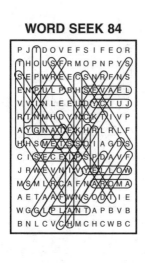

WORD SEEK 85

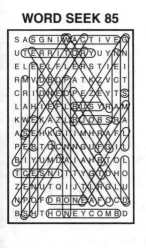

WORD SEEK 86

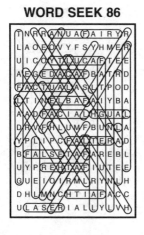

WORD SEEK 87

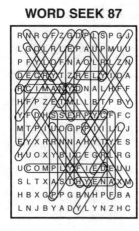

WORD SEEK 88

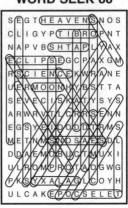

WORD SEEK 89

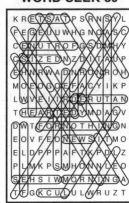

WORD SEEK 90

WORD SEEK 91

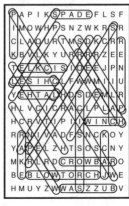

WORD SEEK 92

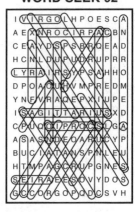

WORD SEEK 93

WORD SEEK 94

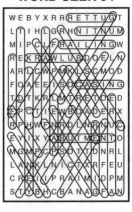

WORD SEEK 95

WORD SEEK 96

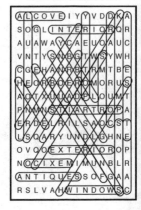

WORD SEEK 97

WORD SEEK 98

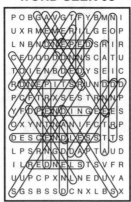

WORD SEEK 99

WORD SEEK 100

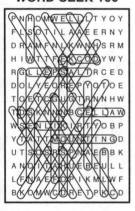

WORD SEEK 101

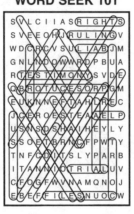

WORD SEEK 102

WORD SEEK 103

WORD SEEK 104

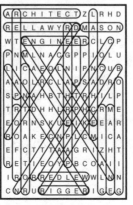

WORD SEEK 105

357

WORD SEEK 106

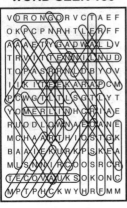

WORD SEEK 107

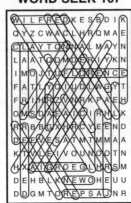

WORD SEEK 108

WORD SEEK 109

WORD SEEK 110

WORD SEEK 111

WORD SEEK 112

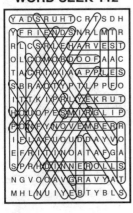

WORD SEEK 113

WORD SEEK 114

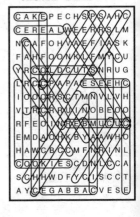

WORD SEEK 115

WORD SEEK 116

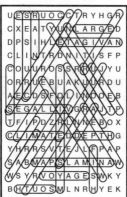

WORD SEEK 117

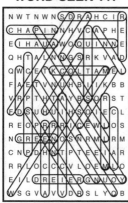

WORD SEEK 118

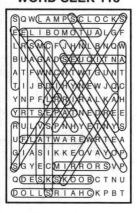

WORD SEEK 119

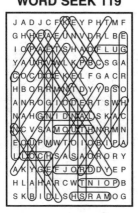

WORD SEEK 120

WORD SEEK 121

WORD SEEK 122

WORD SEEK 123

WORD SEEK 124

WORD SEEK 125

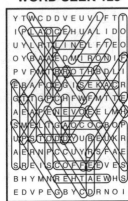

WORD SEEK 126

WORD SEEK 127

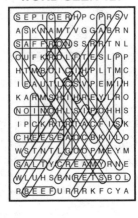

WORD SEEK 128

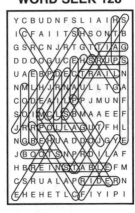

WORD SEEK 129

WORD SEEK 130

WORD SEEK 131

WORD SEEK 132

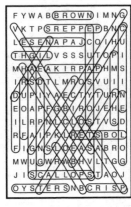

360

WORD SEEK 133

WORD SEEK 134

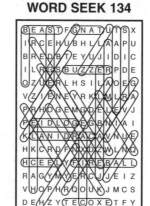

WORD SEEK 135

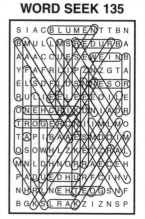

WORD SEEK 136

WORD SEEK 137

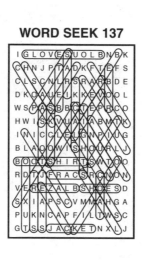

WORD SEEK 138

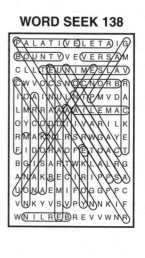

WORD SEEK 139

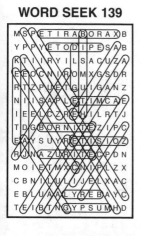

WORD SEEK 140

WORD SEEK 141

361

WORD SEEK 142

WORD SEEK 143
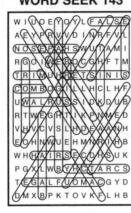

WORD SEEK 144

WORD SEEK 145
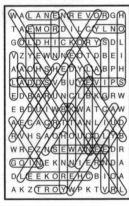

WORD SEEK 146
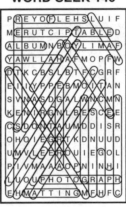

WORD SEEK 147

WORD SEEK 148

WORD SEEK 149
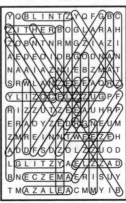

WORD SEEK 150

WORD SEEK 151

```
C Z Z D R Y E N I H R M Y E
N B B M I S S O U R I Z E U
V U E Z T G N A Y S O H H S
A R E G I N D U S A G L O V
M A C K E N Z I E N G D D Y
A L O L M U S Z A T A R S C
Z S S R A S A U C R N K U E
O O G E I X H B O T D K R M
N G L P B X N E L N Y E O U A
A I P E M B O K G S I I P T
N U Z I U C D C O H D E K T
E I N N L Y U K O N U G R A
U D A D O S E G N A G V L V
T D O L C U B U P T B R M Z
```

WORD SEEK 152

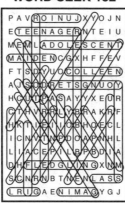

```
P A V R O I N U J X Y O J N
E T E E N A G E R N T E I U
M E M L A D O L E S C E N T
M A I D E N C G X H F F E V
F T S D Y U O C O L L E E N
A J S O D R E T S G N U O Y
H C U D P A S A Y Y X E U R
C T H V R R L Y B R A K R F
H R Y X E Y I O B H O E C L
I C N X Y N X P D O A P N H L
L I A C E P I L B P B D I A
D H F L E D G L X I N G X N M
S C N R N B T N E N L A S S
L R U G A E N I M A G Y G J
```

WORD SEEK 153

```
I N D U C E R U G I F E R C
A G A A O H U W E I V E R P
N F O G N A M R Z A K S D R
P P P R C G I I L N U A E R
S O I E L T N U I M I F E E
Z S N E U W A H U N N F N D
S E E D D T P V I N I E I
S T Z U E I E T P O M R L S
E O L I G R C T C R C M T N
S V L W R O U E G A O T O
S A S V N O D I G I E C
A A T C E L E E C H O O S E
E S U M H D D H E J U D G E
F R E A S O N K T M U L L R
```

WORD SEEK 154

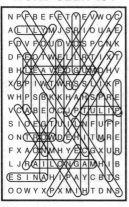

```
N P F B E F E T Y E W O C
A L I L Y M J S R I O U A E
F D V F O U D V O S P C N K
D F E O T W E L L R T X X T
B H L E A V E D G U X M O H V
X B P I W T W R S S L I K P
W H P S B K K H A R S P R E
V C A B E O C J P T U L I P
S I O E G T U I X N F U F P
O N T R O W D E H I T M R E
F X A O X N M H Y E C G X U R
L J R A I L O N G A M H I B
E S I N A H I P A Y C B T S
O O W Y X P X M I H T D N S
```

WORD SEEK 155

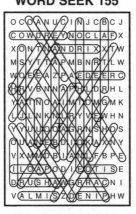

```
O C O A N U C I N J C B C J
C O W D R E Y N O C L A F X
X O N I X M A N D R I X X T W
M S Y T Y A P M B N R T L W
W O E E A Z P A E D E E R C
H R V B N N A P H L D R H L
X A T N O A I M T O M G M K
L J L N K N L R Y V E W H N
Y Y L U O O A G R N S H O S
O U A X E B D I O K A X N Y
V X M M D B J A N L F B P E
I L O X A P O D I P O T I S E
D R U S H A W G R R A C N I
V A L M I S Z D E N I P H W
```

WORD SEEK 156

```
L H V X E N N A P H W X T E
G F O G O V F P V L U I X G
W X R P F D A P S J N F T N
S E X C U R E W E C K W F R L
M C S O L T M N N W A A K E
B E K P L E G D I X R B S F L
C D A M C O M C G O B T O P
E T I D M D T E T O J E D U
S W R K U R L M C W N N N O
R U N O E N R E N X I B M O C
H I X T C H A I N W G L M B C
L M A U H C A X I X T A E P J J
R L O I R B X N O E C N R S C
X G O D O V E X T A I L D N I B
```

WORD SEEK 157

```
C A L A T H U S H O U Z C L
A E T H J O R U M L A Z K R
N Z N C E X P E T T E R U B
N Z Z I C C F X I R K I N I X
I U C A R D B E L L D W S J
K L Y U O R S L M L O S C S
I K S O U S E R E A X T A J
N E Z C O D Y X E R Z G A N
O H U D I L N M T E T E J H
G C A E I P A S L L S R S
G I S X G C M U I W T O O R
I T U G Q G X N C O T K F C
N O I B A G H D B R N R L J
F P U N N E T Y J G S S A T
```

WORD SEEK 158

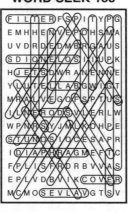

```
F I L T E R F S P I T Y P G
E M H H E N V E P O H S M A
U V D R D E D M B R G A U S
S D I O N E L O S I I U P K
H J E T S D W R A N E N N E
Y L U T E L L A B G W I G T
M R A X V E G O F S P T U S
I L N E R O D S V L E R L W
W P N R S Y J M L X O H P E
S T U N O S I O C E S A P R
I D I A P H R A G M E F T C
F P L I S F R D R B V V A S
E P L V D B V I K C O V E R
M C M O S E V L A V G T S V
```

WORD SEEK 159

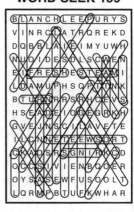

```
B L A N C H L E E P U R Y S
V I N R C L A T R Q R E K D
D Q B B L A I E I M Y U W H
N U O I D E S D L S C W E N
E X F R E S H E S T E X A M I
L D A M U P H S O P T X N K
B T U R N R R S R H C E V S
H S E A O E I O G E G R X H
G V E J N S C I L A V E T E
I X C N N E T E E W S X O R T
C K A O S R S G N I R X C D
O C C S I V I E N B O O E R
O Y S A S E W F U S O O L T
U Q R M P B T U F K W H A R
```

WORD SEEK 160

WORD SEEK 161

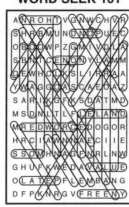

WORD SEEK 162

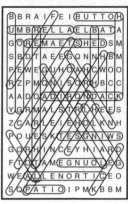

WORD SEEK 163

WORD SEEK 164

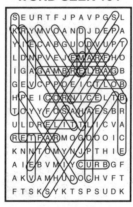

WORD SEEK 165

WORD SEEK 166

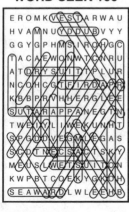

WORD SEEK 167

WORD SEEK 168

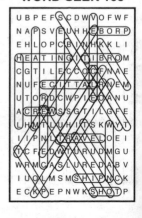

364

WORD SEEK 169

WORD SEEK 170

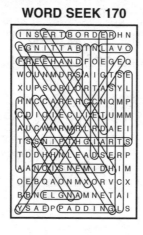

WORD SEEK 171

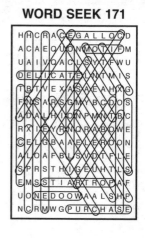

WORD SEEK 172

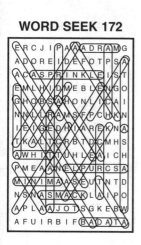

WORD SEEK 173

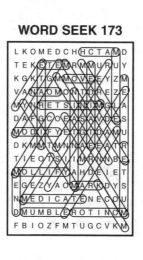

WORD SEEK 174

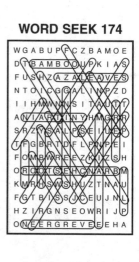

WORD SEEK 175

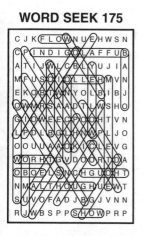

WORD SEEK 176

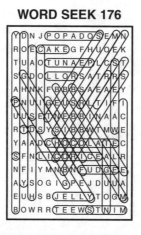

WORD SEEK 177

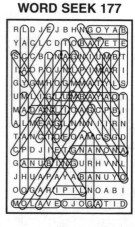

365

WORD SEEK 178

WORD SEEK 179

WORD SEEK 180

WORD SEEK 181

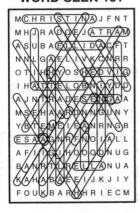

WORD SEEK 182

WORD SEEK 183

WORD SEEK 184

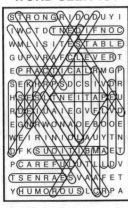

WORD SEEK 185

WORD SEEK 186

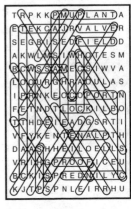

366

WORD SEEK 187

WORD SEEK 188

WORD SEEK 189

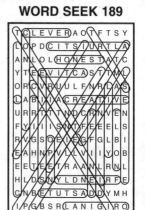

WORD SEEK 190

WORD SEEK 191

WORD SEEK 192

WORD SEEK 193

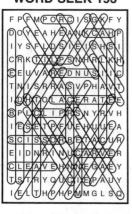

WORD SEEK 194

WORD SEEK 195

WORD SEEK 196

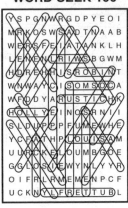

WORD SEEK 197

WORD SEEK 198

WORD SEEK 199

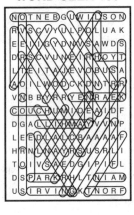

WORD SEEK 200

WORD SEEK 201

WORD SEEK 202

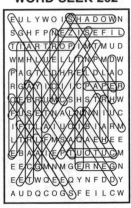

WORD SEEK 203

WORD SEEK 204

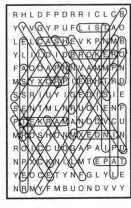

368

WORD SEEK 205

WORD SEEK 206

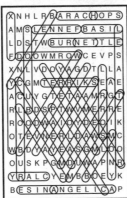

WORD SEEK 207

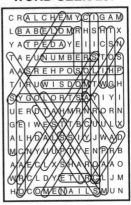

WORD SEEK 208

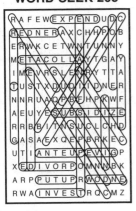

WORD SEEK 209

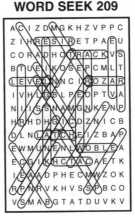

WORD SEEK 210

WORD SEEK 211

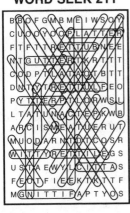

WORD SEEK 212

WORD SEEK 213

369

WORD SEEK 214

WORD SEEK 215

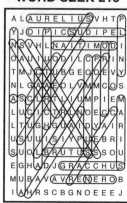

WORD SEEK 216

WORD SEEK 217

WORD SEEK 218

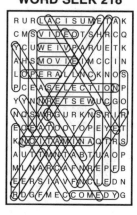

WORD SEEK 219

WORD SEEK 220

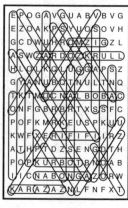

WORD SEEK 221

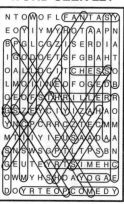

WORD SEEK 222

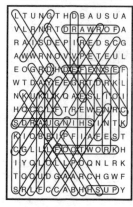

370

WORD SEEK 223

WORD SEEK 224

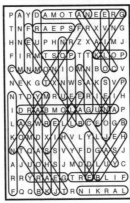

WORD SEEK 225

WORD SEEK 226

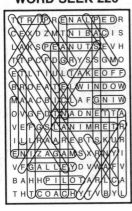

WORD SEEK 227

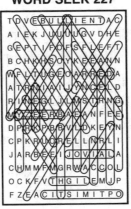

WORD SEEK 228

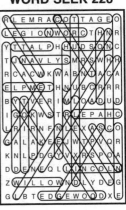

WORD SEEK 229

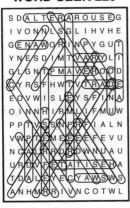

WORD SEEK 230

WORD SEEK 231

WORD SEEK 232

WORD SEEK 233

WORD SEEK 234

WORD SEEK 235

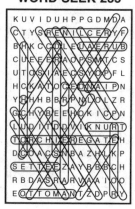

WORD SEEK 236

WORD SEEK 237

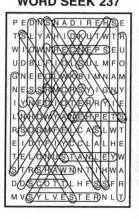

WORD SEEK 238

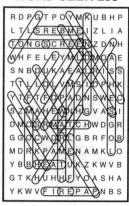

WORD SEEK 239

WORD SEEK 240

WORD SEEK 241

WORD SEEK 242

WORD SEEK 243

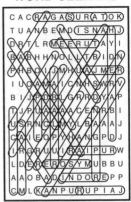

WORD SEEK 244

WORD SEEK 245

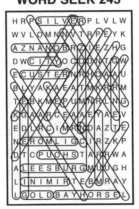

WORD SEEK 246

WORD SEEK 247

WORD SEEK 248

WORD SEEK 249

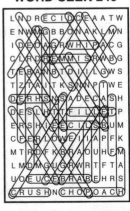

373

WORD SEEK 250

WORD SEEK 251

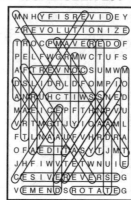

WORD SEEK 252

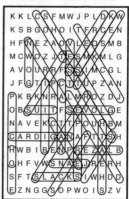

WORD SEEK 253

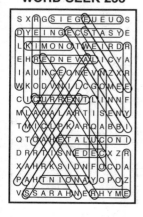

WORD SEEK 254

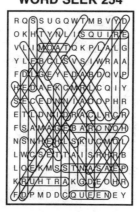

WORD SEEK 255

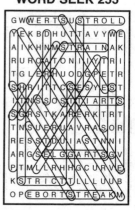

WORD SEEK 256

WORD SEEK 257

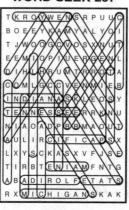

WORD SEEK 258

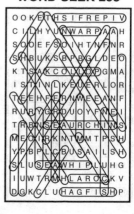

374

WORD SEEK 259

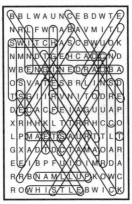

WORD SEEK 260

WORD SEEK 261

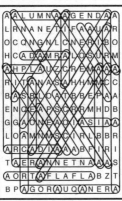

WORD SEEK 262

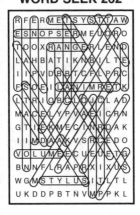

WORD SEEK 263

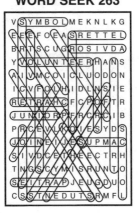

WORD SEEK 264

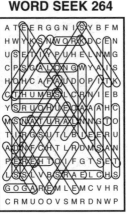

WORD SEEK 265

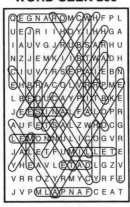

WORD SEEK 266

WORD SEEK 267

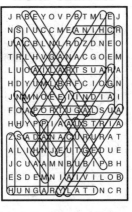

375

WORD SEEK 268

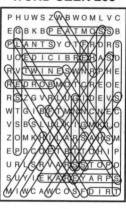

WORD SEEK 269

WORD SEEK 270

WORD SEEK 271

WORD SEEK 272

WORD SEEK 273

WORD SEEK 274

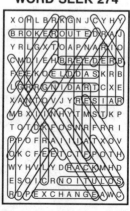

WORD SEEK 275

WORD SEEK 276

WORD SEEK 277

WORD SEEK 278

WORD SEEK 279

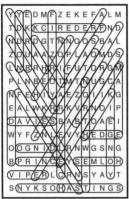

WORD SEEK 280

WORD SEEK 281

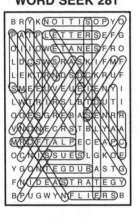

WORD SEEK 282

WORD SEEK 283

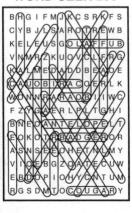

WORD SEEK 284

WORD SEEK 285

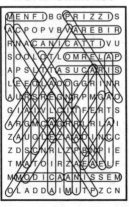

377

WORD SEEK 286

WORD SEEK 287

WORD SEEK 288

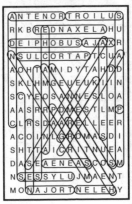

WORD SEEK 289

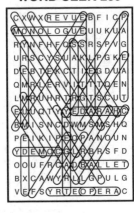

WORD SEEK 290

WORD SEEK 291

WORD SEEK 292

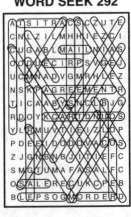

WORD SEEK 293

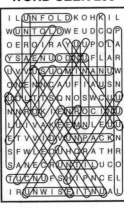

WORD SEEK 294

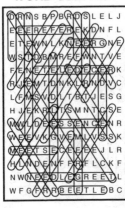

378

WORD SEEK 295

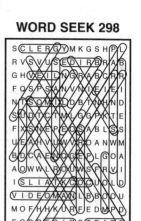

WORD SEEK 296

WORD SEEK 297

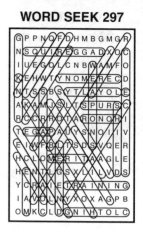

WORD SEEK 298

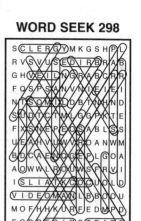

WORD SEEK 299

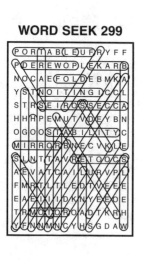

WORD SEEK 300

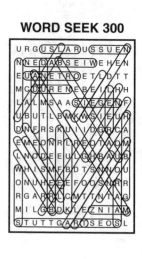

WORD SEEK 301

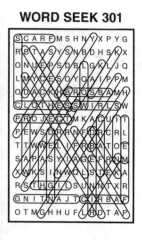

WORD SEEK 302

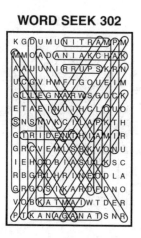

WORD SEEK 303

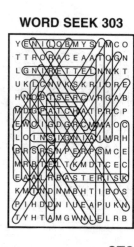

379

WORD SEEK 304

WORD SEEK 305

WORD SEEK 306

WORD SEEK 307

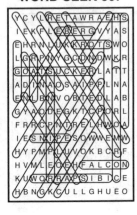

WORD SEEK 308

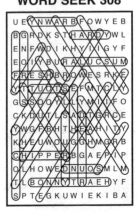

WORD SEEK 309

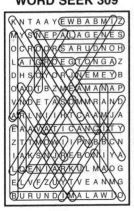

WORD SEEK 310

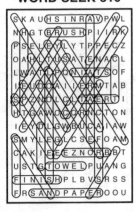

WORD SEEK 311

WORD SEEK 312

380

WORD SEEK 313

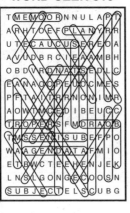

WORD SEEK 314

WORD SEEK 315

WORD SEEK 316

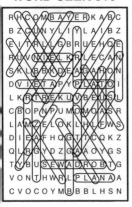

WORD SEEK 317

WORD SEEK 318

WORD SEEK 319

WORD SEEK 320

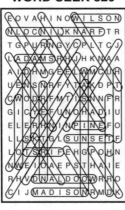

WORD SEEK 321

WORD SEEK 322

WORD SEEK 323

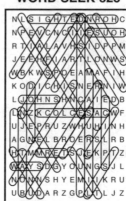

WORD SEEK 324

WORD SEEK 325

WORD SEEK 326

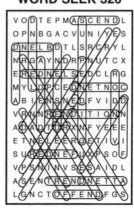

WORD SEEK 327

WORD SEEK 328

WORD SEEK 329

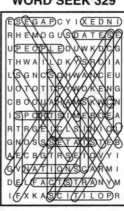

WORD SEEK 330

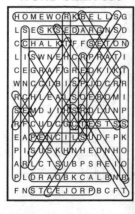

382

WORD SEEK 331

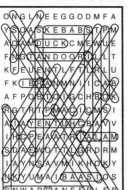

WORD SEEK 332

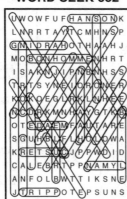

WORD SEEK 333

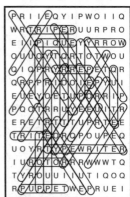

WORD SEEK 334

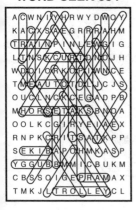

WORD SEEK 335

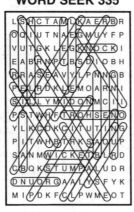

WORD SEEK 336

WORD SEEK 337

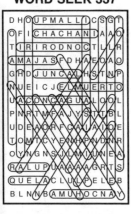

WORD SEEK 338

WORD SEEK 339

383

WORD SEEK 340

WORD SEEK 341

WORD SEEK 342

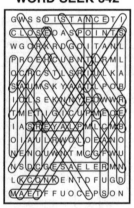

WORD SEEK 343

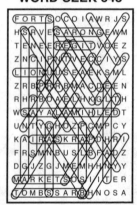